MIND AND COSMOS

Volume 3   *University of Pittsburgh Series*
                   in the Philosophy of Science

Mind

Editor

ROBERT G. COLODNY

HERBERT A. SIMON

DUDLEY SHAPERE

SYLVAIN BROMBERGER

CARL G. HEMPEL

WESLEY C. SALMON

JOSEPH CLARK, S.J.

THOMAS GOLD

HENRY MARGENAU

and Cosmos

Essays in Contemporary
Science and Philosophy

University of Pittsburgh Press

Library of Congress Catalog Card Number 66–16762

© Copyright 1966 University of Pittsburgh Press

Manufactured in the United States of America

Preface

Since 1960, the Center for Philosophy of Science at the University of Pittsburgh has annually presented a number of public lectures on various current topics in the philosophy of the physical, biological, and social sciences as a permanent part of its program of instruction and research. *Frontiers of Science and Philosophy*, the first volume of such lectures by scholars from diverse institutions, was edited by Professor Robert G. Colodny and appeared in 1962 under the imprint of the University of Pittsburgh Press. The second volume, entitled *Beyond the Edge of Certainty* and also edited by Professor Colodny, was published by Prentice-Hall in 1965.

The present book of lectures is the third in the series of volumes on the philosophy of science published under the Center's auspices.

Adolf Grünbaum
Andrew Mellon Professor of Philosophy and
Director of the Center for Philosophy of Science,
University of Pittsburgh

Contents

Figures

ROBERT G. COLODNY
University of Pittsburgh

Introduction

> Philosophers have removed the great cosmic drama of
> Copernican thought from the dominion of reality to the
> dominion of metaphor. Kant described his critical philosophy
> as a Copernican revolution in metaphysics. . . . As a result
> of this radical modification, the knowing mind and the known
> world acquired the appearance of being relative to each other.
> But this kind of relativity remained merely symbolic. Nothing
> had changed in the detail or the principles of coherence of
> knowledge. Empiricism and rationalism remained face to face
> and incapable of achieving either true philosophical coopera-
> tion or mutual enrichment.
>
> The philosophic virtues of the Einsteinian revolution could
> be quite differently effective, as compared to the philosophic
> metaphors of the Copernican revolution, if only the philos-
> opher were willing to seek all the instruction contained in
> relativity science. A systematic revolution of basic concepts
> begins with Einsteinian science.
>
> —Gaston Bachelard
> "The Philosophic Dialectic of the Concepts
> of Relativity" in *Albert Einstein, Philosopher-
> Scientist*, II [1]

IN ONE OF THE halls of the Vatican, Raphael painted a fresco, *The
School of Athens*. Here, surrounded by the philosophers and scholars
of Hellas, Plato and Aristotle engage in conversation. The former points
with his finger to the heavens; the latter reaches with open hand toward
the earth.[2]

The Renaissance vision of the dialectical unity of the poles of scientific
thought can be instructive to the contemporary world which is so deeply
conscious of the dynamic, revolutionary flux of science and its philoso-

phy. The web of the world that scientists weave may no longer appear as seamless, so deep are some of the discontinuities produced by an intellectual activity which constantly questions and restructures its foundations; that questing for fugitive certainty makes critical doubt an ingredient of its methods.

In the beginning of the modern phase of science and its philosophy when new theories of astronomy heralded the first great scientific revolution, Jean Fernel, humanist and physician, wrote:

But what if our elders, and those who preceded them, had followed simply the same path as did those before them? . . . Nay, on the contrary it seems good for philosophers to move to fresh ways and systems; good for them to allow neither the voice of the detractor, nor the weight of ancient culture, nor the fullness of authority, to deter those who would declare their own views. In that way each age produces its own crop of new authors and new arts. This age of ours sees art and science gloriously re-risen, after twelve centuries of swoon. Art and science now equal their ancient splendour, or surpass it. This age need not, in any respect, despise itself, and sigh for the knowledge of the Ancients. . . . Our age today is doing things of which antiquity did not dream. . . . Ocean has been crossed by the prowess of our navigators, and new islands found. The far recesses of India lie revealed. The continent of the West, the so-called New World, unknown to our forefathers, has in great part become known. In all this, and in what pertains to astronomy, Plato, Aristotle, and the old philosophers made progress, and Ptolemy added a great deal more. Yet, were one of them to return today, he would find geography changed past recognition. A new globe has been given us by the navigators of our time.[3]

Yet, it seems not so wildly improbable that were the figures represented in *The School of Athens* to be reassembled in the lecture halls of a great modern university where the perplexities of modern science were discussed in terms of philosophic implications, they would recognize at least the import of the issues discussed in this volume, for it seems that the deeper probes into the physical cosmos and the profounder questions about the knowing mind involve problems that have stimulated and directed human thought uninterruptedly from the beginning of the Western tradition in the far reaches of the Mediterranean. Icarus fulfilled in our time by the chemical thrust of engines forged in lands unknown to Ptolemy or Archimedes only updates paradoxes posed by Zeno, while Tarski and Gödel add new dimensions to the antique structures of the logics that mold the rules of demonstration and validation puzzled over in peripatetic and platonist schools.

Thus, while echoing the exaltation of the Renaissance writer, philosophers of science in this revolutionary age are deeply conscious of the fact that many of their debates are older than the confrontation between Kant and Hume and that the intuitions of a venerable past occasionally illuminate vistas of new terrain for thought. These discoveries are often coeval with the dismantling of philosophical structures of much more recent vintage, such as certain versions of positivism and empiricism.

This concern with a tradition of philosophical labor and discourse represents the inclusion of a fruitful historicism in the current stream of philosophy of science. This has been accentuated not by a discovery of the never-forgotten history of philosophy, but by the convergence of the work of the new historians of science. Experts in this relatively new discipline became aware of the fact that mythologies encrusting the traditional view of the progress of scientific knowledge could be overthrown only by uncovering the motivations and philosophical presuppositions of each scientific epoch. From Pierre Duhem to Thomas Kuhn the philosophies of science have been indispensable to an understanding of the histories of science. In this process the enlightenment has been a two-way exchange and, as the essays of this volume demonstrate, discourse about the role of experience, scientific principles, laws, theories, rules of evidence, and standards of logical structure become more meaningful to the extent that they are studied in concrete historical contexts.

As the foregoing might suggest, the dialogues herein recorded are sometimes against the grain of time and sometimes the polemics are as contemporary as the last issue of a learned journal. It is no longer necessary to wait for a Hume to rouse a Kant from dogmatic slumber. Philosophers of science confront each other not only in the pages of their professional publications, but on public platforms, international conference seminars, and in the pages of special series of volumes, such as this one.

The truths all participants seek are no longer those derived from private intuitions or speculative dreams. They are to be submitted to the scrutiny of public judgment and exposed to the same rigorous tests as propositions of the exact sciences that are their origin.

As Barrows Dunham wrote with reference to other aspects of a public philosophy: "For our hope must be to establish throughout the world a social order such that, though there remain lively disputation, there will be no orthodoxy and no heresy at all. Then we shall behave in politics as we now behave in science and we shall have peace."

The division of this volume into two unequal parts is motivated by a desire to exhibit two distinct but related aspects of contemporary philosophy of science: studies of cognitive processes and logic and searching examinations of frontiers of ongoing scientific inquiry—in this volume, cosmology and quantum theory.

Part I, *Mind,* is introduced by Professor Herbert Simon's essays, "Thinking by Computers" and "Scientific Discovery and the Psychology of Problem Solving." Simon's work adds a significant and exciting new dimension to the traditional problem of analyzing cognitive processes. This arises from data and models derived from the study of the modern computers. These machines, descended from Pascal, Leibniz, Boole, and Babbage, in combination with modern programming languages, provide, according to the author, possibilities of accounting for some of the principal information processing mechanisms involved in human problem solving. The quasi mechanistic procedures employed by man in searching for solutions to well-formulated problems may be duplicated by machines. *Mutatis mutandis,* the activity of the well-programmed machine may be followed by the analyst, be he engaged in solving mundane problems or pioneering on some esoteric frontier of science.

Although theories derived from machine activity may affront the sensibilities of some traditionalists, and although metaphoric flights to android robot sapiens are not here implied, there can be no doubt that a cybernetic component must hereafter be taken seriously by all philosophers of mind and its creations.

Dudley Shapere poses the critical issue of the nature and logic of scientific change. In a searching critique of the theories of Paul K. Feyerabend and Thomas Kuhn, he finds a clue to an interpretation of the progressive quality of scientific growth which, in his view, has been distorted by the analyses and accounts of other philosopher-historians of science.

The rationale of scientific evolution is not disclosed by a mere description of the temporal sequence of the great episodes in the history of science, but is uncovered by a careful determination of the conceptual innovations, as mapped onto a received tradition and available bodies of evidence. Shapere treats this interdisciplinary question not as a problem of a static metaphysics, but as a case study in actual scientific activity. He seeks through a study of the relations between classical mechanics and its predecessors and successors to illustrate the often-concealed logic of this complex process.

As this was one of the unifying themes in Volume II of the series, *Beyond the Edge of Certainty,* readers can usefully consult, *inter alia,* Norwood Russell Hanson, "Newton's First Law: A Philosopher's Door into Natural Philosophy," Brian Ellis, "The Origin and Nature of Newton's Laws of Motion," and Paul K. Feyerabend, "Problems of Empiricism." In Volume I of this series, Feyerabend's essay, "Problems of Microphysics," is also relevant to this debate.

Sylvain Bromberger introduces a novel approach to a core problem in the philosophy of science: the logic of explanation. This field has been thoroughly explored by such powerful minds as Carnap, Reichenbach, Pap, Popper, Nagel, and Hempel in recent times. Around it has appeared a rich and vigorous literature which seemed to bracket all possible avenues of approach. Yet Bromberger's "Why-Questions," by an ingenious and subtle restating of one aspect of the general problem, the specificity of types of explanation, has opened new windows to the world of logic.

The central part of his essay is concerned with the structure and *implications* of why-questions as stated in "ordinary" English, but the final analysis is formulated in universal logical terms that abstract from the peculiarities of any specific language. Thus, light is shed on a new aspect of the logic of explanation and validation. In this series, readers may consult in Volume I, Carl G. Hempel, "Explanation in Science and in History" and in Volume II, Paul K. Feyerabend, "Problems of Empiricism."

Logic burns with a very cold light. Its seminal properties are rarely revealed by dramatic and revolutionary episodes (although the cases of Hume and Gödel are infused with explosive consequences). Yet, this discipline is a dynamic element in modern scientific culture. It presided over the birth of non-Euclidean geometry; it inspired much of the mid-nineteenth-century rigorization of the calculus, with the attendant expansion of the power of mathematical analysis, and one finds a creative element of logical consideration in the Einsteinian revolution.

It is thus abundantly clear that a deeper understanding of the nature of logical systems *a fortiori* expands our intellectual grasp of the entire scientific enterprise. This high aim—supremely difficult of achievement —is attained by the papers of Hempel and Salmon.

Hempel, in "Contemporary Problems of Induction," argues that the classical problem of justification of inductive procedures calls for a clearer characterization of what is to be justified. This leads to a reexamination of rules governing the inductive appraisal of hypotheses and theories. Second, the intended objectives of the procedure must be indicated, for a justification of *any* procedure will have to be relative to the ends it is intended to serve. Hempel thus makes a novel assessment of hidden valuational aspects of the efforts to clarify the rules of inductive inference. He discovers, in fact, a range of paradoxes and problems that reflect the difficulties of an enterprise on the frontiers of knowledge.

Salmon presents a comprehensive survey of the philosophical problems of probability and induction in his two-part essay, "Inductive Inference in Science." Departing from Hume's skeptical arguments regarding the justification of induction, the history of this central issue is traced through competing philosophical systems, and the varied solutions offered are subjected to criticism and found unsatisfactory.

The leading theories of probability are then examined in the light of the impact of Hume's problem of induction on them. These discussions form, then, a background for a penetrating discussion of scientific hypotheses and their confirmation. The deductivist, the hypothetico-deductive, and the Bayesian approaches are considered. Salmon uncovers new relationships in the conjunction of interpretations of probability and the issue of the justification of induction. These insights illuminate not only the structure of scientific inference, but the full range of human cognitive activity as well.

Joseph Clark, in "The Physiognomy of Physics," explores the relations between the mathematical and empirical content of scientific theories. In a magnificent display of pedagogical skill, he clarifies the logical problems of the isomorphism that obtain between statements about physical objects and processes and a mathematical language empty of material content. His total vision of the operation of scientific inference and mathematically controlled deductive statement sheds light on the historical process of scientific change, particularly for those branches of science with high mathematical content. This essay has interesting points of intersection with those of Shapere, Bromberger, and Salmon.

In "Science and Some Other Components of Intellectual Culture," Clark examines the roles of science, philosophy, and theology in the cultural tradition of the Western world. By drawing careful distinctions between different aspects of each discipline and the kind of language each uses, he urges a drastic revision in the received tradition concerning the methods and goals of these intellectual enterprises. With a pugnacious wit, he sketches the evolution of the epistemological problem from Plato to positivism and argues for cooperation between the three sets of scholars who, he maintains, cannot logically contradict each other and whose joint efforts are required to achieve a total knowledge of total reality.

Wilfrid Sellars' essay, "Philosophy and the Scientific Image of Man," in *Frontiers of Science and Philosophy*, also surveyed the broad terrain of cultural history as a function of science and philosophy.

The human mind and imagination created models of the universe in the misty epochs before the dawn of any activity even remotely resembling science. In fact, the intellectual history of man would be meaningfully periodized by mapping it on a linear sequence of cosmological models.

Thomas Gold is one of the architects of the steady state cosmological model. Here, in "Cosmic Processes and the Nature of Time," he undertakes to examine the manner in which the nature of time is related to certain large-scale cosmic processes, particularly those that involve a relativistic cosmos and where the properties of thermodynamic processes are considered primary. This poses the problem of counterintuitive temporal symmetry and the nature of reversible and irreversible processes in the large-scale world.

In his exposition of this cosmic problem, Gold exhibits the kind of intersection of philosophical and physical thought that is responsible for our claims to *understand* the physical world in its aspect of totality.

Adolf Grünbaum's "The Nature of Time" in Volume I and Philip Morrison's "Physics of the Large" in Volume II can be consulted here.

It is a truism of our time that the most persistent and stimulating sources of scientific and philosophical thought are the boundlessly large cosmos and the vanishingly small subatomic worlds. Relativistic cosmology and quantum physics as yet have no generally accepted bridge between them. Hence, they both represent mandatory fields for the philosopher of science. In fact, the broad features of the philosophy of science as a current cohesive discipline owe their origins in large measure to a sustained interest in these two sets of problems.

Henry Margenau, in the concluding essay, "The Philosophical Legacy of the Quantum Theory," asserts that his purpose is to offer an exposition of certain novel features in the philosophy of science that are called for by the current nature of scientific evidence. He accomplishes this by a penetrating account of the epistemology of science, by confronting the important concepts and axioms of quantum theory with their classical counterparts and then drawing the important philosophical consequences of this confrontation for the epistemological theories of science.

Paul Feyerabend's "Problems of Empiricism" in Volume I and Hilary Putnam's "A Philosopher Looks at Quantum Mechanics" in Volume II are parts of this great litigation.

As Margenau states the large issue: "Inasmuch as science is a dynamic, progressive, never-ending enterprise which harbors no stagnant certainties, philosophy of science likewise is a changing field of knowledge which, though it may ask questions of eternal relevance, does not pretend to give eternally valid answers."

NOTES

1. The thematic quotes in this book from *Albert Einstein, Philosopher-Scientist* are taken from the Torchbooks Science Library edition, I, II (New York: Harper & Row, 1959). The Leibniz thematic quotes are from *Leibniz Selections,* ed. Philip P. Weiner (New York: Charles Scribner's Sons, 1951).
2. We were reminded of this Renaissance episode by Paul Henri Michel in *Histoire Genèrale des Sciences,* ed. René Taton (Paris: Presses Universitaires, 1957), I, p. 260.
3. Quoted by J. D. Bernal, *Science in History,* 2d ed. (London: Watts, 1957), p. 277.

Part I / MIND

HERBERT A. SIMON
Carnegie Institute of Technology

Thinking by Computers

That is the aim of that great science which I am used to calling *Characteristic,* of which what we call Algebra, or Analysis, is only a very small branch, since it is this *Characteristic* which gives words to languages, letters to words, numbers to Arithmetic, notes to Music. It teaches us how to fix our reasoning, and to require it to leave, as it were, visible traces on the paper of a notebook for inspection at leisure. Finally, it enables us to reason with economy, by substituting characters in the place of things in order to relieve the imagination. . . .

—Leibniz
On the Method of Universality (1674)

IT IS HARDLY possible to talk about thinking by computers without saying something first about thinking by people. There are two reasons why this is so. First, the only definitions of thinking that are of any use at all are ostensive ones. We can point to a person in a certain state of activity and say, "Thinking is a set of processes like those now taking place in the central nervous system of that person." Alternatively, we can point to the statement of a problem and to its solution and say, "Thinking is a set of processes like those that enabled a person to produce this problem solution from this problem statement." I do not mean that these two definitions are necessarily equivalent, but they might serve equally well as a basis for delimiting the set of phenomena we wish to understand when we investigate thinking.

The second reason why we must talk about thinking by people in order to talk about thinking by computers is that the history of the latter phenomenon is inextricably interwoven with research efforts to understand the former. In most cases where a computer has done something

3

that might reasonably be called "thinking," the occasion for this activity was an investigation aimed at explaining human thinking.

Human Thinking

I have defined human thinking as a set of processes occurring in the central nervous system, and *par excellence* in the human central nervous system. What do we know about these processes? It is conventional to refer to our abysmal ignorance of them. It would not surprise me if a word count revealed that the adjective most commonly associated with the phrase "thought processes" is "mysterious." [1]

That adjective is no longer appropriate. Today we have a substantial and rapidly growing body of knowledge about thinking processes, both at the neurological level and at the level of what I shall call elementary information processes. There are still very large gaps in this knowledge— and particularly gaps between the two levels, as I shall point out. But I think it more useful to follow the example of the physical sciences—to describe what we already know before moving on to the frontier of knowledge—than to observe the vow of ignorance that has been traditional in the social sciences.

Neurological and Information Processing Explanations

The notion of levels of explanation is familiar from physics, chemistry, and biology. From classical Greek times, if not before, unobservable atomic particles have been hypothesized to explain the observable processes going on in chemical reactions. The atomic hypothesis, quantified by Dalton and his contemporaries at the beginning of the nineteenth century, led to one triumph after another in the regularization, systemization, and explanation of chemical phenomena during the course of that century. Only in our own century did atoms acquire an existence partially independent of their hypothesized participation in chemical reactions. Thus, we had a highly developed explanation of chemical reactions at the level of atomic processes long before the latter processes received explanation and confirmation, in turn, at the level of nuclear physics.[2]

Genetics provides an example of levels of explanation that is even more instructive than atomic theory for our purposes. In its initial introduction as the unit of inheritance, the gene had exactly the same hypothetical status as did the atom in Dalton's theory.[3] If one assumed there were genes with certain properties, one could explain some of the gross macroscopic phenomena of inheritance. The gene hypothesis, in its initial form, did not require the genes to be localized in space or to have any specific existence as chemical or protoplasmic entities. The gene hypothesis was compelling because it regularized, systemized, and explained those macroscopic phenomena.

The gene, like the atom, turned out to be "realer" than any of those who proposed it had defensible reasons for predicting. Some of the most beautiful achievements of biology in our generation have been the advances toward the explanation of genes in terms of more microscopic and fundamental levels of biochemical process. The great strides toward deciphering the so-called genetic code within the past few years are only the most recent of these achievements.

Two lessons can be drawn from these examples. First, explanation in science is frequently achieved in successive levels. We explain reactions in terms of atoms and molecules, atoms and molecules in terms of the so-called "elementary" particles. We explain inherited characteristics in terms of genes, genes in terms of organic molecules and their reactions.

Second, the fact that we have succeeded in "reducing" a first-level explanation by means of a more fundamental explanation of its entities and laws does not make the original explanation otiose or dispensable. It is important and gratifying to know that complex chemical reactions can *in principle* be explained by the laws of quantum mechanics. In practice, of course, the chemist could not get along without an intermediate level of chemical theory, for the in-principle reduction has been carried out *in practice* only in the very simplest cases.[4] Similarly, there is no reason to suppose that direct explanation of inheritance in terms of cellular biochemical processes will ever in practice replace explanations in terms of genes. Hierarchy is as essential to the organization and application of knowledge as to its original discovery.

These two examples provide encouraging historical precedents for what is now going on in psychology. Today, the explanation of thinking is progressing at two levels. We are succeeding in explaining ever-widening spheres of human mental activity in terms of hypothesized "atoms" called *elementary information processes*. At the same time, we are making substantial progress toward explaining the fundamental electrochemical processes of synaptic action and nerve signal transmission, and the organization of these processes in various parts of the peripheral and central nervous system.[5] If there is a significant difference between these developments in psychology and the corresponding developments that I have described in genetics and chemistry, it is that the work of constructing explanations at the two levels is going on more nearly simultaneously in psychology than it did in the two other instances cited.

Perhaps the greatest gulf of ignorance today is not *within* neurophysiology or *within* information-processing psychology—although there is no lack of work to be done in each of these areas—but *precisely between them.* Although we can give a considerable account of thinking in terms of elementary information processes, we know almost nothing about the specific physiological basis for these information processes. We do not know what the engram is—how and where symbolized information is stored in the brain. We do not know how symbols are compared, copied, or associated. Neurophysiologists boring from one side of the mountain have not yet made contact with information-processing psychologists boring from the other side.

Yet this state of affairs should be no cause for discouragement, especially for the psychologist who is interested in using psychological theory to understand and work with human higher mental processes. He is no worse off, in his theoretical foundations, than chemists were during the period of most vigorous development of their science. He is no worse off than geneticists were during the twenties of this century. And basing his prognostications on those sciences, he can look forward to a future in which the symbols and symbolic processes hypothesized by information-processing theory will be encased in such hard "reality" as chemistry can provide to entities.

There is one respect in which the information-processing psychologist today is distinctly better off than the geneticist was a generation ago. Belief in the possibility of a mechanistic explanation for the gene hypothesis was then largely an act of faith.[6] Today, although we do not know what protoplasmic processes correspond to the elementary information processes, or how these processes fit into the architecture of the brain, we do have a proof that such processes *can* be provided with mechanistic explanations, for although we do not know how the elementary symbolic processes that are capable of explaining thinking are accomplished physiologically in the brain, we do know how these processes can be accomplished electronically in a digital computer. The possibility of providing a mechanistic explanation for thinking has been demonstrated by programming computers to think.

An Information-Processing Explanation of Thinking

Thinking is a dynamic process—using that term in its technical sense. Classical dynamical theories, of which Newtonian mechanics is the standard example, have generally taken the form of differential equations. The *state* of the system at any given moment of time is specified by the values of a set of variables, the state variables, at that moment. Then the differential equations determine how the state variables will change; they predict the state of the system at the "next" moment as a function of the present state.[7]

Before a system can be described in differential equations of the classical sort, a set of state variables must be discovered. One of the difficulties that has plagued psychology is that no satisfactory way has been found for characterizing thought processes in terms of the kinds of state variables that are suitable for classical differential equations. That difficulty has now been bypassed with the invention of information-processing languages, a special class of computer programming languages, whose variables are not numbers but symbolic structures.[8]

A computer program is quite analogous, at an abstract level, to a system of differential equations (more precisely, of difference equations). Given the memory contents of the computer at any given moment of time (these characterizing its state at that moment), the program determines how the memory contents will change during the next computing cycle and what the contents will be at the end of the cycle. Thus, a computer program can be used as a theory of a dynamic system in exactly the same way as can a set of differential equations. The basic methodological problems of theory construction and theory testing are identical in the two cases. The theory is tested by providing a specific set of initial and boundary conditions for the system, using the equations to predict the resulting time path, and comparing this predicted path with the actual path of the system.

The advantage of an information-processing language over classical mathematical languages for formulating a theory of thinking is that an information-processing language takes symbolic structures rather than numbers as its variables. Since thinking processes are processes for manipulating symbols and structures of symbols (Figure 1), these processes can be represented directly, without requiring elaborate translations or scaling techniques, in an information-processing language.

Let us make this point more specific by considering a particular thinking task.[9] Suppose that a human subject in the psychological laboratory is confronted with a sequence of symbols—ABMCDMEFM, say—and asked to continue it. After a few moments, he will very likely give the continuation GHMIJM, and so on. Now one way in which he might

A———> B———> M———> C———> D———> M

A *list.* Each item is associated with the previous one by the relation of *next* (→).

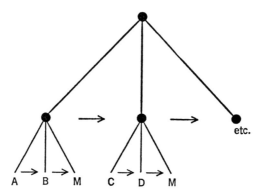

A *tree,* or list of lists. Each item on the main list is itself a list (in this case, a list of three items).

Figure 1. Some simple symbol structures.

accomplish this—and, from the available evidence, the way in which most subjects do accomplish it—is the following:

1. He scans the original list looking for repetitions of identical symbols, discovering that each third symbol is M.

2. He constructs a symbolic structure in memory that represents the periodicity and the recurrence of the M. In order to talk about this structure, let us represent it as (**M), where the asterisks stand for unspecified symbols. Of course, we should not suppose that the symbolic structure in memory "looks" like this sequence in any literal sense, but we can use the sequence in our theory as a fairly straightforward representation of the structure in memory.

3. Now the subject again scans the original list to see whether there are consistent relations between pairs of symbols that occupy corresponding positions in different periods of the sequence. We may think of him as now representing the given sequence thus: ABM CDM EFM, so that A, C, and E are in the first positions in their respective periods, and B, D, and F in the second positions. The relations he searches for are relations of *identity* and of *next on a familiar alphabet* (Figure 2). In the

example before us, he will discover that the second symbol in each period is next to the first symbol, in the English alphabet, and that the first symbol in each period is next to the second symbol in the preceding period. These relations, then, provide a general description of the sequence, as well as a means for extrapolating it. Leaving out details, we might describe the sequence symbolically as (nnM), where "n" stands

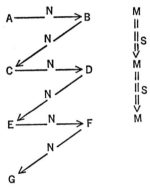

Figure 2. A *pattern*. Each triad (list) can be generated from the previous one by listing the relations of *next* (——)) and *same* (==)) on the English alphabet.

for "next on the English alphabet." Given one period of the sequence, the subject can now construct an indefinite number of the following periods.

It is easy to write a program in an information-processing language that explains this dynamic process in terms of elementary information processes. We need processes for copying symbols, for constructing compound symbols (lists and "trees") from simple symbols, for comparing symbols for identity, for finding the next symbol on a list, and a few others.

A review of the steps that the subjects were described as taking in the illustrative example above shows that these processes are essentially the ones mentioned. In step 1, the original list of symbols could be scanned by a process for finding the *next* symbol on a list. The repetitions of the letter M could be detected by a process for comparing symbols for identity. Step 2 could be carried out by a process for constructing compound symbols—in this case, the list **M. Step 3 again calls for processes that compare symbols for identity and find the next symbol on a list and processes that construct the final pattern nnM from the incomplete pattern **M. The extrapolation of the sequence, finally, calls for applications of the same kinds of processes, under the control of the pattern.

Thus, the program constructed from these processes, and organized to carry out the steps 1 through 3, provides an explanation of how humans detect the patterns in sequences like the one illustrated, how they represent such patterns in memory, and how they use the pattern representations to extrapolate the sequences. It is a theory of human information processing in the series generation task.

This theory has been tested by programming a computer to behave in the manner described and examining the behavior of the computer when it is given the same series completion tasks that were given to the human subjects. The predictions of the theory—that is, the output of the computer under these conditions—can be compared directly with the human behavior. No mathematization of the human behavior is required. One gross test is to check whether the problems the program solves are the same ones that were solved by the largest number of human subjects. Much more specific tests—comparison, for example, of the specific errors made by program and subjects—are possible. With the evidence available to date, the theory has given a fairly good account of itself.

The information-processing explanation of series completion would have only rather narrow interest if it were not for the fact that the same small set of processes that represents the core of this explanation also turns up in a central role in the information-processing theories that have been devised to explain human thinking in quite different contexts. In the first place, the program for the series completion task can be generalized without too much difficulty to apply to a much wider range of pattern recognizing tasks:

1. With a few additions (primarily of the numerical operations of addition, subtraction, multiplication, and division), it will handle number series—e.g., 1 4 9 16 25 . . .

2. It can be extended to various kinds of analogy tasks—e.g., "*a* is to *c* as *r* is to __?" or "a rectangle is to a square as a parallelogram is to a _____?"

Similar programs, employing the same elementary information processes, have had considerable success in explaining subjects' behavior in partial reinforcement experiments.[10]

Finally, quite distinct information-processing programs which, however, employ essentially the same elementary processes, explain a considerable number of other kinds of human thinking: among them, discovering proofs for theorems in logic, geometry, and trigonometry, playing chess and bridge, harmonizing a musical theme, making investment decisions, memorizing nonsense syllables, or learning foreign language vocabulary.[11]

On the basis of experience with these theories, it now appears highly probable that elementary processes like the ones described, operating on symbols and structures of symbols (that is, lists and trees of symbols), are the fundamental means by which human thinking is accomplished. Because the theories take the form of programs in information-processing languages, and because we can program digital computers to execute such programs, we have incontrovertible evidence that these processes are *sufficient* to account for performance of the kinds of tasks that have been mentioned. And because the computers so programmed do prove theorems, play games, compose music, make investment decisions, and memorize, the theories provide examples of thinking by computers that, from the evidence at hand, closely parallel some kinds of thinking by human beings.[12]

Some Characteristics of Thinking Processes

What are some of the generalizations about thinking that have emerged from the information-processing theories? It will not be necessary, in stating these generalizations, to distinguish particularly between human thinking and computer thinking, because the computer thinking referred to occurs in the context of programs designed to simulate human thinking as closely as possible. The generalizations apply to both.

One qualification should be made, however. Existing information-processing theories of thinking undoubtedly fall far short of covering the whole range of thinking activities in man. It is not just that the present theories are only approximately correct. Apart from limits on their correctness in explaining the ranges of behavior to which they apply, much cognitive behavior still lies beyond their scope.

The first generalization—that all thinking processes are constructed out of a small set of elementary information processes—has already been sufficiently stressed. Nothing has been said about the organization of these processes, the way in which they are put together in programs. Two additional generalizations apply here:

1. The processes are organized hierarchically.[13] A sequence of elementary processes can be combined into a compound process. Sequences of compound and elementary processes can be combined again into still more elaborate and complex processes, and so on. If there is a limit on the number of levels in such a hierarchy, experimentation thus far has not revealed that limit—or even indicated that it exists.

In the example of the sequence completion program, the three major program steps represent compound processes organized from elementary ones. The first step determines the periodicity of the sequence; the second step constructs an incomplete representation of the pattern; the third step completes the representation. These three "subroutines," to use computer terminology, are combined into the complete pattern-detection process. The pattern-detection process, in turn, is combined with the extrapolation process in order to carry out the experimental task—continuing the series.

2. The processes are executed serially. Implicit in the principal information-processing theories that have been constructed is the hypothesis that the central nervous system can only do one or a few things at a time. "At a time" means in an interval of a few milliseconds.

Because existing digital computers are serially organized devices, it is simplest to construct information-processing theories that operate serially.[14] However, there is considerable evidence that the human system is organized in the same way—or at least that large parts of it are. The observably narrow limits on span of human attention are one symptom of the serial organization of thinking. There exists also some contrary evidence—for example, the ability of a person to hear his own name softly spoken even when he is attending to something else. On balance, however, it does not appear inaccurate to describe thinking as essentially a serial process.

The generalizations stated thus far—that thinking is a hierarchically organized, serially executed symbol-manipulating process—apply to virtually all the information-processing theories that have been constructed to date. There are several additional important generalizations that refer more specifically to the kinds of thinking activities called "problem solving."

1. Problem solving involves a highly selective trial-and-error search of solution possibilities. The terms "highly selective" and "trial and error" may seem contradictory. They are not. Problem-solving searches require trial and error in that they generally do not go directly to the solution without traversing and retracing some blind alleys—sometimes many, sometimes few. When a person solves a problem without any backtracking whatsoever, we are apt to deny that he needed to think at all. We say, "He knew the answer," or "he didn't have to think; he did it by rote."

Problem-solving searches are selective in that they generally explore only a miniscule fraction of the total (and usually immense) number of possibilities. In most cases of interest, the selection of the paths to be searched is not governed by foolproof, systematic procedures, but by rules of thumb we call *heuristics*.

In a few cases a good deal is known about the size of the problem space, about the heuristics that are used to explore it selectively, and about the quantitative reduction in search that these heuristics achieve.[15] The game of chess is one such case. It is known that a player typically has freedom to choose among about twenty or thirty legal moves. To each of these, the opponent may have a similar number of replies. Thus, the tree of possible game continuations branches geometrically nearly a thousand-fold for a single set of move possibilities and their replies. A complete analysis of continuations two moves deep would typically require the exploration of nearly one million branches; three moves deep, one billion, and so on.

It is now pretty well established that experienced chess players, even in difficult middle-game positions or in exploring deep combinations, seldom examine as many as one hundred continuations. The number examined appears to be almost independent of the player's skill. What distinguishes very good players from less good players is not the amount of exploration they do, but their relative success in identifying the significant continuations to be explored—the selective power of their heuristics.

A detailed investigation of this question has been made for mating combinations—sequences of moves that force a checkmate.[16] An information-processing program has been written that examines continuations in potential mating positions very selectively, using heuristics gleaned from the chess literature and chess experience. This program is able to find combinations as many as eight or more moves deep by examining far fewer than one hundred branches of the game tree. The program, examined in comparison with records of historical chess games, appears to capture successfully some of the main heuristics that are actually used by strong players in complex mating positions.

The positions to which the mating combinations program is relevant allow the players less freedom than many other chess positions, and our previous estimate of the branching rate of the game tree—a thousand-fold per move—is probably too high when applied to them. Let us take one hundred as a more conservative estimate. With this branching rate, *exhaustive* exploration of an eight-move combination would mean examining 10^{16} positions! A program that examines only one hundred is therefore more efficient by a factor of 10^{14}—one hundred thousand billion—than a random search program that tries all possibilities.

Similar calculations have been made for the power of the heuristics in some of the theorem-proving programs, with the finding, again, of gain factors of orders of magnitude similar to those in chess.

2. Means-end analysis is one of the basic heuristics in human problem solving.[17] Means-end analysis, as it appears in human behavior, and as it is formalized in information-processing theories of problem solving, is organized somewhat as follows:

a) The present situation is compared with the desired situation (problem goal), and one or more *differences* between them noticed. (E.g., "I have a board five feet long; I want a two-foot length; there is a difference in length.")

b) Memory is searched for an *operator* or operators associated with one of the differences that has been detected. By "operator" is meant some process that will change the present situation. (E.g., "sawing," "planing," "drilling.") Operators become associated with particular differences as a result of experiences that show that these operators are capable of reducing or eliminating the differences in question. (E.g., "Sawing changes lengths.")

c) An attempt is made to apply the operator to change the present situation. Sometimes, in the course of making the attempt, it is discovered that the operator cannot be applied until some other aspect of the situation has been altered. (E.g., "A board must be held fast in order to saw it.") In these cases a new goal of type (a) may be set up, with satisfaction of the conditions for applying the operator as the "desired situation." (E.g., "Hold the board fast.")

Examination of a large number of human protocols in problem-solving situations reveals that the largest part of the activity is means-end analysis. Considerable success in simulating such problem-solving behavior has been achieved in an information-processing program called the General Problem Solver.

Means-end analysis is a special case of a selective heuristic. By identifying the specific differences between the present and desired situation, it becomes unnecessary to consider all possible ways in which the situation might be changed. Only those operations need be examined that are relevant (at least potentially, on the basis of past experience) to the actual differences that exist. When a tailor alters a suit, he obtains, at the fitting, not only the qualitative nature of the difference—whether the sleeves are too short or long—but the precise amount of the alteration that is needed. He thereby achieves a laudable reduction in the amount of trial and error that is required to make the suit fit.

Intermingled with means-end analysis in problem solving are heuristics that may be called *planning*.[18] Planning consists in omitting some of the detail of the actual problem by abstracting its essential features, solving the simplified problem, then using the solution of the simplified problem as a guide, or plan, for the solution of the full problem. Again, it can be shown quantitatively that planning can increase speed of solution in favorable circumstances by many orders of magnitude. Speaking generally, the larger the number of steps in the complete problem solution, the greater the increase in efficiency achievable through planning.

3. Another heuristic of wide applicability is the procedure of factoring a problem into subproblems, and tackling first the subproblems containing the smallest number of "unknowns." In this way the number of combinations of possible solutions that have to be examined is greatly reduced. Consider, for example, puzzles of the following kind:

$$\begin{array}{r} D \; O \; N \; A \; L \; D \\ + G \; E \; R \; A \; L \; D \\ \hline R \; O \; B \; E \; R \; T \end{array}$$

The problem task is to substitute distinct digits—from o to 9—for distinct letters in such a way that the resulting expression will be a correct example of addition. The hint is given that $D = 5$.[19]

Only one unknown now remains in the last column, and this is immediately solved to give $T = 0$, with a carry to the fifth column. Also, the value 5 for D can be substituted in the first column. Now, subjects generally turn their attentions to columns two, four, or five, since each of these has a duplication of letters, hence, only two unknowns each. They soon discover that $E = 9$, and that R must be an odd number greater than 5, hence $R = 7$. The process is continued until the answer is obtained:

$$\begin{array}{r} 526485 \\ + 197485 \\ \hline 723970 \end{array}$$

The significant point about the example is that successful subjects almost never explore at random or consider possible combinations of digits that might "work." They carry through the solution with a minimum of combinations by always working at points where there are only a few unknowns to be determined.

4. In some very well-structured problem domains, formal procedures, usually called algorithms, are available for finding systematically the solution that is best or maximal by some criterion. Elementary calculus provides an example of a simple algorithm of this kind: to find the max-

imum of a function, take the first derivative, set it equal to zero, and solve the resulting equation.

In most problem-solving domains of everyday life, however, and even in many formal ones, like chess, no such algorithm has been discovered. A modest number of possible solutions can be considered, and there is no way of telling whether a given solution is the best, since many other possibilities must, perforce, go unexamined. In these domains, human problem solvers and the computer programs that simulate them do not search for the "best" solution, but for a solution that is "good enough" by some criterion. Heuristics that proceed on this basis are sometimes called "satisficing" heuristics.[20]

Suppose, for example, that someone wishes to sell a house. He does not know exactly how much he can get for it, but he can make an estimate. If bids come in close to this figure, he holds to it; if they do not, he gradually reduces it. When a bid comes in that meets the revised figure, he accepts it.

The criterion of "good enough" that adjusts in this way is called an *aspiration level*. Satisficing behavior that makes use of aspiration levels is prominent in the selection of chess moves. We have already seen that there is no practical possibility of evaluating all possible moves. Instead, the player can form a preliminary estimate of the value of his position and look for a move that meets this estimate. As his search continues, if he does not find such a move, he revises the estimate downward. Satisficing heuristics are widely applicable and widely applied in problem domains where the number of possible solutions is far too great to permit exhaustive search and where an efficient maximizing algorithm is not available.

Motivation and Emotion in Thinking

Satisficing heuristics bring us to a consideration of the relation between thinking processes and those aspects of human behavior that we call motivation and emotion. Thinking is activity directed toward goals, and as we have just seen, involves considerations of whether a proposed solution is the best, or is good enough, in terms of a criterion. If the level of aspiration is very high, search for a satisfactory solution will be more prolonged than if it is low. The thinking program will also contain parameters, or constants, that determine how long exploration will continue in a particular direction and when it will turn to a new direction. (E.g., "If not successful in five minutes, try something else.") It may contain procedures to determine which of several alternative subproblems will be explored next (the "minimize-unknowns" heuristic is an example of this).

Thus, thinking programs, whether for human or computer, contain motivational components.[21] This is not to say that the aspects of motivation that have been represented in information-processing theories to date come anywhere near to representing the totality of motivational factors in human behavior. Ulric Neisser has pointed out that, as compared with human behavior in the large, the behavior predicted by existing information-processing theories is exceedingly single-minded, stubborn, but otherwise unemotional.[22] He observes that human beings are capable of turning from one activity to another and of being interrupted in an activity.

Can information-processing theories be broadened to encompass the motivational and emotional mechanisms we observe in human behavior? Although there has been little concrete progress in this direction, there have been some speculations suggesting the directions that progress might take.

Imagine a computer with a rather large memory—a combination of magnetic core and tape, say—that contains, among others, the general problem-solving program augmented by programs for specific tasks like playing chess, detecting serial patterns, solving differential equations, inverting matrices, calculating correlation coefficients, and so on. Each job that is input to the computer is examined and assigned a priority (on some basis that need not concern us) that gradually changes with the length of time the job has been waiting to be processed. When the priority of a job reaches a sufficiently high level, the job that is currently being processed is interrupted and replaced by the high priority job.

Such a computer (and, of course, systems organized in this general way are already in existence) would exhibit, in its behavior, motivation and a set of values. If we noticed that it gave high priorities to matrix inversions, we would say that this was an activity it preferred. Suppose we also noticed that when certain brief new jobs were input, it immediately interrupted what it was doing to undertake one of the new tasks before returning to the original one. We might say that it was easily distracted, or even that it was exhibiting emotion.

I do not propose here to develop in detail the idea that the core of the behavior we call emotional derives from a mechanism for interrupting the ongoing stream of activity. However, this notion is consistent with a good deal of empirical evidence about the nature of emotion and provides an interesting avenue of exploration into the relation of emotion to cognitive activity. It suggests that we shall not be able to write programs for computers that allow them to respond flexibly to a variety of demands, some with real-time priorities, without thereby creating a system that, in a human, we would say exhibited emotion.

Conclusion

In the foregoing I have tried to describe some of the general characteristics of human thinking, as we know them from constructing and testing information-processing theories. These are also, of course, the characteristics of computer thinking, since most computers that think, think in simulation of man.

I have not tried to answer the standard objections that "of course" computers do not think at all. To most of these objections, very satisfactory answers have been given by others—the delightful article by Alan Turing, for example, and the paper by Professor J. J. C. Smart.[23] The best answers, probably, are given by the structure of the programs themselves that embody our information-processing theories of human thinking.

I cannot forebear, however, a brief comment on one of the commonest objections: that computers do only what they are programmed to do. The assertion is undoubtedly true, but it does not imply that computers cannot think. That conclusion would only follow if it were true that human beings, when they are thinking, do *not* do what they are programmed to do. The progress of information-processing theories of human thinking requires a denial of this latter premise. The processes of human thinking, in fact, can be very effectively stated in the form of programs. We do not know what physiological mechanisms store these programs in the brain and execute them; but we have as much reason to believe there are such mechanisms as earlier generations had to believe that there are mechanisms underlying the valences of atoms and the control of heredity by genes.

A human being is able to think because, by biological inheritance and exposure to a stream of experience in the external world, he has acquired a program that is effective for guiding thought processes. If we wish to seek an efficient cause for his behavior, it lies in that program in its interaction with ongoing stimuli.

We know a great deal today about the structure and content of human thinking programs. We know very little about which parts of these programs are inherited and which parts are acquired. We know little about the biological substrate for the programs. We know far less than we need to know about how thinking programs can be modified and improved through education and training. Computers, programmed to simulate human thinking, continue to offer a powerful research tool in investigating these unanswered questions. And programs in information-processing languages offer powerful means for expressing our theories of human thought processes.

NOTES

The work on which this chapter is based was supported in part by a grant from the Carnegie Corporation and in part by Research Grant MH-07722-01 from the the National Institutes of Health. Several of my examples are drawn from joint work with K. Kotovsky, P. A. Simon, and L. W. Gregg. My debts to Allen Newell are too numerous to acknowledge in detail. To all of these, I give thanks and offer absolution for the particular conclusions reached here, which are my own.

1. A typical example is Edna Heidbreder's concluding comment in her article on "Thinking" in the 1960 Encyclopedia Brittanica: "Thinking remains one of the unsolved problems of psychology."
2. It might be mentioned that although there was much resistance to the atomic hypothesis through the first two-thirds of the nineteenth century, the grounds for this resistance were not what a radical operationalist might suppose. There were few objections to atoms because of their hypothetical character—only a few philosophers of science, like Mach, Poincaré, and Russell, anachronistically stressed this toward the end of the century. The main objection was to the neglect of the "qualities," like color, in a theory that took mass as the significant atomic property. The sceptics were humanists, not operationalists. See Stephen Toulmin and June Goodfield, *The Architecture of Matter* (New York: Harper & Row, 1962), pp. 234–37, 263–68; or *Harvard Case Histories in Experimental Science*, eds. James B. Conant and Leonard K. Nash (1950) I, 215–321.
3. Toulmin and Goodfield, pp. 365–68.
4. Compare Kekulé's prescient observation, "Should the progress of science lead to a theory of the constitution of chemical atoms, it would make but little alteration in chemistry itself. The chemical atoms will always remain the chemical unit . . ." (Quoted by Toulmin and Goodfield, p. 265.) "Little alteration" sounds too strong in the light of modern physical chemistry, but the import of the statement, that there is a distinct "chemical" level, is still substantially correct.
5. Symbolic of this progress was the award of the 1963 Nobel Prize in Physiology and Medicine to Eccles, to Hodgkin, and to Huxley for their work on transmission of neural signals. See the brief appreciation of this work, by M. G. F. Fuortes, in *Science*, 142 (1963), 468–70.
6. See Note 3 above.
7. Of course "next" must be put in quotation marks since the differential equations describe the changes in the limit as the time interval is taken shorter and shorter.

8. Allen Newell et al., *IPL-V Programmers' Reference Manual* (New York: Prentice-Hall, 2d ed., 1964).

9. The analysis here is based on H. A. Simon and K. Kotovsky, "Human Acquisition of Concepts for Serial Patterns," *Psychological Review*, 70 (1963), 534–46. For similar theories applied to closely related tasks, see J. Feldman, F. Tonge, and H. Kanter, "Empirical Explorations of a Hypothesis-Testing Model of Binary Choice Behavior," in *Symposium on Simulation Models*, eds. Hoggatt and Balderston (Cincinnati: South-Western Publishing, 1963), pp. 55–100; and K. R. Laughery and L. W. Gregg, "Simulation of Human Problem-Solving Behavior," *Psychometrika*, 27 (1962), 265–82.

10. In the partial reinforcement experiment, the subject is asked to predict whether the next stimulus in a series will be a "plus" or "minus." The sequence is in fact random, each symbol having a certain probability of occurring. Subjects, however, typically search for patterns: "a run of plusses," "an alternation of plus and minus," or the like. See the chapter by J. Feldman in *Computers and Thought*, eds. Feigenbaum and Feldman (New York: McGraw-Hill, 1964).

11. For a survey of these theories see A. Newell and H. A. Simon, "Computers in Psychology," *Handbook of Mathematical Psychology*, eds. Luce, Bush, and Galanter (New York: Wiley, 1963), I, and the references therein.

12. See references in "Computers in Psychology," to the work of Hiller and Isaacson on musical composition, Clarkson on investment decisions, and Feigenbaum and Simon on memorizing.

13. See H. A. Simon, "The Architecture of Complexity," *Proceedings of the American Philosophical Society*, 106 (1962), 467–82; Naom Chomsky, *Syntactic Structures* (The Hague: Mouton, 1957); and Toulmin and Goodfield, pp. 301–02.

14. For reasons both of economics and organizational simplicity, a typical computer has only a few "active" memory locations (sometimes called accumulators) where processing can be carried out. Information is brought in from "passive" storage locations, processed, then returned to storage. Thus, the steps involved in adding the number in storage location A to the number in storage location B and storing the sum in C might be the following: (1) copy contents of A into accumulator, (2) add contents of B to contents of accumulator, (3) store contents of accumulator in C. With only one or a few active accumulators, the action of such a system is necessarily serial rather than parallel. Increasing the number of accumulators is expensive; it also creates an extremely difficult problem of coordinating their activity.

15. For some quantitative analysis, see A. Newell, J. C. Shaw, and H. A. Simon, "The Processes of Creative Thinking," *Contemporary Approaches to Creative Thinking*, eds. Gruber, Terrell, Wertheimer (New York: Atherton Press, 1962), Chap. 3; and H. A. Simon, and P. A. Simon, "Trial and Error Search in Solving Difficult Problems: Evidence from the Game of Chess," *Behavioral Science*, 7 (1962), 425–29.

16. Simon and Simon, op. cit.

17. The organization of thinking around means-end analysis has been extensively explored with a program called the General Problem Solver (GPS). Descriptions of GPS have been published in several places, including "Computers in Psychology" and "The Processes of Creative Thinking."

18. The planning heuristic is described briefly in "The Processes of Creative Thinking," pp. 91–96.

19. Data on the behavior of subjects performing the Donald-Gerald task will be found in Sir Frederic Bartlett, *Thinking* (New York: Basic Books, 1958), Chap. 4.

20. A discussion of satisficing heuristics and aspiration levels will be found in H. A. Simon, *Models of Man* (New York: Wiley, 1957), Introduction to Pt. IV and Chap. 14 and 15.

21. D. W. Taylor, "Toward an Information-Processing Theory of Motivation," *Nebraska Symposium on Motivation*, ed. Jones (Lincoln: U. of Nebraska Press, 1960); Walter R. Reitman, "Personality as a Problem-Solving Coalition," and Silvan S. Tomkins, "Simulation of Personality," *Computer Simulation of Personality*, eds. Tomkins and Messick (New York: Wiley, 1963).

22. Ulric Neisser, "The Imitation of Man by Machine," *Science*, 139 (1963), 193–97.

23. A. M. Turing, "Computing Machinery and Intelligence," *Mind*, 59 (1950), 433–60, reprinted in *The World of Mathematics*, ed. James R. Newman (New York: Simon & Schuster, 1956), IV, and in Feigenbaum and Feldman, op. cit.; J. J. C. Smart, "Gödel's Theorem, Church's Theorem, and Mechanism," *Synthèse*, 13 (June 1961), 105–10.

HERBERT A. SIMON
Carnegie Institute of Technology

Scientific Discovery and the Psychology of Problem Solving

> The very fact that the totality of our sense experiences is such that by means of thinking (operations with concepts, and the creation and use of definite functional relations between them, and the coordination of sense experiences to these concepts) it can be put in order, this fact is one which leaves us in awe, but which we shall never understand. One may say "the eternal mystery of the world is its comprehensibility." It is one of the great realizations of Immanuel Kant that the setting up of a real external world would be senseless without this comprehensibility.
>
> —Albert Einstein
> *Out of My Later Years*

IN THE PREVIOUS CHAPTER a theory of human problem solving was put forward with references to some of the evidence for its validity. The theory has been formalized and tested by incorporating it in programs for digital computers and studying the behavior of these programs when they are confronted with problem-solving tasks.

The thesis of the present chapter is that scientific discovery is a form of problem solving, and that the processes whereby science is carried on can be explained in the terms that have been used to explain the processes of problem solving. In particular, I shall undertake to show how the theory of problem solving described in the previous chapter can account for some of the principal reported phenomena of scientific discovery.

For a description of these phenomena, the analysis will draw heavily upon previous published accounts. Discussions of scientific discovery have always been highly anecdotal, most of our specific information on the subject deriving from reports of specific examples, recorded in some instances by historians and philosophers of science, in some instances by psychologists, but often by the discoverers themselves. The classics in the latter category are Henri Poincaré's celebrated lecture, translated as "Mathematical Creation" (New York: The Science Press, 1913), and the delightful essay by Jacques Hadamard, *The Psychology of Invention in the Mathematical Field* (Princeton: Princeton U. Press, 1945). Chapter 10 of Max Wertheimer's *Productive Thinking* (New York: Harper & Row, enlarged ed., 1959) reports a series of interviews with Albert Einstein on the course of events that led to the invention of the theory of special relativity.

The literature on the topic produced by philosophers of science is substantial, but has been for purposes of this analysis, on the whole, less useful. (I will mention two important exceptions in a moment.) The reason is that philosophers of science tend to address themselves to the normative more than to the descriptive aspects of scientific methodology. They are more concerned with how scientists *ought to* proceed, in order to conform with certain conceptions of logic, than with how they *do* proceed. Notions of how they ought to proceed focus primarily on the problem of induction: on how generalizations might validly arise from data on particulars and on the degree to which a corpus of data logically confirms a generalization. These are interesting questions of philosophy, but they turn out to have relatively little relation to the actual behavior of scientists—and perhaps less normative value than has been supposed.

In the past few years, two philosopher-historians of science, both originally trained in physics, have made particularly significant contributions to the psychology and sociology of scientific discovery. Both have been quite explicit in distinguishing the processes of discovery from the traditional canons of "sound" scientific method. I shall make considerable use of their work and ideas. One of these men, Norwood Russell Hanson, has set forth his views most extensively in *Patterns of Discovery* (Cambridge: Cambridge University Press, 1958). The other, Thomas S. Kuhn, has produced an original and stimulating account of *The Structure of Scientific Revolutions* (Chicago: University of Chicago Press, 1962).

To explain scientific discovery is to describe a set of processes that is sufficient—and *just* sufficient—to account for the amounts and directions of scientific progress that have actually occurred. For a variety of reasons, perhaps best understood by psychoanalysis, when we talk or write about scientific discovery, we tend to dwell lovingly on the great names and the great events—Galileo and uniform acceleration, Newton and universal gravitation, Einstein and relativity, and so on.[1] We insist that a theory of discovery postulate processes sufficiently powerful to produce these events. It is right to so insist, but we must not forget how rare such events are, and we must not postulate processes so powerful that they predict a discovery of first magnitude as a daily matter.

On the contrary, for each such event there is an investment of thousands of man-years of investigation by hundreds of talented and hardworking scientists. This particular slot machine produces many stiff arms for every jackpot. At the same time that we explain how Schrödinger and Heisenberg, in 1926, came to quantum mechanics, we must explain why Planck, Bohr, Einstein, de Broglie, and other men of comparable ability struggled for the preceding twenty years *without* completing this discovery. Scientific discovery is a rare event; a theory to explain it must predict innumerable failures for every success.

The great events do not, of course, represent sudden leaps forward, unrelated to previous exploration. While modern quantum mechanics clearly did not exist in 1924, and clearly did in 1926, the approach to it was gradual and steady, involving all the illustrious scientists mentioned in the previous paragraph and many hundreds more. And the particular advance that we identify as "the discovery" was followed by many man-years of exploitation and consolidation, just as it was preceded by man-years of exploration and anticipation. The central point remains: scientific discovery, when viewed in detail, is an excruciatingly slow and painful process.

Related to the rarity of great discoveries—and relevant to our understanding of the process—is the rarity of great discoverers. If there are only a few great discoveries, and if a great discoverer is someone who makes a great discovery, then such persons must be rare by definition. But there is a substantive question too. Does science depend, for its major progress, upon heroes who have faculties not possessed by journeymen scientists? Or are the men whose names we associate with the great discoveries just the lucky ones—those who had their hands on the lever at the precise moment when the jackpot showered its rewards.

A case could be made for either view, and my own hunch is that the truth lies somewhere between. If it is luck, a few men in each generation appear more skillful in wooing the goddess than are their fellows. On the other hand, I have encountered no evidence that there exist significant differences between the processes that great scientists use in achieving their discoveries and the processes used by those men we regard merely as "good" scientists.

The theory of scientific discovery I propose to set forth rests on the hypothesis that there are no qualitative differences between the *processes* of revolutionary science and of normal science, between work of high creativity and journeyman work. I shall not claim that the case can be proven conclusively. My main evidence will be data indicating that the processes that show up in relatively simple and humdrum forms of human problem solving are also the ones that show up when great scientists try to describe how they do their work. How convincing the evidence is can better be judged at the end of the chapter.

Let us return, then, to the problem-solving theory proposed in the last chapter and confront that theory with the recorded phenomena of scientific discovery.

The problem-solving theory asserted that thinking is an organization of elementary information processes, organized hierarchically and executed serially. In overall organization, the processes exhibit large amounts of highly selective trial-and-error search using rules of thumb, or heuristics, as bases for their selectivity. Among the prominent heuristic schemes are means-end analysis, planning and abstraction, factorization, and satisficing. Our task is to show how a system with these characteristics can behave like a scientist.

Selective Trial-and-Error Search

The prominence of selective trial-and-error processes in accounts of scientific discovery makes an extended discussion of this phenomenon unnecessary.[2] Examples of such accounts that come immediately to mind, out of a multitude that could be cited, are Hanson's analysis of the development of Kepler's theories (*Patterns of Discovery*, pp. 73–84), and Wertheimer's report of his conversations with Einstein on the theory of special relativity (*Productive Thinking*, Chapter 10).

Wertheimer's book is particularly interesting in this connection, because he can be regarded as a hostile witness. As a Gestaltist he maintains the greatest skepticism about the processes, like trial-and-error, postulated by associationists to account for problem solving. In fact, he almost never uses the phrase "trial and error" without prefixing the adjective "blind." His chapter certainly provides no evidence that Einstein engaged in "random" search. It does provide ample evidence that he made many attempts at solutions that failed—that a great deal of *selective* trial and error took place over the decade or more during which Einstein struggled with the problem of the velocity of light.

Hadamard (*The Psychology of Invention in the Mathematical Field,* p. 48) has expressed the point metaphorically: "It is well known that good hunting cartridges are those which have a proper scattering. If this scattering is too wide, it is useless to aim; but if it is too narrow, you have too many chances to miss your game by a line. I see quite similar circumstances in our subject."

The theory and empirical explorations described above call for precisely this kind of mixture of search and aim. Except where an algorithm is available—that is, in areas that are already well structured, hence, well behind the frontiers of discovery—some amount of trial and error is essential. On the other hand, the sizes of the problem spaces encountered even in relatively simple laboratory tasks show that without powerful heuristics, principles of selectivity, the search could only rarely reach its object.

The theory has a further implication. Evidences of trial and error should be most prominent in those areas of problem solving where the heuristics are least powerful, least adequate to narrow down the problem space. Hence, the paths leading to discoveries we would call creative might be expected to provide even more visible evidences of trial and error than those leading to relatively routine discoveries. We have no quantitative evidence to test this prediction. Moreover, it rests implicitly on a somewhat doubtful *ceteris paribus* assumption: that the heuristics of persons who make creative discoveries are no more powerful than those of their contemporaries who do not.

Let us examine the question more closely. One characteristic of a discovery that marks it as creative is its unexpectedness. To say that it is "surprising" or "unexpected" is to say that it would not readily be chanced upon. But chanced upon by whom? Presumably by scientists working at the time of the discovery. Since it was, by definition, chanced upon or found by the actual discoverer, we must conclude (1) that he was lucky, (2) that he searched longer and harder than his contemporaries, or (3) that he had more powerful selective heuristics than they did. The most plausible hypothesis is that all three conditions are generally met, in varying proportions. Of these three conditions conducive to discovery, the first, luck, implies nothing about the amount of trial and error, or its selectivity.[3] To the extent that the second condition, persistence, is present, trial-and-error search should be prominently visible. If the third condition, superior heuristics, is chiefly responsible for the discovery, no more trial-and-error search will be present than would appear normal in cases of less creative activity.

The evidences of a high degree of persistence in pursuing fundamental problems are numerous in the biographies of creative scientists. Persistence does not always mean continual conscious preoccupation with the problem, or orderly, organized pursuit, but concern with the problem over a considerable period of years, indicated by recurrent attention to it. One could conjecture that while the biographies of "journeyman" scientists might reveal persistent attention to a problem *area* over comparable periods of time, the activity would more likely than in the case of highly creative scientists represent attacks upon, and solutions of, a whole series of relatively well-structured problems within the general area (e.g., determinations of structures of a number of molecules, or of the parameters of a system under a range of experimental conditions). However, the data on this point remain to be gathered.

A good deal less conjectural is the hypothesis that superior problem solvers in a particular area have more powerful heuristics and that they will produce adequate solutions with less search, or better solutions with equivalent search as compared with less competent persons. A. de Groot, for example, compared the searches of grandmasters and ordinary chess players for a good move in a middle-game position. Both classes of players searched for about the same length of time (which was partly an artifact of the laboratory situation), and examined approximately the same number of branches of the game tree. In fact, it was impossible to distinguish, from the statistics of the search, between the grandmasters and the ordinary players. They were easily distinguished by one datum, however: In the particular position examined, all five grandmasters attained better solutions to the problem (chose moves that could be shown to be objectively better) than any of the solutions attained by the ordinary players. While the grandmasters did not engage in more search than the others, their superior selective heuristics allowed them to search more significant and relevant parts of the game tree.[4]

Whence do the superior heuristics, the secret weapons, of the creative scientist come? Frequently, they derive from his possession of a superior technique of observation or of representation. Examples of the former are commonplace: Leeuwenhoek and his microscope, Galileo and his telescope, Lawrence and his cyclotron, and so on. God is on the side of the highest resolutions. The classic example of the interaction between apparatus for symbolizing or representation and scientific discovery is the relation of the calculus to the birth and growth of Newtonian mechanics. One might ask how the creative scientist comes to possess superior techniques. The answer would again be in terms of luck, persistence, and superior heuristics. The answer is not really circular, for it is quite legitimate, in dynamic systems, to explain chickens by the hatching of eggs, and eggs by the laying processes of chickens.

The theory of problem solving set forth in these two chapters itself provides an example of apparatus and representation as sources of heuristic. The idea that problem solving is a process of selective trial and error is an old one. The idea remained vague and largely untested until a formalism became available (list-processing language for computers) that was powerful enough to state the theory formally and precisely and until an instrument became available (the digital computer) that was powerful enough to draw out the implications and predictions of the theory for human problem-solving behavior. The scientists who have been active in developing and testing this theory were all in one way or another —sometimes in very "accidental" ways—thrown into contact with computers soon after these instruments were invented.

Incubation and Unconscious Processes in Discovery

The phenomena of incubation and sudden illumination have held immense fascination for those who have written on scientific discovery. Poincaré's experience on boarding the bus at Coutances takes its place in the annals of illumination along with Proust's madeleine dipped in tea:

Just at this time I left Caen, where I was then living, to go on a geological excursion under the auspices of the school of mines. The changes of travel made me forget my mathematical work. Having reached Coutances, we entered an omnibus to go some place or other. At the moment when I put my foot on the step the idea came to me, without anything in my former thoughts seeming to have paved the way for it, that the transformations I had used to define the Fuchsian functions were identical with those of non-Euclidean geometry.[5]

Hadamard places particular emphasis on the role of the unconscious in mathematical invention. While he proposes no specific theory of the processes that go on during incubation, he argues strongly that these are active processes and not merely a forgetting of material generated during conscious work that is inhibiting the problem solution.

The theory of problem solving proposed in the last chapter does not assign any special role to the unconscious—or, for that matter, to the conscious. It assumes, implicitly, that the information processes that occur without consciousness of them are of the same kinds as the processes of which the thinker is aware. It assumes, further, that the organization of the totality of processes, conscious and unconscious, is fundamentally serial rather than parallel in time.

Our examination of the phenomena of incubation and illumination and their explanation will proceed in several stages. First, I shall describe briefly the phenomena themselves. Second, I shall consider the question of why the phenomena should be regarded as surprising and in what sense they require special explanation. Finally, the information-processing theory of problem solving will be applied to provide an explanation of the main features of incubation and illumination.

The phenomena themselves are relatively simple, and their occurrence is well documented. In the case of many important scientific discoveries (we do not know in what proportion of all cases), the discoverer reports three main stages in the progress of his inquiry. The first stage, which Hadamard calls "preparation," involves conscious, prolonged investigation that is more or less unsuccessful in solving, or sometimes even satisfactorily framing, the problem. Ultimately, frustration becomes intense, and the problem is dropped from conscious attention. Some time later, often suddenly and with little or no warning (as in the instance reported by Poincaré), or immediately upon awakening from sleep, the central idea for the solution presents itself to the conscious mind, only the details remaining to be worked out. The period between this illumination and the preceding preparation is the incubation period.

While there is little question about the phenomena, they provide no clues as to what goes on during incubation. In the absence of a full-fledged theory of problem solving, one can fill that period with almost any imaginable activity. Illumination is a vivid experience for the person who experiences it, because he is given no hint as to what occasioned the problem solution. Worse, since the incubation processes apparently go on independently of his conscious efforts to solve the problem (and best after these efforts have ceased), the experience gives him few cues as to what he should do when he next encounters a difficult problem—other than to "sleep on it." He must wait until the god decides to seize him.

We can see readily why the phenomenon should be puzzling and surprising to the illuminatee. The solution to a problem that has resisted his hardest efforts suddenly, and without further work, reveals itself to his conscious mind. The notions of continuity in space and time are intrinsic to most of our ideas of causation, and illumination appears to violate this continuity. One must say "appears" because, of course, the laws are only violated in the way they are violated when a magician produces a rabbit from a hat. When we watch the magician, we do not cease to believe in the spatial and temporal continuity of causation, but only in our ability to observe the connections. The same distinction applies to illumination.

If illumination is surprising to a scientist who experiences it, it is less easy to see why it should surprise a psychologist.[6] It is commonplace that many, if not most, of the processes of the central nervous system are inaccessible to consciousness. The subconscious plays a major role in modern theories of motivation, emotion, and psychopathology. There is no a priori reason, then, to assign the problem-solving processes to the conscious rather than the unconscious. From the phenomenal evidence, they in fact belong to both.

I have been using the terms "conscious" and "unconscious" (or "subconscious"—for present purposes, no distinction is made between unconscious and subconscious) to distinguish between what a person is aware of and can report, and what he is not aware of and cannot report. The reports of illumination contain numerous instances that occurred immediately on awakening, but also numerous others that occurred when the discoverer had been awake for some time. Hence, "unconscious" is a more comprehensive term than "asleep." For the sake of parsimony, we shall assume that unconscious processes of the same kinds can occur both in the sleeping and waking states.

It has sometimes been argued that the evidence for unconscious processes is evidence that the information processing in the brain is parallel rather than serial. This argument only has force, of course, for unconscious processes that occur in the waking state when, presumably, they are operating in parallel with the conscious processes and are capable (viz., the Poincaré episode) of interrupting the latter. One can show, however, that a serial system is capable (through a "time-sharing" organization of its processing) of behaving in the observed manner, and the explanation I shall propose for illumination is compatible with either a serial or a parallel organization of cognitive processing.

With these preliminaries out of the way, let us return to incubation and illumination. I should like to describe two mechanisms currently employed in the information-processing theories that appear to go a long way toward accounting for these phenomena. The first of these mechanisms is called *familiarization*, the second is called *selective forgetting*. The familiarization mechanism emerged in the course of constructing a theory of human rote memory, the forgetting mechanism in the course of trying to discover why the organization of the first theorem-proving program, the Logic Theorist, was more effective in solving problems than the organization of early versions of the General Problem Solver. Neither mechanism was devised, then, with incubation and illumination in mind; they were introduced into the theory to meet other requirements imposed by the data on problem solving.

1. *Familiarization.* Thinking processes make use of certain means in the central nervous system for holding symbols in short-term or "immediate" memory. Little is known of the neurophysiological substrate of immediate memory, but a good deal is known about its phenomenal characteristics. Most important, the number of symbols that can be stored in immediate memory is severely limited—in George Miller's words, "seven, plus or minus two." But a "symbol" can serve as the name for anything that can be recognized as familiar and that has information associated with it in permanent memory. Thus "*a*" is a symbol; so is "Lincoln's Gettysburg Address." For most native speakers of English "criminal lawyer" is a symbol, but for a person just learning the language, the phrase may constitute a pair of symbols denoting a lawyer with certain antisocial tendencies.

The important facts are (1) that only about seven symbols can be held and manipulated in immediate memory at one time and (2) that anything can become a symbol through repeated exposure to it, or familiarization. Familiarization involves storing in *permanent* memory information that allows the symbol to be recognized and a single symbol or "name" to be substituted for it.

Since immediate memory can only hold a few symbols at a time, complex structures can only be acquired by gradually building them up from substructures which are formed, in turn, from still smaller substructures. As each substructure is learned and stored in permanent memory, the symbol that serves as its "name" internally can be used in immediate memory as a single chunk when combining it with other substructures. Thus, a total structure of unlimited size can be assembled without the need for holding more than a few symbols in immediate memory at any given moment. Lincoln's Gettysburg Address is memorized by assembling phrases out of words (which are already familiar units), sentences out of phrases, paragraphs out of sentences, and so on.

Familiarization processes, for reconciling the limits of immediate memory with the needs for storing information structures of unlimited size and complexity in permanent memory, are incorporated in the information-processing theory of memorization called EPAM (Elementary Perceiver and Memorizer), a program that has successfully accounted for a wide range of laboratory data on human memorizing.[7] We will assume here that these same processes go on during complex problem solving, so that in later stages of problem solving complex units are available that existed only as disconnected particulars at an earlier stage.

In proving mathematical theorems it is common first to introduce and prove some subsidiary theorems, or lemmas, which then enter as premises in the proof of the final theorem. The lemma serves to sum up a whole segment of the proof so that the name of the lemma can be used as premise in place of that segment. It should not be assumed that all or most familiarization is as deliberate or conscious as this use of lemmas by mathematicians, but the processes are analogical and perform the same function.

2. *Selective Forgetting.* A second mechanism to be found in information-processing theories of problem solving that is essential to our proposed explanation of incubation and illumination involves more rapid forgetting of some memory contents than of others. The selective forgetting rests, in turn, on the distinction between forms of short-term and long-term memory.

In the typical organization of a problem-solving program, the solution efforts are guided and controlled by a hierarchy or "tree" of goals and subgoals. Thus, the subject starts out with the goal of solving the original problem. In trying to reach this goal, he generates a subgoal that will take him part of the way (if it is achieved) and addresses himself to that subgoal. If the subgoal is achieved, he may then return to the now-modified original goal. If difficulties arise in achieving the subgoal, sub-subgoals may be erected to deal with them.

The operation of such a process requires the goal hierarchy to be held in memory. If a subgoal is achieved, it can be forgotten, but the tree of unattained goals must be retained. In human problem solvers this retention is not always perfect, of course. When part of the structure is lost, the subject says, "Where am I?" or "Now why was I trying to get that result?" and may have to go over some of the same ground to get back into context—i.e., to locate himself in that part of the tree that has been retained in memory. If we were designing such a system, instead of probing the one that human beings possess, we would specify that the goal tree be held in some kind of temporary memory, since it is a dynamic structure, whose function is to guide search, and it is not needed (or certainly not all of it) when the problem solution has been found. Our hypothesis is that human beings are also constructed in this way—that the goal tree is held in a relatively short-term memory.

During the course of problem solving, a second memory structure is being built up. First of all, new complexes are being familiarized, so that they can be handled by the processing system as units. In addition, the problem solver is noticing various features of the problem environment and is storing some of these in memory. If he is studying a chess position, for example, in the course of his explorations he may notice that a particular piece is undefended or that another piece is pinned against the queen.

This kind of information is perceived while the problem solver is addressing himself to particular subgoals. What use is made of it at the time it is noted depends on what subgoal is directing attention at that moment. But some of this information is also transferred to more permanent forms of memory and is associated with the problem environment—in this example, with the chess position. This information about the environment is used, in turn, in the processes that erect new subgoals and that work toward subgoal achievement. Hence, over the longer run, this information influences the growth of the subgoal tree. To have a short name for it (since it is now a familiar unit for us!), I will call the information about the task environment that is noticed in the course of problem solution and fixated in permanent (or relatively long-term) memory the "blackboard."

The course of problem solving, then, involves continuous inter-action between goal tree and blackboard.[8] In the course of pursuing goals, information is added to the blackboard. This information, in turn, helps to determine what new goals and subgoals will be set up. During periods of persistent activity, the problem solver will always be working in local goal contexts, and information added to the blackboard will be used, in the short run, only if it is relevant in those contexts.

What happens, now, if the problem solver removes himself from the task for a time? Information he has been holding in relatively short-term memory will begin to disappear, and to disappear more rapidly than information in long-term memory. But we have hypothesized that the goal tree is held in short-term memory, the blackboard in long-term memory. Hence, when the problem solver next takes up the task, many or most of the finer twigs and branches of the goal tree will have disappeared. He will begin again, with one of the higher level goals, to reconstruct that tree—but now with the help of a very different set of information, on the blackboard, than he had the first time he went down the tree.

In general, we would expect the problem solver, in his renewed examination of the problem, to follow a quite different path than he did originally. Since his blackboard now has better information about the problem environment than it did the first time, he has better cues to find the correct path. Under these circumstances (and remembering the tremendous differences a few hints can produce in problem solution), solutions may appear quickly that had previously eluded him in protracted search.

There is almost no direct evidence at the present time for the validity of this explanation of incubation and illumination. (I have been able, introspectively, to account for my most recent illumination experience quite simply in these terms, but perhaps my introspections are compromised as witnesses.) It invokes, however, only mechanisms that have already been incorporated in problem-solving theories. It does leave one aspect of the phenomena unaccounted for—it does not explain how the problem that the problem solver has temporarily (consciously) abandoned is put back on the agenda by unconscious processes. It does, however, account for the suddenness of solution without calling on the subconscious to perform elaborate processes, or processes different from those it and the conscious perform in the normal course of problem-solving activity. Nor does it postulate that the unconscious is capable of random searches through immense problem spaces for the solution.

It is difficult, in brief compass, to give an actual example of the tree-blackboard scheme in operation, but a schematized hypothetical example will show in general how the mechanism operates. Suppose that we assign "values" to nodes on the goal tree, the values representing estimates of the reward that could be achieved by searching further from the corresponding nodes. The purpose of the search is to find a node with a value of at least 20—such a node represents a solution of the problem (Figure 1).

A reasonable search rule, starting from any given node, would be to search next from the subbranch with the highest value. Thus, if the problem solver were at node G he would pick up branch J, with value 12, next, then the subbranch P (value 15) of that branch, the sub-subbranch Q (value 8), and so on.

Suppose that, in addition, each time a new node was generated, its name and value were added to a list on a blackboard, and that as soon as the subnodes of that node had been generated, the name and value of the node was erased. The blackboard would then contain, at any moment, the names and values of all nodes that had been generated but had not yet been explored. A possible search rule, different from the one previously mentioned, would be always to pick for next exploration the node on the blackboard with the highest value.

Using the first search rule, the search of this particular hypothetical tree would proceed: *A-B-E-G-J-P-Q-* . . . Using the second search rule, the search of the tree would proceed: *A-B-E-C-F-I-M*, reaching the solution. For, the branch *C* with value 11, generated at the same time as *B*, but not immediately investigated, would be selected from the blackboard in preference to the subgoal *G*, with value only 9, of goal *E*.

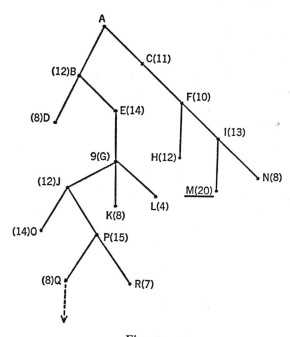

Figure 1

Now our theory of incubation and illumination derives from the hypothesis that during continued attention to a problem, search tends to be context-determined and to follow something like the first rule. During incubation, the tree disappears, leaving the blackboard, and when search resumes, it begins on the basis of the second rule.

Experiments with programs for discovering mating combinations in chess have shown that very different exploration trees are generated in game situations by the two rules, and that the second rule usually finds the mating combinations with far less search than the first. It would be easy, then, to reproduce incubation and illumination phenomena with these programs—by starting a search with a program using the first rule, but maintaining a blackboard, then at some point switching for a short time to the second rule.

As was mentioned earlier, the same point is demonstrated by comparison of the problem-solving power of the Logic Theorist with the power of early versions of the General Problem Solver. Without going into detail, it can simply be stated that the Logic Theorist used a form of the tree-and-blackboard scheme, while search in the General Problem Solver was always determined in the local context of current goals.[9]

Problem Formulation in Scientific Discovery

The theories described in the previous section postulate organized systems of processes which, when a problem of an appropriate kind is posed, will go to work on that problem and attempt to solve it. Scientific development involves not only solving problems, but posing them as well. In some discussions of creativity, asking the right questions is regarded as the crucial creative act; answering questions, in this view, is a relatively routine activity once the questions have been properly posed.

The view that question asking rather than question answering is the critical part of the creative process would be hard to defend in its extreme form. Perhaps it even illustrates itself, for in implying a sharp boundary between question asking and question answering, it may be posing the wrong question. If the issue were properly stated, we would see, first, that reformulation of questions—more generally, modification of representations—is one of the problem-solving processes; second, that the task of formulating a problem can itself be posed as a problem to a problem-solving system.

In exploring the relation of question asking to question answering, Thomas Kuhn's distinction between normal and revolutionary science becomes relevant. Normal science, he argues, does not have to pose its own questions. These questions have already been formulated for it by previous scientific revolutions. The textbooks and classics of science, incorporating the revolution, served "for a time implicitly to define the legitimate problems and methods of a research field for succeeding generations of practitioners." They can do this for two reasons: "Their achievement [is] sufficiently unprecedented to attract an enduring group of adherents away from competing modes of scientific activity. Simultaneously, it [is] sufficiently open-ended to leave all sorts of problems for the redefined group of practitioners to resolve."

Kuhn refers to achievements that share these two characteristics as "paradigms," and he defines normal science as scientific activity within the framework of received paradigms, revolutionary science as scientific activity that establishes new paradigms.[10] Within Kuhn's theory, it is easy to state who poses the problems for investigators engaged in normal science: Their problems come from the paradigms themselves. We must either define "creativity" so that it does not imply question asking as well as question answering, or we must conclude that creativity is not involved in normal science. The choice is one of definition.[11]

Is it necessary to adduce entirely new mechanisms to account for problem formulation in revolutionary science? Kuhn argues that it is not, for the paradigms of any given revolution arise out of the normal science of the previous period. Normal science, in Kuhn's account, leads to the discovery of anomalies, of facts that are difficult or impossible to reconcile with the accepted paradigms. The new problem then—the problem to which the prospective revolutionists address themselves—is to modify the paradigm, or replace it with another that is consistent with the facts, including the new anomalous ones.

In sum, we do not need a separate theory of problem formulation. A problem-solving system of the kind we have been considering—capable of generating subproblems from an initial problem, and capable of testing the adequacy of its solutions by generating new data about the environment—such a system will continue indefinitely to create new problems for itself. Problem formulation in science is to be understood by looking at the continuity of the whole stream of scientific endeavor.

A theory of scientific discovery adequate to explain revolutionary as well as normal science must account not only for the origins of problems, but for the origins of representations, of paradigms, as well. I do not underestimate the importance of this topic, but I shall not undertake to deal with it at any length here. In a previous paper, my colleagues A. Newell and J. C. Shaw, and I have made some general observations about it to which I refer the reader.[12] I shall add just a few more comments.

New representations, like new problems, do not spring from the brow of Zeus, but emerge by gradual—and very slow—stages. The caution stated in the opening pages of this chapter may be recalled: We must not overestimate the capacity of the human mind to invent new representations. The number of such inventions in human history has been very small.

Problem solvers use representations of the spatial relations of objects (engineering drawings are a relatively sophisticated and formalized example). They use representations of the abstract relations of objects (as, for example, in flow charts, genealogical charts, and chemical formulae). They use representations of programs (for example, systems of differential equations, computer programs). One can list a small number of other basic forms of representation and a somewhat larger number of specialized formats within each of these basic forms. The list is not long, and it is hard to find items for it whose history does not go back beyond the Christian era. (The *program* is probably the most recently developed broad form of representation, but it must not be forgotten that a recipe is a program, as is an algorithm like Eratosthenes' sieve. The differential equation represents a highly important subclass within this broad class of representations.)

Thus, our general answer to the question, "Where do representations come from?" is the same as our answer to the question, "Where do problems come from?" Representations arise by modification and development of previous representations as problems arise by modification and development of previous problems. A system that is to explain human problem solving and scientific discovery does not need to incorporate a highly powerful mechanism for inventing completely novel representations. If it did contain such a meachanism, it would be a poor theory, for it would predict far more novelty than occurs.

Conclusion

Theories are now available that incorporate mechanisms sufficient to account for some of the principal phenomena of problem solving in at least certain relatively well-structured situations. The aim of this chapter has been to ask how much these theories need to be modified or extended in order to account for problem solving in science. The general tenor of the argument has been that problem solving in science, like problem solving in the psychological laboratory, is a tedious, painstaking process of selective trial and error. Our knowledge of it does not suggest the presence of completely unknown processes far more powerful than those that have been observed in the laboratory.

Several kinds of objections can be raised, and have been, against this "minimalist" theory. One objection is that it does not account for striking phenomena like incubation and illumination. To meet this objection, a mechanism has been proposed that is believed sufficient to produce exactly these kinds of phenomena.

Another objection is that the theory only explains how problems are solved that have already been stated and for which there exist well-defined representations. This objection has not been answered in detail, but an answer has been sketched in terms of the broader social environment within which scientific work takes place. Most scientific activity goes on within the framework of established paradigms. Even in revolutionary science, which creates those paradigms, the problems and representations are rooted in the past; they are not created out of whole cloth.

We are still very far from a complete understanding of the whole structure of the psychological processes involved in making scientific discoveries. But perhaps our analysis makes somewhat more plausible the hypothesis that at the core of this structure is the same kind of selective trial-and-error search that has already been shown to constitute the basis for human problem-solving activity in the psychological laboratory.

NOTES

The preparation of this chapter has been aided by research grants from The Carnegie Corporation and the National Institutes of Health (MH-07722-01). Most of the ideas in it have been developed in collaboration with my colleague Allen Newell. See his "Some Problems of Basic Organization in Problem-Solving Programs," in *Self-Organizing Systems,* eds. Yovits, Jacobi, and Goldstein (New York: Spartan Press, 1962).

1. Obviously, I am not immune to this tendency.
2. For further discussion, see the previous chapter and A. Newell, J. C. Shaw, and H. A. Simon, "The Processes of Creative Thinking" in Gruber *Contemporary Approaches to Creative Thinking,* eds. Gruber, Terrell, and Wertheimer (New York: Atherton Press, 1962).
3. There are numerous anecdotes, some true, some fictitious, about the role of luck in invention. It is clear, however, that chance events played a role in: discovering vulcanization of rubber, the sweetening power of saccharine, developers in photography, and many other discoveries. See Joseph Rossman, *The Psychology of the Inventor* (Washington: The Inventors Publishing Co., 1931), Chap. 7.
4. A. de Groot, *Thought and Choice in Chess* (Amsterdam: Mouton, 1965).
5. Henri Poincaré, *Mathematical Creation,* reprinted in *The World of Mathematics,* ed. James R. Newman, IV, 2041–50.
6. Mary Henle begins her essay on "The Birth and Death of Ideas" with the sentence, "Perhaps the most astonishing thing about creative thinking is that creative thinkers can tell us so little about it" (in *Contemporary Approaches to Creative Thinking,* Chap. 1). Why astonishing? Would we say: "Perhaps the most astonishing thing about neurotic behavior is that persons suffering from neuroses can tell us so little about it?" Why would we expect, a priori, self-consciousness to be more characteristic of the one than of the other?
7. For an introduction to EPAM see E. A. Feigenbaum, "The Simulation of Verbal Learning Behavior," pp. 297–309 in *Computers and Thought,* eds. Feigenbaum and Feldman (New York: McGraw-Hill, 1964).
8. The role of goal tree and blackboard in the organization of problem solving have been discussed by Allen Newell, in "Some Problems of Basic Organization."

9. See A. Newell, J. C. Shaw, and H. A. Simon, "Empirical Explorations of the Logic Theory Machine," and A. Newell and H. A. Simon, "GPS, A Program that Simulates Human Thought," in Feigenbaum and Feldman, eds., pp. 109–33, 279–93.

10. Kuhn, pp. 10–12.

11. This account elides some important details. Generating subgoals from a more general goal is a form of question asking also, which is a part both of normal science and of our problem-solving theories. Since this process has already been considered, our only present concern is with problems whose generation cannot be explained in this way.

12. "The Processes of Creative Thinking," pp. 98–104.

DUDLEY SHAPERE

University of Chicago

Meaning and Scientific Change

The laboratory technician has succeeded in *implementing* by means of the atomic pile the Einsteinian principle of inertia of energy. The reality which slumbered in his materials was *provoked* by mathematically-founded experiments. Seen from the nuclear level, one might well say that matter evokes a neo-materialism in which substance and energy are interchangeable entities. Reality is no longer nature pure and simple. It must be wrought to become the object of scientific experiment. Thus, the philosophy of contemporary science as it issued from the revolutions of the beginning of the century appears as a dialectic of enlightened rationalism and elaborated realism. In order to lose none of the philosophical implications of science the two concepts of invariance and conservation must be synthesized in an *abstract-concrete* philosophy by introducing an additional unifying trait in the form of an *invariance-conservation*. Here is a philosophical *doublet* which would be mutilated by an unilateral philosophical interpretation, whether rationalistic or realistic. Science requires hereafter a bi-certitude. It must satisfy the requirements of mathematical coherence and minute experimental verification.

> —Gaston Bachelard
> "The Philosophic Dialectic of the Concepts
> of Relativity," in *Albert Einstein, Philoso-*
> *pher-Scientist,* II

The Revolt Against Positivism

IN THE PAST DECADE, a revolution—or at least a rebellion—has occurred in the philosophy of science. Views have been advanced which claim to be radically new not only in their doctrines about science and its evolution and structure, but also in their conceptions of the methods appropriate to solving the problems of the philosophy of science, and even as to what those problems themselves are. It will be the primary purpose of this paper to examine some of the tenets of this revolution, in order to determine what there is in them of permanent value for all people who wish to understand the nature of science.

But before proceeding to this study, it will be worthwhile to examine some of the sources of these new views; and the first thing to do in this regard will be to summarize (at considerable risk of oversimplification) some of the main features of the approach to the philosophy of science against which these new approaches are in part reacting.[1]

The mainstream of philosophy of science during the second quarter of this century—the so-called "logical empiricist" or "logical positivist" movement and related views—was characterized by a heavy reliance on the techniques of mathematical logic for formulating and dealing with its problems. Philosophy of science (and, indeed, philosophy in general) was pronounced to be "the logic of science," this epithet meaning to attribute to the subject a number of important features. First, philosophy of science was to be conceived of on the analogy of formal logic: just as formal logic, ever since Aristotle, has been supposed to be concerned with the "form" rather than with the "content" of propositions and arguments, so also philosophy of science was to deal with the "form"—the "logical form"—of scientific statements rather than with their "content," with, for example, the logical structure of *all possible* statements claiming to be scientific laws, rather than with any particular such statements; with the logical skeleton of *any possible* scientific theory, rather than with particular actual scientific theories; with the logical pattern of any possible scientific explanation, rather than with particular actual scientific explanations; with the logical relations between evidence-statements and theoretical conclusions, rather than with particular scientific arguments. Of course, the philosophical conclusions arrived at were supposed, in principle, to be tested against actual scientific practice, but the actual work of the philosopher of science was with the construction of adequate formal representations of scientific expressions in general, rather than with the details of particular current scientific work (and much less with past scientific work).[2]

Alternatively, the analogy between logic and "the logic of science" can be drawn in another manner which is in some ways even more revealing. Just as modern logicians make a distinction between logic proper—particular systems of logic, formulated in an "object language"—and metalogic, which consists of an analysis of expressions (like "true," "provable," "is a theorem") which are applied to statements and sequences of statements expressed in the object language, so also "the logic of science" can be seen as concerning itself primarily with the analysis of expressions which are applied to actual scientific terms or statements—which are used in talking about science (expressions like "is a law," "is meaningful," "is an explanation," "is a theory," "is evidence for," "confirms to a higher degree than").

On the basis of either analogy, some conclusions can be drawn which will be of importance for our later discussion. First, since philosophy of science, so conceived, does not deal with particular scientific theories, it is immune to the vicissitudes of science—the coming and going of particular scientific theories, for those changes have to do with the content of science, whereas the philosopher of science is concerned with its structure; not with specific mortal theories, but with the characteristics of any possible theory, with the meaning of the word "theory" itself. It also follows that the philosopher of science, insofar as he is successful, will provide us with a *final* analysis of the expressions which he analyzes; in giving us the characteristics of, for instance, all possible explanations, he is *a fortiori* giving us the formal characteristics of all future explanations. It is thus assumed that a revealing account can be given of such terms as "explanation" which will hold true always, although particular scientific explanations may change from theory to theory, nevertheless that which is *essential* to being an explanation—those features of such accounts which make them deserve the title "explanation"—can be laid down once and for all; and furthermore, those essential characteristics can be expressed in purely logical terms, as characteristics of the form or structure of explanation.

Besides conceiving of the philosophy of science along the lines of formal logic as a model, the "logical empiricist" tradition also *used* the techniques of modern mathematical logic in approaching their problems. Thus, fatal objections were raised against proposed views because of some flaw in the logical formulation of the position; and such difficulties were to be overcome not by abandoning the safe ground of formulation in terms of the already well-developed mathematical logic, but rather by giving a more satisfactory reformulation in terms of that logic. Again, scientific theories were conceived of as being, or as most easily treated as being, axiomatic (or axiomatizable) systems whose connection with experience was to be achieved by "rules of interpretation," the general characteristics of which could again be stated in formal terms. The conclusions of philosophy of science were therefore supposed to be applicable only to the most highly developed scientific theories, those which had reached a stage of articulation and sophistication which permitted treating them as precisely—and completely—formulated axiomatic systems with precise rules of interpretation. (Whether any scientific theory has ever achieved such a pristine state of completeness, or whether it even makes sense to talk about precision in such an absolute sense in connection with scientific concepts and theories, is questionable.) Hence, an examination of the history of science was considered irrelevant to the philosophy of science. This concentration on perfected (even idealized) systems was part of what was embodied in the slogan, "There is no logic of discovery." Insofar as the development of science was considered at all, it tended to be looked upon as a process of ever-increasing accumulation of knowledge, in which previous facts and theories would be incorporated into (or reduced to) later theories as special cases applicable in limited domains of experience.

All this, in summary, constituted the "logical" aspect of logical empiricism. The "empiricist" aspect consisted in the belief, on the part of those philosophers, that all scientific theory must, in some precise and formally specifiable sense, be grounded in experience, both as to the meanings of terms and the acceptability of assertions. To the end of showing how the meanings of terms were grounded in experience, a distinction was made between "theoretical terms" and "observation terms," and a central part of the program of logical empiricism consisted of the attempt to show how the former kind of terms could be "interpreted" on the basis of the latter. Observation terms were taken to raise no problems regarding their meanings, since they referred directly to experience. As to the acceptability of assertions, the program was to show how scientific hypotheses were related to empirical evidence verifying or falsifying them (or confirming or disconfirming them); and if there were any other factors (such as "simplicity") besides empirical evidence influencing the acceptability of scientific hypotheses, those other factors, if at all possible, should be characterized in formal terms as rigorously as the concept of verification (or confirmation).

The views which have been presented to date within the general logical empiricist framework have not met with unqualified success. Although analyses of meaning, of the difference between theoretical and observation terms and of the interpretation of the former on the basis of the latter, of lawlikeness, of explanation, of acceptability of theories, etc., have been developed in considerable detail, they have all been subjected to serious criticism. Continuing efforts have been made to adjust and extend those analyses to meet the criticisms—and, after all, the logical empiricist programs are not self-contradictory *enterprises,* so that the hope can always be held out that they will yet be carried through to success. But because of the multitude of difficulties that have been exposed, many philosophers think that an entirely new approach to the problems of the philosophy of science is required.[3]

In addition to such criticisms of specific views, however, objections have also been raised against the general logical empiricist approach of trying to solve the problems of the philosophy of science by application of the techniques of, and on analogy with, formal logic. For in its concentration on technical problems of logic, the logical empiricist tradition has tended to lose close contact with science, and the discussions have often been accused of irrelevancy to real science. Even if this criticism is sometimes overstated, there is surely something to it, for in their involvement with logical details (often without more than cursory discussion of any application to science at all), in their claim to be talking only about thoroughly developed scientific theories (if there are any such), and in their failure (or refusal) to attend at all to questions about the historical development of actual science, logical empiricists have certainly laid themselves open to the criticism of being, despite their professed empiricism, too rationalistic in failing to keep an attentive eye on the facts which constitute the subject matter of the philosophy of science.

Such disenchantment with the general mode of approach that has been dominant in the philosophy of science since at least the early days of the Vienna Circle has been reinforced by developments in other quarters. Many proponents of the "rebellion" against logical empiricism have been heavily influenced by the later philosophy of Ludwig Wittgenstein,[4] which was itself partly a reaction against the attempt to deal, through the "ideal language" of logic, with all possible cases. Wittgenstein warned that a great many functions of language can be ignored if language is looked upon simply as a calculus, and philosophers of science have found application for this warning by pointing out functions of, say, scientific laws which could not be noticed by looking at them solely in terms of their logical form.[5]

Other thinkers have been influenced in turning to a new, nonpositivistic approach to philosophy of science by developments in science itself. This is particularly the case with Paul Feyerabend, whose work departs not only from a reaction against contemporary empiricism, but also from his opposition to certain features of the Copenhagen Interpretation of quantum theory.[6] Feyerabend attacks as dogmatic the view of the Copenhagen Interpretation according to which all future developments of microphysical theory will have to maintain certain features of the present theory, or will otherwise fall into formal or empirical inconsistency. He characterizes this view as being opposed to the spirit of true empiricism; but, as we shall see shortly, he finds the same sort of dogmatism inherent in contemporary (and past) versions of empiricism also, particularly in current analyses of the nature of scientific explanation and of the reduction of one scientific theory to another.

But by far the most profound influence shaping the new trends in the philosophy of science has come from results attained by the newly professionalized discipline of the history of science. I have already mentioned that the logical empiricist tradition has tended to ignore the history of science as being irrelevant to the philosophy of science, on the ground that there could be no "logic of discovery," the processes by which scientific discovery and advance are achieved being fit subject matter for the psychologist and the sociologist, but hardly for the logician. I also noted that, insofar as logical empiricists considered the history of science at all, they tended to look on it as largely a record of the gradual removal of superstition, prejudice, and other impediments to scientific progress in the form of an ever-increasing accumulation and synthesis of knowledge—an interpretation of the history of science which Thomas Kuhn has called "the concept of development-by-accumulation." [7] This interpretation, coupled with the logical empiricists' exclusive concern with "completely developed" theories, led them to ignore as unworthy of their attention even the ways in which incomplete theories ultimately eventuated in "completely developed" (or more completely developed) ones. But in the years since the pioneering historical research of Pierre Duhem early in this century, the history of science has come a long way from the days when most writers on the subject were either themselves confirmed positivists or else scientists, ignorant of the details of history, who read the past as a record of great men throwing off the shackles of a dark inheritance and struggling toward modern enlightenment. The subject has developed high standards of scholarship, and much careful investigation has brought out features of science which seemed clearly to conflict with the positivist portrayal of it and its evolution. Many older theories that were supposedly overthrown and superseded—Aristotelian and medieval mechanics, the phlogiston and caloric theories—have been found to contain far more than the simple-minded error and superstition which were all that was attributed to them by earlier, less scholarly and more positivistic historians of science. Indeed, those theories have been alleged to be as deserving of the name "science" as anything else that goes by that name. On the other hand, previous pictures of the work of such men as Galileo and Newton have been found riddled with errors, and the "Galileo-myth" and the "Newton-myth," products of an excessively Baconian and positivistic interpretation, have been mercilessly exposed.[8] Newton made hypotheses after all, and rather alarmingly nonempirical ones at that; and, it is suggested, he had to make them. Galileo, now often demoted to a status little above that of press agent for the scientific revolution, did not base his views on experiments, and even when he performed them (which was more rarely and ineffectively than had previously been supposed), he did not draw conclusions from them, but rather used them to illustrate conclusions at which he had already arrived—ignoring, in the process, any deviations therefrom.

Further, the *kind* of change involved in the history of science has been found (so the story continues) not to be a mere process of accumulation of knowledge, synthesized in more and more encompassing theories. Contemporary historians of science have emphasized again and again that the transition from Aristotelian to seventeenth-century dynamics required not a closer attention to facts (as older histories would have it), but rather, in the words of Herbert Butterfield, "handling the same bundle of data as before, but placing them in a new system of relations with one another by giving them a different framework, all of which virtually means putting on a different kind of thinking-cap."[9] Such words as "virtually" tend to be dropped as deeper and more sweeping conclusions are drawn. The underlying philosophy of the sixteenth- and seventeenth-century scientific revolution has been held to have been strongly infused, not with Baconian empiricism, but rather—irony of ironies!—with Platonic rationalism.[10] Such conclusions have been generalized still further: While experiment plays far less of a role than many philosophers have supposed in the great fundamental scientific revolutions, certain types of presuppositions, not classifiable in any of the usual traditional senses as "empirical," play a crucial role. The most pervasive changes in the history of science are to be characterized, according to these writers, in terms of the abandonment of one set of such presuppositions and their replacement by another. It is no wonder that Thomas Kuhn begins his influential book, *The Structure of Scientific Revolutions*, with the words, "History, if viewed as a repository for more than anecdote or chronology, could produce a decisive transformation in the image of science by which we are now possessed."[11] And it is no wonder, either, that many of the leaders in presenting this new image—Kuhn, Alexandre Koyré—have been historians of science. Nor is it any accident that many philosophers dissatisfied with current logical empiricist approaches to science—Paul Feyerabend,[12] N. R. Hanson,[13] Robert Palter,[14] Stephen Toulmin[15]—have found inspiration for their views in the work of contemporary historians of science, and have even, in some cases, made original contributions to historical research.

The view that, fundamental to scientific investigation and development, there are certain very pervasive sorts of presuppositions, is the chief substantive characteristic of what I have called the new revolution in the philosophy of science (although the authors concerned do not usually use the word "presupposition" to refer to these alleged underlying principles of science). Of course, there have been presupposition analyses of science before, but the present movement (if it can be called that) is different from its predecessors in certain important respects. Any consistent body of propositions, scientific or not, contains "presuppositions" in one sense, namely, in the sense of containing a (really, more than one) subset of propositions which are related to the remainder of the propositions of the set as axioms to theorems. But these new sorts of presuppositions are alleged to be related to scientific methods and assertions not simply (if at all) as axioms to theorems, but in some other, deeper sense which will be discussed in the course of this paper. For most writers, these presuppositions are not what are ordinarily taken to be fundamental scientific laws or theories or to contain the ordinary kind of scientific concepts; they are more fundamental even than that —more "global,"[16] as Kuhn says. Even when they are called "theories," as by Feyerabend, it turns out (as we shall see) that the author does not really mean that word in any usual sense; and even when the author speaks of a certain scientific law as having the character of a fundamental presupposition—as Toulmin describes the law of inertia—he reinterprets that law in an entirely novel way.

Again, in opposition to what might be called a "Kantian" view, the presuppositions are held to vary from one theory or tradition to another; indeed, what distinguishes one theory or tradition from another ultimately is the set of presuppositions underlying them. Hence, although these writers hold that *some* presuppositions always have been made and (at least according to some authors) must always be made, there is no single set which must always be made. In defending these views, as has been suggested above, the authors make extensive appeal to cases from the history of science.

More positively, different writers characterize these "presuppositions," as I have called them, in different ways—but, as we shall see, with much in common, despite significant differences. Koyré speaks of a "philosophic background" [17] influencing the science of a time; Palter, too, speaks of "'philosophic' principles which tend to diversify scientific theories." [18] Toulmin, in *Foresight and Understanding,* calls them "ideals of natural order" or "paradigms," and describes them as "standards of rationality and intelligibility" [19] providing "fundamental patterns of expectation." [20] "We see the world through them to such an extent that we forget what it would look like without them"; [21] they determine what questions we will ask as well as "giving significance to [facts] and even determining what are 'facts' for us at all." [22] Finally, "Our 'ideals of natural order' mark off for us those happenings in the world around us which do require explanation, by contrasting them with 'the natural course of events'—i.e., those events which do not." [23] He suggests that "These ideas and methods, and even the controlling aims of science itself, are continually evolving"; [24] and inasmuch as what counts as a problem, a fact, and an explanation (among other things) change with change of ideal, it follows that we cannot hope to gain an understanding of these basic features of science by merely examining logical form; we must examine the content of particular scientific views. "In studying the development of scientific ideas, we must always look out for the ideals and paradigms men rely on to make Nature intelligible." [25]

Kuhn's *The Structure of Scientific Revolutions* presents a view which is in many respects similar to that of Toulmin. Analyzing the notion of "normal science" as a tradition of workers unified by their acceptance of a common "paradigm," Kuhn contrasts normal science with scientific revolutions: "Scientific revolutions are . . . non-cumulative episodes in which an older paradigm is replaced in whole or in part by an incompatible new one." [26] Kuhn considers his paradigms as being not merely rules, laws, theories, or the like, or a mere sum thereof, but something more "global," [27] from which rules, theories, and the like can be abstracted, but to which no mere statement of rules, theories, and so forth can do justice. A paradigm consists of a "strong network of commitments—conceptual, theoretical, instrumental, and methodological"; [28] among these commitments are "quasi-metaphysical" [29] ones. A paradigm is, or at least includes, "some implicit body of intertwined theoretical and methodological belief that permits selection, evaluation, and criticism"; [30] it is "the source of the methods, problem-field, and standards of solution accepted by any mature scientific community at any given time." [31] Even what counts as a fact is determined by the paradigm. Because of this pervasive paradigm-dependence, "the reception of a new paradigm often necessitates a redefinition of the corresponding science. . . . And as the problems change, so, often, does the standard that distinguishes a real scientific solution from a mere metaphysical speculation, word game, or mathematical play. The normal-scientific tradition that emerges from a scientific revolution is not only incompatible but often actually incommensurable with that which has gone before." [32] Thus, a paradigm entails "changes in the standards governing permissible problems, concepts, and explanations" [33]—changes that are so fundamental that the meanings of the terms used in two different paradigm traditions are "often actually incommensurable," incomparable.

It thus appears that there are at least the following theses held in common by a number of proponents of the "new philosophy of science" (including, as we shall see, Feyerabend):

a) A *presupposition theory of meaning:* the meanings of all scientific terms, whether "factual" ("observational") or "theoretical," are determined by the theory or paradigm or ideal of natural order which underlies them or in which they are embedded. (This thesis is in opposition to the traditional view of logical empiricism to the effect that there is an absolute, theory-independent distinction between "theoretical terms" and "observation terms," the latter having the same meanings, or at least a core of common meaning, for all (or at least for competing) scientific theories, and against which different theories are judged as to adequacy. It also opposes the attempt to distinguish, in a final manner, "meaningful" ("verifiable," "confirmable," or perhaps "falsifiable") statements from "meaningless" ("metaphysical") ones.

b) A *presupposition theory of problems* that will define the domain of scientific inquiry, *and of what can count as an explanation* in answer to those problems. (Most obviously, this thesis is directed against the attempt of Hempel and others to give a "deductive-nomological and statistical" analysis of the concept of scientific explanation.)

c) A *presupposition theory of the relevance of facts to theory, of the degree of relevance* (i.e., of the relative importance of different facts), *and, generally, of the relative acceptability or unacceptability of different scientific conclusions* (laws, theories, predictions). (This thesis is directed primarily against the possibility, or at least the value as an interpretation of actual scientific procedure, of a formal "inductive logic" in Carnap's sense.)

It will be the purpose of this essay to examine critically some aspects of this revolutionary philosophy of science, especially what I have called the "presupposition theory of meaning," although, in later parts of the paper, something will be said also about other facets of these new ideas. I will focus my critical examination on one particular view, that presented by Paul Feyerabend in a number of papers, especially in his "Explanation, Reduction, and Empiricism," "Problems of Microphysics," and "Problems of Empiricism." After discussing his views as presented in those papers, I will consider his recent attempt, in a paper entitled "On the 'Meaning' of Scientific Terms," to clarify his position. At the end of this discussion of Feyerabend's work, I will compare my criticisms of him with criticisms which I have raised previously against Kuhn.[34] This comparison will enable us to see not only some deeply underlying mistakes (or rather excesses) of the "new philosophy of science," but also, through an examination of a case study in the development of science, some of the not insignificant elements of positive value in it.

Feyerabend bases his position on an attack on two principles following from the theory of explanation which is "one of the cornerstones of contemporary philosophical empiricism."[35] These two principles are (1) *the consistency condition:* "Only such theories are . . . admissible in a given domain which either *contain* the theories already used in this domain, or which are at least *consistent* with them inside the domain"; (2) *the condition of meaning invariance:* "meanings will have to be invariant with respect to scientific progress; that is, all future theories will have to be framed in such a manner that their use in explanations does not affect what is said by the theories, or factual reports to be explained."[36]

In opposition to these two conditions, Feyerabend argues (1) that scientific theories are, and ought to be, inconsistent with one another, and (2) that "the meaning of every term we use depends upon the theoretical context in which it occurs. Words do not 'mean' something in isolation; they obtain their meanings by being part of a theoretical system."[37] This dependence of meaning on theoretical context extends also to what are classified as "observation terms"; such terms, like any others, depend for their meanings on the theories in which they occur. The meanings of theoretical terms do not depend (as they were alleged to by the logical empiricist tradition) on their being interpreted in terms of an antecedently understood observation-language; on the contrary, Feyerabend's view implies a reversal

in the relation between theory and observation. The philosophies we have been discussing so far [i.e., versions of empiricism] assumed that observation sentences are meaningful *per se*, that theories which have been separated from observations are not meaningful, and that such theories obtain their interpretation by being connected with some observation language that possesses a stable interpretation. According to the point of view I am advocating, the meaning of observation sentences is determined by the theories with which they are connected. Theories are meaningful independent of observations; observational statements are not meaningful unless they have been connected with theories. . . . It is therefore the *observation sentence* that is in need of interpretation and *not* the theory.[38]

What, then, of the traditional empiricist view that a theory must be tested by confrontation with objective (theory-independent) facts and that one theory is chosen over another because it is more adequate to the facts —facts which are *the same* for both theories? Such factual confrontation, Feyerabend tells us, will not work for the most fundamental scientific theories.

It is usually assumed that observation and experience play a theoretical role by producing an observation sentence that by virtue of its meaning (which is assumed to be determined by the nature of the observation) may *judge* theories. This assumption works well with theories of a low degree of generality whose principles do not touch the principles on which the ontology of the chosen observation language is based. It works well if the theories are compared with respect to a background theory of greater generality that provides a stable meaning for observation sentences. However, this background theory, like any other theory, is itself in need of criticism.[39]

But the background theory cannot be criticized on its own terms; arguments concerning fundamental points of view are "invariably *circular*. They show what is implied in taking for granted a certain point of view, and do not provide the slightest foothold for a possible criticism." [40] How, then, are such theories to be criticized? The theory-dependence of meanings, together with the fact that each theory specifies its own observation-language, implies, according to Feyerabend, that "each theory will have its own experience." [41] This, however, does not prevent the facts revealed by one theory from being relevant to another theory. This means, in Feyerabend's eyes, that in order to criticize high-level background theories, "We must choose a point outside the system or the language defended in order to get an idea of what a criticism would look like." [42] It is necessary to develop alternative theories.

Not only is the description of every single fact dependent on *some* theory . . . , but there also exist facts that cannot be unearthed except with the help of alternatives to the theory to be tested and that become unavailable as soon as such alternatives are excluded.[43]

Both the relevance and the refuting character of many decisive facts can be established only with the help of other theories that, although factually adequate, are not in agreement with the view to be tested. . . . Empiricism demands that the empirical content of whatever knowledge we possess be increased as much as possible. Hence, *the invention of alternatives in addition to the view that stands in the center of discussion constitutes an essential part of the empirical method.*[44]

An adequate empiricism itself therefore requires the detailed development of as many different alternative theories as possible, and "This . . . is the methodological justification of a plurality of theories." [45]

Since meanings vary with theoretical context, and since the purpose of such theoretical pluralism is to expose facts which, while relevant to the theory under consideration, cannot be expressed in terms of that theory, and would not ordinarily be noticed by upholders of that theory (or speakers of that language), it follows that we cannot be satisfied with alternatives that are "created by arbitrarily denying now this and now that component of the dominant point of view." [46] On the contrary, "Alternatives will be the more efficient the more radically they differ from the point of view to be investigated." [47] In fact, "It is . . . better to consider conceptual systems all of whose features deviate from the accepted points of view," [48] although "failure to achieve this in a single step does not entail failure of our epistemological program." [49] Thus "the progress of knowledge may be by replacement, which leaves no stone unturned, rather than by subsumption. . . . A scientist or a philosopher must be allowed to start completely from scratch and to redefine completely his domain of investigation." [50]

There are a number of difficulties with these views, both as to interpreting what, exactly, they are supposed to assert, and—when one can arrive at an interpretation—as to whether they are adequately defended or, even if not, whether they are correct.

First, it is not clear whether Feyerabend believes that it is impossible ever to change a theoretical context (to change a theory) without violating the conditions of meaning invariance and consistency—so that the older empiricist viewpoint cannot be correct—or whether, while those conditions *can*, in some cases at least, be satisfied, it is inadvisable or undesirable to do so. On the one hand, we are led to believe that the theory-dependence of meanings is a necessary truth, that since the meaning of *every* term depends on its theoretical context, therefore a change of theory *must* produce a change of meaning of every term in the theory. But on the other hand, we learn that the two conditions *are* "adopted by some scientists":

The quantum theory seems to be the first theory after the downfall of the Aristotelian physics that has been quite explicitly constructed, at least by some of the inventors, with an eye both on the consistency condition and on the condition of meaning invariance. In this respect it is very different indeed from, say, relativity, which violates both consistency and meaning invariance with respect to earlier theories.[51]

That is to say, the Copenhagen Interpretation of quantum theory, restated by Feyerabend as a "physical hypothesis," holds that the terms "space," "time," "mass," etc., are used by quantum theory in their classical senses; and Feyerabend declares himself "prepared to defend the Copenhagen Interpretation as a physical hypothesis and I am also prepared to admit that it is superior to a host of alternatives." [52] Thus, Feyerabend alleges that this view is evidence for the *possibility* of upholding meaning invariance. If, however, meanings *must* vary with theoretical context, and if—as surely must be admitted under any reasonable interpretation of the expression "difference of theoretical context"—those classical terms occur in a different theoretical context when they occur in quantum-theoretical contexts, then they should have meanings which are *different* from their meanings in classical physics. In short, in Feyerabend's own terms we are hard put to understand his contention, in *Problems of Microphysics*, that the Copenhagen Interpretation (restated as a physical hypothesis), while it is overly dogmatic in barring theories which are inconsistent with it and whose terms differ in meaning from its own, is nevertheless a satisfactory scientific theory.

These difficulties concerning the general thesis of the theory-dependence of meanings have implications for the more specific view that there is no core of observational meaning which is common to all theories and which provides the basis for testing and comparing them. *Can* there be no observational core? Or is it merely *undesirable* to maintain one? Despite the suggestions conveyed by Feyerabend's statements about the relations between theories and meanings, we find that "it is completely up to us to have knowledge by acquaintance and the poverty of content that goes with it or to have hypothetical knowledge, which is corrigible, which can be improved, and which is informative." [53] Again, he tells us that "the ideal of a purely factual theory . . . was first realized by Bohr and his followers . . ." [54]—"factual" because everything in quantum theory, on Bohr's view, is to be expressed in "purely observational" terms, the classical terms "space," "time," "mass," etc. being taken (strangely!) as "purely observational."

Again, although we are told that "the meaning of *every* term we use depends upon the theoretical context in which it occurs" [55]—suggesting that the slightest alteration of theoretical context alters the meaning of every term in that context—Feyerabend introduces, at numerous points, qualifications which appear to contradict this thesis. Thus, "High-level theories . . . *may not* share a single observational statement," [56] although one would suppose that, if they are really different theories, all their terms would be different in meaning, so that it is difficult to see how they *could* share *any* statement. Similar difficulties arise with regard to the qualifications made in such remarks as the following:

Statements that are empirically adequate and are the result of observation (such as "here is a table") *may* have to be reinterpreted . . . because of changes in sometimes very remote parts of the conceptual scheme to which they belong.[57]

. . . the methodological unit to which we must refer when discussing questions of test and empirical content is constituted by a *whole set of partly overlapping, factually adequate, but mutually inconsistent theories.*[58]

The root of such difficulties is, of course, the lack of sufficient explanation and detailed defense which Feyerabend offers of his doctrine of the theory-dependence of meanings. We are given no way of deciding either what counts as a part of the "meaning" of a term or what counts as a "change of meaning" of a term. Correspondingly, we are given no way of deciding what counts as a part of a "theory" or what counts as a "change of theory." Hence, it is not clear what we should say when confronted with proposed objections to Feyerabend's analysis. We may be confronted, for example, with cases of theoretical changes which seem too minor to affect the meanings of the expressions concerned (much less terms "far removed" from the area of change): the addition of an epicycle; a change in the value of a constant; a shift from circular to elliptical orbits; [59] the ascription of a new property to some type of entity. Yet such cases might not be accepted by Feyerabend as counting against him; he might consider such changes as not really being changes of theory (perhaps they are only changes *in* theory, but at what point, exactly, do such changes become major enough to constitute changes of theory— i.e., to affect meanings?). Or, alternatively, perhaps he would consider that the mere difference itself *constitutes* a change of meaning of all terms in the theory—so that the doctrine that "meanings change with change of context" becomes a tautology.

It seems sensible to ask whether every change constitutes a change of meaning, but what Feyerabend would say about this is unclear. Much the same must be said about the question of whether every change constitutes a change of theory. What, on Feyerabend's view, is the appropriate reply to objections such as the following: Do mere extensions or applications of a theory make a difference to the "theoretical context," and so to the meanings, of the terms involved? Do alternative axiomatizations constitute different theoretical contexts, so that the meanings of the expressions axiomatized change with reaxiomatization? And do logical terms, like "and" and "if-then," change their meanings under alteration of theory? Presumably, one would want to answer such questions in the negative; but Feyerabend does not deal with such points, and his statements about the relation between meaning changes and changes of theory leave much to be desired. (Remember: "The meaning of every term we use depends upon the theoretical context in which it occurs.")

Further, what counts as part of a theory? Did Kepler's mysticism determine the meanings of the terms used in his laws of planetary motion? And did the meanings of those laws change when they were removed from that context and incorporated in the Newtonian theory? Or to consider a more difficult question: Are Newton's conceptions of "absolute space" and "absolute time" relevant parts of the theoretical context of his mechanical theory, or are they essentially irrelevant? Where does one draw the line? These difficulties might at first appear rather minor; one might want to reply, "But we can at least point to clear examples of theories, and this is all Feyerabend needs to make his point clear enough." This impression disappears, however, and the difficulty takes on crucial importance, when one looks closely at what Feyerabend means in talking about "theories." The usual idea, made familiar to us by logicians, is that a theory is a set of statements formulable in a language, in which language alternatives (e.g., the denial) to the theory can also be expressed. Perhaps this is true for Feyerabend's "lower-level" theories (although this is not clear), but it certainly does not do justice to his conception of higher-level background theories. On the contrary, such theories are *presupposed by* a language, and in terms of that language, alternatives to the background theory are absurd, inconceivable, self-contradictory. A theory is "a way of looking at the world";[60] it is really a philosophical point of view, a metaphysics, although it need not be so precise or well formulated; superstitions also count as theories. Thus, we have the following (the only) explanation of what he means by a "theory":

In what follows, the term "theory" will be used in a wide sense, including ordinary beliefs (e.g., the belief in the existence of material objects), myths (e.g., the myth of eternal recurrence), religious beliefs, etc. In short, any sufficiently general point of view concerning matter of fact will be termed a "theory." [61]

It is this breadth allowed to what can count as a theory that makes it difficult—even impossible—to say, in cases like that of Kepler's mysticism and Newton's absolutes, whether they are to be considered, on Feyerabend's view, as part of the theoretical context.[62] (Was Kepler perhaps holding two *different,* mutually independent theories in adhering to his laws of planetary motion on the one hand and to his mysticism on the other? But Feyerabend has given us no criterion for distinguishing theories—no "principle of individuation" of theories—and so this possibility is of no help either.)

Still more difficulties arise: How is it possible to reject *both* the consistency condition *and* the condition of meaning invariance? For in order for two sentences to contradict one another (to be inconsistent with one another), one must be the denial of the other; and this is to say that what is denied by the one must be what the other asserts; and this in turn is to say that the theories must have some common meaning. Perhaps Feyerabend has in mind some special sense of "inconsistent" (although he claims not to be abandoning the principle of noncontradiction), or else of "meaning"; but in the absence of any clarification, it is difficult to see how one could construct a theory which, while differing in the meanings of all its terms from another theory, can nevertheless be inconsistent with that other theory. It is no wonder that Feyerabend, like Kuhn, often uses the word "incommensurable" to describe the relations between different background theories.[63]

This brings us to what I believe is the central difficulty in Feyerabend's philosophy of science. He tells us that the most desirable kinds of theories to have are ones which are *completely* different from the theory to be criticized—which "do not share a single statement" with that theory, which "leave no stone unturned." Yet—even if we agree to pass over any feelings of uneasiness we may have about what such an absolute difference would be like—how could two such theories be relevant to one another? How is criticism of a theory possible in terms of facts unearthed by another if meaning depends on, and varies with, theoretical context, and especially if there is *nothing* common to the two theories? Facts, after all, on Feyerabend's view, are not simply "unearthed" by a theory; they are *defined* by it and *do not exist* for another theory. ("Each theory will possess its own experience, and there will be no overlap between those experiences.") Even if two sentences in two different theories are written in the same symbols, they will have different meanings. How, then, can evidence for or against a theory be forthcoming because of another theory which does not even talk the same language —and in a much stronger sense than that in which French and English are different languages, since, for Feyerabend's two radically different high-level theories, presumably, translation—even inaccurate translation—appears to be impossible in principle?

But even if facts unearthed by one high-level theory *could* be relevant to the testing of some other, completely different theory, it is hard to see how such relevant criticism could be effective. For why should it not be possible to reinterpret the fact unearthed by the alternative theory so that it either is no longer relevant or else supports our theory? Feyerabend's own words lend credence to this: "Observational findings can be reinterpreted, and can perhaps even be made to lend support to a point of view that was originally inconsistent with them." [64] And he himself asks the crucial question: "Now if this is the case, does it not follow that an objective and impartial judge of theories does not exist? If observation can be made to favor any theory, then what is the point of making observations?" [65]

How, then, does Feyerabend answer this question? What are "the principles according to which a decision between two different accounts of the external world can be achieved," [66] when those two accounts are high-level background theories which are so radically different as to leave no stone unturned? He lists three such principles. "The first [procedure] consists in the invention of a still more general theory describing a common background that defines test statements acceptable to *both* theories." [67] But this third theory is still a different theory, and even though it contains a subset of statements which *look* exactly like statements in the two original theories, the meanings of those statements in the new metatheory will still be different from the meanings of the corresponding statements in either of the two original theories. In fact, the meanings will be *radically* different; for any term in the metatheory will have, as part of the theoretical context which determines its meaning, not only the set of statements corresponding to statements in one of the two original theories, but also a set of statements corresponding to statements in the other, radically different original theory. The context of any term in the new metatheory will thus be radically different from the context in which a corresponding term occurred in one of the two original theories, and so its meaning will be radically different. Thus, the same problems arise concerning the possibility of comparing the metatheory with either of the two original theories as arose with regard to the possibility of comparing the two original theories with one another.

"The second procedure is based upon an internal examination of the two theories. The one theory might establish a more direct connection to observation and the interpretation of observational results might also be more direct." [68] I confess that I do not understand this, since each theory defines its own facts or experience, and what could be more direct than this?

Feyerabend's third procedure for choosing between two different high-level theories consists of "taking the pragmatic theory of observation seriously." [69] He describes this theory as follows:

A statement will be regarded as observational because of the *causal context* in which it is being uttered, and *not* because of what it means. According to this theory, "this is red" is an observation sentence, because a well-conditioned individual who is prompted in the appropriate manner in front of an object that has certain physical properties will respond without hesitation with "this is red"; and this response will occur independently of the *interpretation* he may connect with the statement. [70]

According to the pragmatic theory, then,

observational statements are distinguished from other statements not by their meaning, but by the circumstances of their production. . . . These circumstances are open to observation and . . . we can therefore determine in a straightforward manner whether a certain movement of the human organism is correlated with an external event and can therefore be regarded as an indicator of this event. [71]

This theory provides, according to Feyerabend, a way of choosing between even radically different high-level background theories:

It is bound to happen, then, at some stage, that the alternatives do not share a single statement with the theory they criticize. The idea of observation that we are defending here implies that they will not share a single observation statement either. To express it more radically, each theory will possess its own experience, and there will be no overlap between these experiences. Clearly, a crucial experiment is now impossible. It is impossible not because the *experimental device* would be too complex or expensive, but because there is no universally accepted *statement* capable of expressing whatever emerges from observation. *But there is still human experience as an actually existing process,* and it still causes the observer to carry out certain actions, for example, to utter sentences of a certain kind. Not every interpretation of the sentences uttered will be such that the theory furnishing the interpretation predicts it in the form in which it has emerged from the observational situation. Such a combined use of theory and action leads to a selection even in those cases where a common observation language does not exist. . . . the theory—an acceptable theory, that is—has an inbuilt syntactical machinery that *imitates* (but does not *describe*) certain features of our experience. This is the *only* way in which experience judges a general cosmological point of view. Such a point of view is not removed because its observation *statements* say that there must be certain experiences that then do not occur. . . . It *is* removed if it produces observation *sentences* when observers produce the *negation* of these sentences. It is therefore still judged by the predictions it makes. However, it is not judged by the truth or falsehood of the prediction-statements—this takes place only after the general background has been settled—but by the way in which the prediction sentences are ordered by it and by the agreement or disagreement of this *physical* order with the *natural* order of observation sentences as uttered by human observers, and therefore, in the last resort, with the natural order of sensations.[72]

It turns out that there is, after all, something that is theory-independent and against which we can compare and test theories: It is "human experience as an actually existing process," which causes the well-conditioned observer to utter a sequence of noises (observation sentences). That this takes place can be determined "in a straightforward manner" (i.e., independently of theory); it is only when we assign meanings to the sequence of noises uttered by the observer that we bring in theoretical considerations. The human organism emits results of experiments or experience (in the form of sequences of noises) which must be interpreted in the light of theory, just as other scientific instruments produce pointer-readings which must then be interpreted in the light of theory. Theories are to be compared and judged, not by reference to their meanings (for those are necessarily different) but by reference to the common domain of "features of experience" which they are concerned to "imitate" or "order": the theory, if it is an acceptable one, "has an inbuilt syntactical machinery" which "produces observation sentences"; and the theory is to be "removed" not when "its observation statements say that there must be certain experiences that then do not occur. . . . It is removed if it produces observation sentences when observers produce the negation of these sentences."

We thus have come back to an older empiricism: There is, after all, something common to all theories, in terms of which they can be compared and judged; only, what is objective, independent of theory, given, is not an observation-language but something nonlinguistic; for Feyerabend's observation-sentences, being mere uninterpreted noises, are no more "linguistic" than is a burp. We place an interpretation on this "given" only when we read meanings into those utterances; and to read in meanings is to read in a theory. Hence, in the light of the pragmatic theory of observation, we must give a conservative interpretation to Feyerabend's more radical declarations—e.g., that "the given is out," that each theory "possesses its own experience." The given is indeed still "in," and there is human observation, experience, which is the same for all theories: It is not theory-independent observation, but a theory-independent observation *language* that Feyerabend is set against.[73]

One can wonder, among other things, whether the view that statements made by human beings pop out as conditioned responses, as the word "Ouch!" sometimes pops out when one is stuck with a pin, is not a drastic oversimplification. More important for present purposes is the question as to whether Feyerabend has shown that theories can really be judged against one another despite the theory-dependence of meanings. The answer, it seems to me, is clearly that he has not; nothing has been said by the pragmatic theory of observation to remove the fatal objection of Feyerabend's own words: "Observational findings can be reinterpreted, and can perhaps even be made to lend support to a point of view that was originally inconsistent with them"; and Feyerabend has still given no reason why the qualification "perhaps" is included in this statement. Knowledge by acquaintance—raw, meaningless "human experience" (including uninterpreted "observation statements"), after all, according to Feyerabend, exhibits a complete "poverty of content": Such experience tells us nothing whatever; uninterpreted observation statements convey no information whatsoever and, therefore, cannot convey information which would serve as a basis for "removing" a theory. They can do so only when they are assigned meanings and, thereby, are infused with a theoretical interpretation. This "poverty of content," therefore, not only leaves open the possibility of interpretation, but even *requires* that interpretation be made in order to allow judgment of theories. It is not any help to say that theories must at least "imitate" the "order" of experiences ("and ultimately the order of sensations"). For scientific theories often, as a matter of fact, *alter* that order rather than imitate it; and in many cases, some of the elements of experience are declared irrelevant. So "interpretation," rather than "imitation," takes place even with regard to the alleged "order" of experience or sensations. And with the liberty—no, rather with the license—which Feyerabend grants us for interpreting experience, for assigning meanings to observation statements, we must conclude that, with regard either to single "experiences" (or observation statements) or allegedly ordered sets of them, anything goes: We are always able to interpret experience so that it supports, rather than refutes, our theory. The truth of the matter is thus that Feyerabend's kind of experience is altogether *too weak,* in its pristine, uninterpreted form, to serve as grounds for "removal" of any theory; and his view of meaning is *too strong* to preclude the possibility of *any* interpretation whatever of what is given in experience.[74]

I have confined the above remarks to those sorts of high-level background theories which "leave no stone unturned." One might suppose that the situation is less serious with less radically different theories. There, at least, there are some similarities, and perhaps relevance can be established and comparison made of the two theories on the basis of those similarities. One might suppose, for example, that a slight amendment of Feyerabend's position, introducing the notion of degrees of likeness of meaning, might answer the question of how theories all of whose terms must differ in meaning can yet, in some cases at least, be mutually relevant, since the relevance could be established through the likenesses, despite the differences. This view would also remove our difficulties, discussed above, with Feyerabend's description of some background theories as, e.g., "partially overlapping." *Prima facie,* this seems a promising move to make, although the notion of "degrees of likeness of meaning" may well introduce complications of its own; and in any case, making this move, as will become clear in what follows, would be tantamount to confessing that Feyerabend's technical notion of "meaning" is an unnecessary obstruction to the understanding of science. In any case, however, it is not a move that Feyerabend himself makes. [75] We have seen that he admits only three ways of comparing and judging two high-level theories: by constructing a metatheory, by examining the relative "directness" of their connection with experience, or via their common domain of experience. Different high-level theories, even those which are "partially overlapping," are apparently not comparable in spite of their similarities; Feyerabend's general tendency is to look on the similarities as rather unimportant, superficial, inessential. And this is only what we would expect if likeness and difference of meaning are not a matter of degree, for if difference of meaning makes *all* the difference, then any two theories must be incommensurable, incomparable, despite any (superficial, inessential) similarities. Thus, all our dire conclusions regarding theories which have nothing in common are extended even to theories which do not turn every stone.

We are thus left with a complete relativism with regard not only to the testing of any single theory by confrontation with facts, but also to the relevance of other theories to the testing of that theory. Feyerabend's attempts "to formulate a methodology that can still claim to be *empirical,*" [76] as well as his efforts to justify a "methodological pluralism," have ended in failure.

In a recent short paper, "On the 'Meaning' of Scientific Terms," Feyerabend has attempted to reply to some criticisms of his views which had been raised by Achinstein and which are similar to some of the questions raised above concerning the interpretation of Feyerabend's views on meaning variance and the dependence of meaning on theoretical context. In that paper, Feyerabend admits that certain changes, although they count as changes of theory, do not involve a change of meaning. He cites as an example a case of two theories, T (classical celestial mechanics) and $\bar{T}$ (like classical celestial mechanics except for a slight change in the strength of the gravitation potential). T and $\bar{T}$, he declares,

> are certainly different theories—in our universe, where no region is free from gravitational influence, no two predictions of T and $\bar{T}$ will coincide. Yet it would be rash to say that the transition $T \to \bar{T}$ involves a change of meaning. For though the *quantitative values* of the forces differ almost everywhere, there is no reason to assert that this is due to the action of different *kinds of entities*.[77]

It thus appears that Feyerabend wants to say that two theories are different theories if they assign different quantitative values to the factors involved ("almost everywhere"); and the meanings of terms involved are different if they have to do with different kinds of entities. He makes his notion of "change of meaning" (and, conversely, of "stability of meaning") explicit in the following passage:

> A diagnosis of *stability of meaning* involves two elements. First, reference is made to rules according to which objects or events are collected into classes. We may say that such rules determine concepts or kinds of objects. Secondly, it is found that the changes brought about by a new point of view occur *within* the extension of these classes and, therefore, leave the concepts unchanged. Conversely, we shall diagnose a *change of meaning* either if a new theory entails that all concepts of the preceding theory have extension zero or if it introduces rules which cannot be interpreted as attributing specific properties to objects within already existing classes, but which change the system of classes itself.[78]

At first glance, this discussion does seem to introduce some clarification, although at the price of adopting what seems an unreasonably extreme notion of "difference of theory" (after all, a slight refinement in the value of a fundamental constant will lead to widespread differences in quantitative predictions, and so, on Feyerabend's criterion, to a new, "different" theory). However, closer inspection reveals that the improvement achieved is by no means substantial. Consider the analysis of "change of meaning" (and, correlatively, of "stability of meaning"). This analysis depends on the notion of being able to collect "entities" ("objects or events") into classes, and this in turn rests on being able to refer to "rules" for so collecting them. If the changes occur only within the extensions of these classes ("kinds of entities," "objects or events"), the meanings have not changed; if the new theory changes the whole system of classes (or "entails that all concepts of the preceding theory have extension zero"), the meanings have changed. However, first, in order to apply this criterion, the rules of classification must be unique and determinate, allowing an unambiguous classification of the "entities" involved. Otherwise, we might not be able to determine whether the system of classes, or merely the extension of the previous classes, has changed. Furthermore, there may be two different sets of rules and consequent systems of classification, according to one of which a change of meaning has taken place, while the other implies that the meaning has not changed. Indeed, this would seem to be generally the case: One can, in scientific as in ordinary usage, collect entities into classes in a great variety of ways, and on the basis of a great variety of considerations ("rules"); and which way of classifying we use depends largely on our purposes and not simply on intrinsic properties of the entities involved by means of which we are supposed to fit them unambiguously into classes. Are mesons different "kinds of entities" from electrons and protons, or are they simply a different subclass of elementary particles? Are the light rays of classical mechanics and of general relativity (two theories which Feyerabend claims are "incommensurable") different "kinds of entities" or not? Such questions can be answered *either* way, depending on the kind of information that is being requested (this is to say that the questions, as they stand, are not clear), for there are differences as well as similarities between electrons and mesons, as between light rays in classical mechanics and light rays in general relativity. They can be given a simple answer ("different" or "the same") only if unwanted similarities or differences are stipulated away as inessential. And even if we agree to Feyerabend's (rather arbitrary) decision "not to pay attention to any *prima facie* similarities that might arise at the observational level, but to base our judgment [as to whether change or stability of meaning has occurred] on the principles of the theory only," [79] the spatiotemporal frameworks of classical mechanics and general relativity are still comparable with respect to their possession of certain kinds of mathematical properties—metrical and topological ones (both theories have something to do with "spaces" in a well-defined mathematical sense). And the question must still arise—and is equally useless and answerable only by stipulation—as to whether the spatiotemporal frameworks involved share the same *kinds* of properties and are the same *kinds* of entities ("spaces") or whether these properties are not "specific" [80] enough to count toward making those frameworks the same "kinds of entities." [81]

Under any interpretation, it is hard to see how *any* theory would entail that *all* the concepts of a rival theory have extension zero or would change the whole system of classes.[82] Even theories having to do with very different subjects—e.g., geological theories of the structure and evolution of the earth on the one hand and physical theories of waves and their transmission on the other—have something in common. (Theories of the structure and evolution of the earth in fact depend intimately on the ways in which earthquake waves are transmitted through different kinds of material.) Of course, one *can* say, in examples like this, that the physical theory is part of the "borrowed background" of the geological theory rather than being *part of* the geological theory. But this again simply throws us back to the question, asked earlier in regard to Feyerabend's views, of what is and what is not supposed to be included in a "theory."

Meanings and the Analysis of Science

We have seen that Feyerabend's interpretation of science eventuates in a complete relativism, in which it becomes impossible, as a consequence of his views, to compare any two scientific theories and to choose between them on any but the most subjective grounds. In particular, his "pragmatic theory of observation," which constitutes his main effort to avoid this disastrous conclusion, does not succeed in doing so for, inasmuch as all meanings are theory-dependent, and inasmuch as theories can be shaped at will, and inasmuch, finally, as all observational data (in his sense) can be reinterpreted to support any given theoretical framework, it follows that the role of experience and experiment in science becomes a farce. In trying to assure freedom of theorizing, Feyerabend has made theory-construction too free; in depriving observation statements of any meaning whatever (independent of theories), he has deprived them also of any power of judgment over theories: They must be interpreted by reading meaning into them, and thus reading theory into them; and we are at liberty to interpret them as we will—as irrelevant, or as supporting evidence. By granting unlimited power of interpretation, on the one hand, over that which allows limitless possibilities of interpretation on the other, Feyerabend has destroyed the possibility of comparing and judging theories by reference to experience. And by holding that all meanings vary with theoretical context, and by implying that a difference of meaning is *a fortiori* a complete difference, an "incommensurability," he has destroyed the possibility of comparing them on any other grounds either.

In the first section of this chapter, I called attention to the very great similarities between Feyerabend's views and those of a number of other recent writers whom I grouped together, on the basis of those similarities, as representatives of a new approach to the philosophy of science. Among those writers is Thomas Kuhn. There are differences, of course, between Kuhn's views and those of Feyerabend. For example, while Feyerabend insists on the desirability of developing a large number of mutually inconsistent alternative theories at all stages of the history of science, Kuhn claims that, both as a matter of desirability and as a matter of fact through most of its actual development, science is "normal," in the sense that there is one dominant point of view or "paradigm" held in common by all the members of the tradition; it is only on the very exceptional and rare occasions of scientific revolutions that we find the development of competing alternatives. However, it is not in the differences, but rather in the similarities between their views that I am interested here.

In view of these similarities, it is only to be expected that Kuhn's and Feyerabend's interpretations of science may be open to many of the same objections. This is indeed the case. In an earlier paper reviewing Kuhn's book, *The Structure of Scientific Revolutions,* I made a number of criticisms of his views which are in fact remarkably like those which I tried to bring out in connection with Feyerabend.[83] Kuhn's notion of a "paradigm," like Feyerabend's notion of a "theory," becomes so broad and general in the course of his discussion that we are often at a loss to know what to include under it and what to exclude. Again, neither author gives us a criterion for determining what counts as a part of the meaning of a term, or what counts as a change of meaning, even though these notions are central to their portrayals of science. They share other criticisms as well; most important for present purposes, however, is the fact (which I tried to establish for Kuhn in my review of his book, and for Feyerabend in this chapter) that both views result in relativism: The most fundamental sorts of scientific change are really complete replacements; the most fundamental scientific differences are really utter incompatibilities. It will be instructive for us to compare the source of this relativism in these two writers, because the trouble, as I think could be shown, is shared by a large number of current writers representative of what I have called "the new philosophy of science," and is, I think, the major pitfall facing that view.

What are the grounds, in Kuhn's view, for accepting one paradigm as better, more acceptable, than another? He manages without difficulty to analyze the notion of progress within a paradigm tradition—i.e., within normal science. There, "progress" consists of further articulation and specification of the tradition's paradigm "under new or more stringent conditions." [84] The trouble comes when we ask how we can say that "progress" is made when one paradigm is replaced, through a scientific revolution, by another. For according to Kuhn, "the differences between successive paradigms are both necessary and irreconcilable"; [85] those differences consist in the paradigms' being "incommensurable": They disagree as to what the facts are, and even as to the real problems to be faced and the standards which a successful theory must meet. A paradigm change entails "changes in the standards governing permissible problems, concepts, and explanations"; [86] what is metaphysics for one paradigm tradition is science for another, and *vice versa*. It follows that the decisions of a scientific group to adopt a new paradigm cannot be based on good reasons of any kind, factual or otherwise; quite the contrary, what counts as a good reason is determined by the decision. Despite the presence in Kuhn's book of qualifications to this extreme relativism (although, as in Feyerabend, these qualifications really only contradict his main view), the logical tendency of his position is clearly toward the conclusion that the replacement of one paradigm by another is not cumulative, but is mere change: Being "incommensurable," two paradigms cannot be judged according to their ability to solve the same problems, deal with the same facts, or meet the same standards. For problems, facts, and standards are all defined by the paradigm, and are different—*radically*, incommensurably different—for different paradigms.

How similar this is to the logical path that leads to relativism in the case of Feyerabend! It is, in fact, fundamentally the same path: meanings, whether of factual or of any other sorts of terms, are theory-(paradigm-) dependent and, therefore, are different for different theories (paradigms); for two sets of meanings to be different is for them to be "incommensurable"; if two theories (paradigms) are incommensurable, they cannot be compared directly with one another. Neither Kuhn nor Feyerabend succeeds in providing any extra-theoretical basis (theory-independent problems, standards, experiences) on the basis of which theories (paradigms) can be compared or judged indirectly. Hence, there remains *no* basis for choosing between them. Choice must be made without any basis, arbitrarily.

When their reasoning (and the objections thereto) is summarized in this way, it becomes obvious that the root of Kuhn's and Feyerabend's relativism, and of the difficulties which lead to it, lies in their rigid conception of what a difference of meaning amounts to—namely, absolute incomparability, "incommensurability." Two expressions or sets of expressions must either have precisely the same meaning or else must be utterly and completely different. If theories are not meaning-invariant over the history of their development and incorporation into wider or deeper theories, then those successive theories (paradigms) cannot *really* be compared at all, despite apparent similarities which must therefore be dismissed as irrelevant and superficial. If the concept of the history of science as a process of "development-by-accumulation" is incorrect, the only alternative is that it must be a completely noncumulative process of replacement. There is never any middle ground and, therefore, it should be no surprise that the rejection of the positivistic principles of meaning invariance and of development-by-accumulation leave us in a relativistic bind, for that is the only other possibility left open by this concept of difference of meaning. But this relativism, and the doctrines which eventuate in it, is not the result of an investigation of actual science and its history; rather, it is the purely logical consequence of a narrow preconception about what "meaning" is. Nor should anyone be surprised that the root of the trouble, although not easy to discern until after a long analysis, should turn out to be such a simple point, for philosophical difficulties are often of just this sort.

Having, then, found the place where Kuhn and Feyerabend took a wrong turn and ended by giving us a complete relativism with regard to the development of science, can we provide a middle ground by altering their rigid notion of meaning? For example, can we say that meanings can be similar, comparable in some respects even while also being different in other respects? For by taking this path, we could hope to preserve the fact that, e.g., Newtonian and relativistic dynamics *are* comparable—something Feyerabend and Kuhn deny—even while being more fundamentally different than the most usual logical empiricist views make them. Thus, we could hope, by this expedient, to avoid the excesses *both* of the positivistic view of the development of science as a process of development-by-accumulation (and systematization), characterized by meaning invariance, *and* of the view of the "new philosophy of science" that different theories, at least different fundamental theories (paradigms), are "incommensurable."

Whether this is a wise path to take depends on how we interpret this new concept of degrees of likeness (or difference) of meanings. For if we still insist on some distinction between what, in the use of a term, is and what is not a part of the meaning of the term, then we expose ourselves to the danger of relegating some features of the use of a term to the "less important" status of not being "part of the meaning." Yet those very features, for some purposes, may prove to be the very ones that are of central importance in comparing two uses, for relative importance of features of usage must not be enshrined in an absolute and a priori distinction between essential and inessential features. It thus seems wiser to allow *all* features of the use of a term to be equally potentially relevant in comparing the usage of the terms in different contexts. But this step relieves the notion of meaning of any importance whatever as a tool for analyzing the relations between different scientific "theories." If our purpose is to compare the uses of two terms (or of the same term in different contexts), and if *any* of their similarities and differences are at least potentially relevant in bringing out crucial relations between the uses—the actual relevance and importance being determined by the problem at hand rather than by some intrinsic feature of the uses (their being or not being "part of the meaning")—then what is the use of referring to those similarities and differences as similarities and differences of "meaning" *at all?* Once more, introducing the term "meaning," and even admitting degrees of meaning, suggests that there may be similarities and differences which are not "part of the meaning" of the terms, and this in turn might suggest that those features are, in some intrinsic, essential, or absolute sense less important than features which *are* "parts of the meaning." For the purpose of seeking out central features of scientific theories, and of comparing different theories, then, it seems unnecessary to talk about meanings, and on the other hand, that notion is potentially misleading. Worse still, we have already seen how that notion, which is made so fundamental in the work of Feyerabend and Kuhn, has *actually* been an obstruction, misleading those authors into a relativistic impasse.

All this is not to say that we *cannot,* or even that we *ought not,* use the term "meaning," even often if we like—so long as we do not allow ourselves to be misled by it, as Kuhn and Feyerabend were misled by it, or as we are liable to be misled by talk about "degrees of likeness of meaning." Nor is it to say that we could not formulate a precise criterion of meaning, which would distinguish between what is, and what is not, to count as part of the meaning, and which would also serve to specify what would count as a change of meaning. Nor is it to say that for some purposes it might not be very valuable to formulate such a precise criterion. All that has been said is that, *if* our purpose is to understand the workings of scientific concepts and theories, and the relations between different scientific concepts and theories—if, for example, our aim is to understand such terms as "space," "time," and "mass" (or their symbolic correlates) in classical and relativistic mechanics, and the relations between those terms as used in those different theories—then there is *no need* to introduce reference to meanings. And in view of the fact that that term *has* proved such an obstruction to the fulfillment of this purpose, the wisest course seems to be to avoid it altogether as a fundamental tool for dealing with this sort of problem.

Both the thesis of the theory-dependence of meanings (or, as I called it earlier—more accurately, as we have seen—the presupposition theory of meaning), and its opponent, the condition of meaning invariance, rest on the same kind of mistake (or excess). This does not mean that there is not considerable truth (as well as distortion) in both theses. There are, for example, as I have argued elsewhere,[87] statements that can be made, questions that can be raised, views that may be suggested as possibly correct, within the context of Einsteinian physics that would not even have made sense—would have been self-contradictory—in the context of Newtonian physics. And such differences, both naturally and, for many purposes, profitably, can be referred to as changes of meaning, indicating, among other things, that there are differences between Einsteinian and Newtonian terms that are not brought out by the deduction of Newtonianlike statements from Einsteinian ones. But attributing such differences to alterations of "meaning" must not blind one—as it has blinded Kuhn and Feyerabend—to any resemblances there might be between the two sets of terms.

It is one of the fundamental theses of Kuhn's view of science that it is impossible to describe adequately in words any paradigm; the paradigm, "the concrete scientific achievement" that is the source of the coherence of a scientific tradition, must not be identified with, but must be seen as "prior to the various concepts, laws, theories, and points of view that may be abstracted from it."[88] Yet why, simply because there are differences between views or formulations of views held by members of what historians classify as a "tradition" of science, *must* there be a single, inexpressible view held in common by all members of that tradition? No doubt some theories are very similar—so similar that they can be considered to be "versions" or "different articulations" of one another (or of "the same subject"). But this does not imply, as Kuhn seems to believe, that there must be a common "paradigm" of which the similar theories are incomplete and imperfect expressions and from which they are abstracted. There need not be, unifying a scientific "tradition," a single inexpressible paradigm which guides procedures, any more than our inability to give a single, simple definition of "game" means that we must have a unitary but inexpressible idea from which all our diverse uses of "game" are abstracted. It would appear that Kuhn's view that, in order for us to be able to speak of a "scientific tradition," there must be a single point of view held in common by all members of that tradition, has its source once again in the error of supposing that, unless there is absolute identity, there must be absolute difference. Where there is similarity, there must be identity, even though it may be hidden; otherwise, there would be only complete difference. If there are scientific traditions, they must have an identical element—a paradigm—which unifies that tradition. And since there are differences of formulation of the various laws, theories, rules, etc. making up that tradition, the paradigm which unifies them all must be inexpressible. Since what is visible exhibits differences, what unites those things must be invisible.

Again, then, Kuhn has committed the mistake of thinking that there are only two alternatives: absolute identity or absolute difference. But the data at hand are the similarities and differences; and why should these not be enough to enable us to talk about more, and less, similar views and, for certain purposes, to classify sufficiently similar viewpoints together as, e.g., being in the same tradition? After all, disagreements, proliferation of competing alternatives, debate over fundamentals, both substantive and methodological, are all more or less present throughout the development of science; and there are always guiding elements which are more or less common, even among what are classified as different "traditions." By hardening the notion of a "scientific tradition" into a hidden unit, Kuhn is thus forced *by a purely conceptual point* to ignore many important differences between scientific activities classified as being of the same tradition, as well as important continuities between successive traditions. This is the same type of excess into which Feyerabend forced himself through his conception of "theory" and "meaning." Everything that is of positive value in the viewpoint of these writers, and much that is excluded by the logic of their errors, can be kept if we take account of these points.

Impetus and Inertial Dynamics: A Case Study

In Part I of this paper, mention was made of the influence of the history of science on recent philosophical interpretations of science. Of all the historical episodes contributing to such philosophical interpretation, none has had greater impact than the Impetus Theory, first brought to the attention of scholars by Pierre Duhem. This theory was advanced in the fourteenth century (and even earlier, as we shall see) in order to meet certain objections to Aristotle's account of projectile motion. Inasmuch as Feyerabend appeals to the Impetus Theory as an example of a theory which, despite appearances to the contrary, is "incommensurable" with Newtonian conceptions of inertia and momentum, and also inasmuch as the Impetus Theory has by now been rather (but by no means completely) well documented and discussed, it provides an excellent case study to illustrate the comparability of scientific concepts and the continuity of their evolution from one "tradition" to another.[89]

Aristotelian physics distinguished sharply between celestial motion— the type of motion characteristic of the heavenly spheres—and terrestrial motion. All celestial motion was held to be circular, the spheres revolving around the center of the universe, carrying the moon, planets, sun, and stars around with them; such motion in a perfect circle was the "natural motion" of the element ether, of which the incorruptible heavenly spheres were made. Sublunar (or terrestrial) motion, however, could be either "natural" or "violent." The four elements—earth, water, air, and fire—tended "by nature" to move rectilinearly, along a radius of the universe, toward a "natural place" in the sublunar domain, and to come to rest upon reaching that natural place. On the other hand, bodies composed of (mixtures of) those elements could also be moved "violently." It is in connection with this latter kind of motion that the focal weakness of Aristotelian physics arose and out of the criticisms of which the inertial conception ultimately evolved. However, the infection of this weakness spread also, as we shall see, to the cases of natural sublunar and of celestial motion; but for the present, we shall for the sake of simplicity ignore these cases.

The basic principle of Aristotelian dynamics, accepted throughout the Middle Ages, was that a force is required to maintain a body in motion: *omne quod movetur ab alio movetur* (everything that moves is moved by something else). Furthermore, this principle was usually (although by no means always) interpreted in a way that can be summarized, in modern quantitative terms, as saying that the greater the force, the greater the velocity. (That is, force is directly proportional to velocity; also, it was conceived of as being inversely proportional to the total resistance offered, e.g., by the medium, this latter proportionality being closely intertwined with the Aristotelian conception of the impossibility of a void. This quantitative formula can be said to hold only if the resistance is less than the force, for otherwise there would be no motion at all. It is also not certain, as Dijksterhuis points out,[90] whether Aristotle would have accepted the conclusion following from this formula that a body a hundred times as heavy as another must take one hundredth the time to fall a given distance.)

For the case of natural sublunar motions—the case which ultimately came to center around the problem of freely falling bodies—the character of this force was a matter of considerable debate; we shall, as was said above, pass over this problem. For the case of violent motion—the motion of projectiles—the force must in any case be external, and that external force must be in contact with the body throughout the motion. Upon removal of the force, the body will (if it is in its natural place) come to rest immediately or (if it is not in its natural place) immediately assume its natural motion. (Aristotelian principles did not allow the combined action of two different forces to produce a "resultant" motion.)

This view, however, faces some rather obvious difficulties, particularly as to why projectiles in fact do continue to move "violently" after being released by the propelling agent. Aristotle himself mentioned two ways of accounting for such continuation of violent motion, in both of which the air serves as the continually operating contact mover. According to the first, the theory of *antiperistasis,* a "mutual replacement" takes place between the projectile and the air, the air pushed out in front of the path by the moving projectile pushing other air out of place and, finally, air rushing in behind the projectile to avoid the creation of a vacuum; this air pushes the projectile on. Aristotle seems to have rejected this view, apparently preferring a second view, according to which the air moved, along with the projectile, by the original mover receives, because of its special nature, the power to act as a mover; this power, communicated in decreasing amounts to the air beyond, continues to carry the projectile along by contact action until the power or force is exhausted.

Already in the sixth century, the Byzantine philosopher John Philoponus rejected both theories on the basis of both rational and empirical considerations; he preferred a view according to which "some incorporeal motive force is imparted by the projector to the projectile, and . . . the air set in motion contributes either nothing at all or else very little to this motion of the projectile." [91] This view, which anticipates the fourteenth-century Impetus Theory, influenced a number of Arabic writers, notably Avicenna and his followers (theory of *mail*). However, we shall consider here only the Impetus Theory as presented by the Fourteenth Century Parisian, Jean Buridan. After rejecting, on the basis of empirical evidence (*experientie*) both of the accounts of the continuation of projectile motion discussed by Aristotle, Buridan declares that:

It seems to me that it ought to be said that the motor in moving a moving body impresses in it a certain impetus or a certain motive force of the moving body [which impetus acts] in the direction toward which the mover was moving the moving body, either up or down, or laterally, or circularly. And by the amount the motor moves that moving body more swiftly, by the same amount it will impress in it a stronger impetus. It is by that impetus that the stone is moved after the projector ceases to move. But that impetus is continually decreased by the resisting air and by the gravity of the stone, which inclines it in a direction contrary to that in which the impetus was naturally predisposed to move it. . . . by the amount more there is of matter, by that amount can the body receive more of that impetus and more intensely. . . .

From this theory also appears the cause of why the natural motion of a heavy body downward is continually accelerated. For from the beginning only the gravity was moving it. Therefore, it moved more slowly, but in moving it impressed in the heavy body an impetus. This impetus now [acting] together with its gravity moves it. Therefore, the motion becomes faster; and by the amount it is faster, so the impetus becomes more intense. Therefore, the movement evidently becomes continually faster.

. . . impetus is a thing of permanent nature, distinct from the local motion in which the projectile is moved. . . . And it also is probable that just as that quality (the impetus) is impressed in the moving body along with the motion by the motor; so with the motion it is remitted, corrupted, or impeded by resistance or a contrary inclination.[92]

A quantitative measure of impetus is at least suggested in this passage: It appears to be equal to the product of the quantity of matter and the velocity of the moved body. Notice also that the impetus is not self-corrupting (although it was according to many adherents of the Impetus Theory); it (and consequently the velocity of the body it pushes) is reduced by contrary or resisting agencies. Furthermore, Buridan extends his impetus account of motion from the case of projectile motion to that of freely falling bodies and thus to natural motions in the sublunar domain. He also proposes an extension of it to the natural motion of the celestial spheres:

Since the Bible does not state that appropriate intelligences move the celestial bodies, it could be said that it does not appear necessary to posit intelligences of this kind, because it would be answered that God, when He created the world, moved each of the celestial orbs as He pleased, and in moving them He impressed in them impetuses which moved them without his having to move them any more except by the method of general influence whereby He concurs as a co-agent in all things which take place. . . . And these impetuses which He impressed in the celestial bodies were not decreased nor corrupted afterwards, because there was no inclination of the celestial bodies for other movements. Nor was there resistance which would be corruptive or repressive of that impetus.[93]

Immediately upon unearthing the Impetus Theory, Duhem and others noticed the striking parallels between that theory and the principle of inertia, and also between that theory and the concept of momentum—equals mass ("quantity of matter") times velocity—in classical mechanics. Since Buridan's impetus would be preserved except for the degenerative effects of counteragencies, only two main steps appeared necessary to achieve the concept of inertia.[94] First, the conception of the possibility of motion in a vacuum and, second, the abandonment of the idea of impetus as an internal force distinct from the body and maintaining it at constant velocity. The Impetus Theory itself contributed to the first of these steps by showing the medium to be unnecessary for the continuation of motion. The second could be seen as the product of a gradual transition, aided perhaps by increasing nominalistic tendencies. With those alterations, the Impetus Theory could be seen as transformed into the principle of inertia, that "Every body continues in its state of rest, or of uniform motion in a right [i.e., straight] line, unless it is compelled to change that state by forces impressed on it." The shift from Aristotelian to Newtonian physics could then be seen as a transition from the view that force is the cause of *motion* (i.e., of velocity) to the modern view that force is the cause of *change of motion* (i.e., of acceleration). The Impetus Theory thus stands as a transitional phase between these two traditions—still in the tradition of Aristotelian physics in its view that impetus is a cause of motion, but heading toward the modern view in making impetus an internal and incorporeal force rather than an external, corporeal one.

Historical evidence, although somewhat sketchy, was also available for the influence of the Impetus Theory on the development of the seventeenth-century scientific revolution. Galileo's early work was definitely in the tradition of the Impetus Theory, and he seems never to have escaped completely from the view that a constant force is required to maintain a body in motion. (Newton, too, was not perfectly clear in his conception of inertia; he sometimes spoke of a *vis inertiae*—not to be confused with the modern conception of "inertial force"—which he conceived of as an internal force maintaining the body in its state of uniform motion.) And a steady, although not always progressive, evolution seemed traceable from Buridan and his equally brilliant successor, Nicole Orêsme, to Newton, although complete details are still lacking. Among the major steps along this road were Galileo's view that bodies, once in "horizontal" motion, would continue to move at a uniform rate along a great circle on the surface of the earth and Descartes' conception that true inertial motion would be realized were it not for the fact that space is filled with (or identical with) incompressible matter, thus requiring all motion to be circular after all. Less famous, but equally revealing of the growing tendency to think in modern terms, were such developments as Benedetti's restriction of impetus to having rectilinear effects and the clear abandonment by Galileo's pupil, Baliani, of the notion of impetus as a cause of motion and his view that motion continues of its own accord.

It is not hard to see that the Impetus Theory (in the form in which it was presented by Buridan, at least) made it possible to think in certain ways that had previously been precluded or at least discouraged by the Aristotelian system. (1) By removing the need for air as the agency responsible for continued motion, it helped make motion in a vacuum conceivable, and thus helped pave the way for thinking about the idealized case of a body moving in the absence of impeding forces. (2) It shifted attention away from the forces causing motion and toward those impeding motion. (3) It made plausible the notion of the composition of forces. (4) It was headed in the direction of concentration on quantitative features of motion. (It is noteworthy in this connection that Orêsme was one of the first, and perhaps the first, person to use graphing methods for the representation of intensive qualities.) (5) By treating celestial and terrestrial motion, and natural and violent motion, in terms of a single kind of cause (impetus), it helped lead toward a unified account of all motion.[95] (6) It provided counterarguments to two of Aristotle's proofs that the earth could not rotate and thus helped pave the way for Copernicus. Aristotle had held that, if the earth rotated, a terrific wind would be set up in the direction opposite to the rotation. The Impetus Theory's answer was that the earth communicates an impetus to the air, which impetus carries the air along with the rotating earth. Aristotle had further argued that, if the earth rotated from west to east, then an object dropped from a height would be left behind by the earth moving out from under it, so that the object would hit the ground at a point due west of the point directly underneath the dropping hand. The answer in terms of the Impetus Theory was as follows: The motion of the falling object is a composite of a downward motion caused by gravity, and an eastward-directed motion due to the impetus conveyed to the body by the dropping hand, which is being carried around by the rotating earth. The composition of the two forces will make the body hit the ground at the point directly beneath the dropping hand despite the rotation of the earth. (Although there is no definite evidence that Copernicus was acquainted with these arguments of the Impetus Theory, he may well have been exposed to them either at the University of Cracow or the University of Padua where he had studied and where the Impetus Theory was taught.)

Despite all this evidence of similarities and continuities between medieval and classical concepts, there has in recent years been a reaction against the claim that the concept of impetus is related to the concepts of inertia and momentum. Significant differences have been pointed out between these concepts,[96] so that some writers have been led to claim that impetus and classical mechanics are not nearly so closely alike as earlier writers had supposed and perhaps are entirely different. Feyerabend follows this reaction in claiming that the two theories are "incommensurable," what happened having been a "complete replacement . . . and a corresponding change in the meanings of all descriptive terms"[97] involved.

Feyerabend admits, quite correctly,[98] that the "inertial law" of the Impetus Theory (which he formulates as, "The impetus of a body in empty space which is not under the influence of any outer force remains constant"[99]) is not in quantitative disagreement with anything asserted by Newton's mechanics: "It is correct that the measure of [momentum] is identical with the measure that has been suggested for the impetus."[100] But such quantitative agreement, as usual, is not enough to satisfy Feyerabend, or even to make any difference at all, as far as he is concerned, to the comparability of the two concepts.

It would be very mistaken if we were, on that account, to identify impetus and momentum. For whereas the impetus is supposed to be something that pushes the body along, the momentum is the result rather than the cause of its motion. Moreover, the inertial motion of classical mechanics is a motion which is supposed to occur by itself, and without the influence of any causes.[101]

But the point made here concerning the difference between impetus and momentum—that one is a cause, the other a result, of motion—seems slim grounds indeed for concluding that the two concepts have nothing at all in common. To put through an argument of this sort, one must first establish that it is relevant to discussing the meaning of a term whether the reference is the cause or the result of something else. (Does putting the cart before the horse change the meanings of "cart" and "horse"?) And, having established that, one must further show that any difference in meaning implies complete difference, "incommensurability," of the concepts. We have seen, however, that Feyerabend gives neither a clear criterion of what is supposed to be part of the meaning of a term, nor a convincing argument that differences of meaning make all the difference to the comparability of concepts.

Similar remarks apply to Feyerabend's alleged differences between impetus and inertia. The two theories differ with regard to what is considered to be the "natural state" of a body. For the Impetus Theory (and, indeed, this constitutes its primary affinity with the Aristotelian tradition), the natural state is the state of rest (in the natural place of the body). In such a place, no force is acting; it is only for bodies in motion that a force is required to maintain the motion. For the Newtonian view, on the other hand (according to Feyerabend), "it is the state of being at rest or in uniform motion which is regarded as the natural state," [102] and thus force is the cause of deviation from a state of rest *or uniform motion* rather than simply from rest. But in the first place, as was pointed out earlier in this part of the present paper, Newton himself is not perfectly clear as to whether inertial motion requires a cause (*vis inertiae*), and so Feyerabend's discussion of "Newton's physics" is misleading on this point. It is true that the inertial conception became clearer in succeeding years and that the notion of a cause of inertial motion is unnecessary to classical mechanics; but Feyerabend's notion of theory gives us no way of distinguishing, here as elsewhere, between what, in Newton's thought, was necessary to his scientific theory and what was not. And furthermore, if we can ask whether the notion of an internal cause of inertial motion is necessary to Newton's physics, why can we not ask also the same question about the necessity of the concept of impetus as a cause of (uniform rectilinear) motion?

A more balanced appraisal can be outlined as follows. The Aristotelian-Scholastic system, through an intricately connected web of concepts and propositions, laid down certain patterns of thought, principles, for example, in terms of which certain sorts of questions could be raised and answered (e.g., that what needed to be explained was, in general, motion; and that motion was to be explained in terms of contact action only—a principle, incidentally, which it shared with later and otherwise far different "traditions"). And in terms of such principles, certain things appeared to be self-contradictory (vacuum, actual infinite) or physically impossible (rotation of the earth). In laying down such principles of investigation, it simultaneously set up obstacles, or limitations, both by theoretical argument and by suggestion, to thinking in certain other ways. In this sense, we can speak of the Aristotelian view as having involved certain "presuppositions" specifying (for example) what could and what could not count as an explanation. To this extent, Kuhn and

Feyerabend have made an important point. But these "presuppositions" were not mysterious, invisible, behind-the-scenes "paradigms" (Kuhn) or "high-level background theories" (Feyerabend), but were involved in the straightforward scientific statements themselves, even though there were disagreements about details (and even about fundamentals), and even though the ways in which they restricted thought, or the importance of those restrictions, could not be seen so easily. (However, these things *were* seen by some people—Philoponus, Buridan, Orêsme, among others —who were taught in that tradition.)

The Impetus Theory, even though it did not go all the way toward thinking outside the Aristotelian limits, did open the door to doing so. This is not to say that the Impetus Theory was a *new* theory, distinct in all respects from its Greek and Scholastic predecessors. On the contrary, it constituted, in its inception, only an adjustment in one seemingly minor area of the total Aristotelian system, the account of projectile motion. It remained within the Aristotelian tradition in holding that without a continually acting force, there can be no continually proceeding motion. But to say all this is not to deny, either, its affinities with later scientific concepts: We can see clearly, from the above discussion, that there are a large number of such resemblances and continuities. Impetus is not yet inertia, nor is it momentum, but it is, in the ways described above, a visible move away from fundamental Aristotelian conceptions (e.g., it allows the sustaining force in projectile motion to be internal and incorporeal) and in the definite direction of classical mechanics. In our fear of falling into "precursoritis"—the mistake of supposing that all great achievements in science were anticipated long before—we must not fall into the opposite error of thinking that every great achievement in science is a "complete replacement" (in Feyerabend's sense) of the old by the new, a thoroughgoing "revolution" (in Kuhn's sense)—that it was not led up to by a succession of developments that can be described as reasonable.

Yet, as such thinkers as Feyerabend, Koyré, and Butterfield have pointed out, that reasonableness did not consist merely in the discovery of new facts, or even—merely—in a closer attention to facts already known. It is true, as Feyerabend notes, that the Impetus Theory can give the same quantitative results as the Newtonian. On the other hand, it must not be concluded from this (as Koyré and others have concluded) that the seventeenth-century scientific revolution was therefore "nonempirical," "rationalistic," or "Platonic": The distinction between "empirical" and "nonempirical" has not been clarified sufficiently by philosophers for either horn of the distinction to serve as an adequate tool for the interpretation of scientific change. And still less should the conclusion be drawn that the choice between impetus and inertial dynamics must be (and must have been in the sixteenth and seventeenth centuries) arbitrary (or a matter of convention). In a sense that still remains to be analyzed satisfactorily by philosophers of science, Galileo's inclined plane experiments were relevant as "factual evidence" for the modern inertial concept. The greater "simplicity" or "economy" of the latter view must be taken into account also.

No doubt many of the characteristics outlined here of the transition from Aristotelian to classical physics via the Impetus Theory are found also in later "scientific revolutions." [103] One must not generalize too hastily, however: It was not too long ago that "medieval" was synonymous with "unscientific," and there may well be very important differences between the case considered here and later "revolutions," e.g., the transition from classical to relativistic dynamics. Conclusions about such matters should be drawn only in the light of careful examination of actual cases: as Dijksterhuis has commented, "The History of Science forms not only the memory of science, but also its epistemological laboratory." [104] There are two possible ways of interpreting this remark: the history of science (and we must include its product, contemporary science) can be looked on as a laboratory either in the sense that an understanding of science can come through an investigation of the logic of its development or in the sense that conceptions of the aims and methods of science may well have been forged and evolved in the practice thereof, just as has the content of science. We can profit by keeping in mind both of these possible interpretations.

In approaching the investigation of science, however, we must beware of analytical tools which, whether they have been employed throughout a long philosophical tradition or in less formal discussions of science, have never been adequately clarified. Such are the distinctions between what is and what is not part of the meaning of a term, and between stability and change of meaning, which have been examined in this essay. Such also are distinctions—some of which have been touched on here— between "meaningful" and "meaningless," "scientific" and "unscientific," and "empirical" and "nonempirical" ("metaphysical"). An adequate vocabulary for talking about science must, of course, be developed if understanding of science is to be achieved. But the vocabulary we adopt must not be laid down in advance of detailed examination of cases, as a set of logical categories which the cases must fit; this was a fault too often with philosophies of science in the past. Nor must our terms be employed without adequate analysis, and in such a way that those fundamental tools themselves determine the outcome of our investigation, as we have found to have been the case with some more recent attempts to interpret science.

NOTES

1. What follows is not meant to be a description of views to all of which any one thinker necessarily adheres, but rather a distillation of points of view which are widespread. Perhaps the writers who come closest to the characterizations given herein are Rudolf Carnap and Carl Hempel, at least in some of their works, although even they might not accept all the doctrines outlined here. The summary does, however, seem to me to represent trends in a great many writings on such subjects as the verifiability theory of meaning, explanation, lawlikeness, counterfactual conditionals, theoretical and observational terms, induction, correspondence rules, etc. Conversely, many writers whose work fits, at least to some degree, the descriptions given here might object to the label "logical empiricist."
2. There were, of course, some notable exceptions to this account—the work of Carnap and Reichenbach on relativity and quantum theory, for example.
3. There have been a number of varieties of efforts to develop new approaches: conspicuous among them, in addition to the views to be discussed in this essay, are the work of Nelson Goodman (*Fact, Fiction, and Forecast*, Cambridge: Harvard University Press, 1955), and of those philosophers who have attempted to develop new sorts of logics ("modal," for example), in the hope that they will prove more suitable for dealing with philosophical problems.
4. L. Wittgenstein, *Philosophical Investigations*, trans. G. E. M. Anscombe (New York: Macmillan, 1953).
5. But Paul Feyerabend, whose views will be discussed in this essay, has not been particularly influenced by this approach and has opposed himself to some of its main features. But he is against overconcentration on formalisms; for example, he says, "Interesting ideas may . . . be invisible to those who are concerned with the relation between existing formalisms and 'experience' only." ("On the 'Meaning' of Scientific Terms," *J. of Philosophy*, 62 (1965), 268.
6. P. Feyerabend, "Problems of Microphysics," *Frontiers of Science and Philosophy*, ed. R. Colodny (Pittsburgh: U. of Pittsburgh Press, 1962), pp. 189–283.
7. T. S. Kuhn, *The Structure of Scientific Revolutions* (Chicago: U. of Chicago Press, 1962), p. 2.
8. For example, see E. J. Dijksterhuis, *The Mechanization of the World Picture* (Oxford: Clarendon Press, 1961), Pt. IV, Chaps. 2, sec. C and 3, sec. L.
9. H. Butterfield, *The Origins of Modern Science* (New York: Macmillan, 1958), p. 1.
10. See, for example, E. A. Burtt, *The Metaphysical Foundations of Modern Physical Science* (New York: Harcourt, Brace, 1925); A. Koyré, "Galileo and Plato," *J. of the History of Ideas*, 4 (1943), 400–28, reprinted in *Roots of Scientific Thought*, eds. P. P. Wiener and A. Noland (New York: Basic Books, 1957), pp. 147–75; A. R. Hall, *From Galileo to Newton* (New York: Harper & Row, 1963). For criticism of the view that the scientific revolution (and

Galileo's philosophy of science in particular) was "Platonic," see L. Geymonat, *Galileo Galilei* (New York: McGraw-Hill, 1965); T. McTighe, "Was Galileo a Platonist?" (to appear in the proceedings of the 1964 Notre Dame Conference on Galileo, edited by E. McMullin and published by the U. of Notre Dame Press); and D. Shapere, "Descartes and Plato," *J. of the History of Ideas,* 24 (1963), 572–76 (specifically concerned with Koyré's views).

11. Kuhn, *Scientific Revolutions,* p. 1.

12. See especially his "Explanation, Reduction, and Empiricism," in *Minnesota Studies in the Philosophy of Science,* eds. H. Feigl and G. Maxwell, *Scientific Explanation, Space, and Time* (Minneapolis: U. of Minnesota Press, 1962), III, 28–97; and "Problems of Empiricism," in *Beyond the Edge of Certainty,* ed. R. Colodny (Englewood Cliffs, N.J.: Prentice-Hall, 1965), pp. 145–260. Feyerabend's views will be discussed in detail later in this essay.

13. N. R. Hanson, *Patterns of Discovery* (Cambridge: Cambridge U. Press, 1958); *The Concept of the Positron* (Cambridge: Cambridge U. Press, 1963). Hanson has also expressed his views in a large number of articles.

14. See especially his article, "Philosophic Principles and Scientific Theory," *Philosophy of Science,* 23 (1956), 111–35.

15. Especially in his *The Philosophy of Science* (New York: Hutchinson, 1953), and *Foresight and Understanding* (Bloomington: Indiana U. Press, 1961), and in his article, "Criticism in the History of Science: Newton on Absolute Space, Time, and Motion," *Philosophical Review,* 68 (1959), 1–29, 203–27. For a critical examination of this article, see my "Mathematical Ideals and Metaphysical Concepts," *Philosophical Review,* 69 (1960), 376–85.

16. Kuhn, *Scientific Revolutions,* p. 43.

17. A. Koyré, "Influence of Philosophic Trends on the Formulation of Scientific Theories," *The Validation of Scientific Theories,* ed. P. Frank (Boston: Beacon, 1954), p. 192.

18. Palter, "Philosophic Principles and Scientific Theory," *Philosophy of Science,* 23 (1956), p. 116.

19. Toulmin, *Foresight and Understanding,* p. 56.

20. Ibid., p. 47.

21. Ibid., p. 101.

22. Ibid., p. 95.

23. Ibid., p. 79.

24. Ibid., p. 109.

25. Ibid., p. 81.

26. Kuhn, *Scientific Revolutions,* p. 91.

27. Ibid., p. 93.

28. Ibid., p. 42.

29. Ibid., p. 41.

30. Ibid., pp. 16–17.

31. Ibid., p. 102.

32. Ibid., p. 102.

33. Ibid., p. 105.

34. D. Shapere, "The Structure of Scientific Revolutions," *Philosophical Review,* 73 (1964), pp. 383–94.

35. Feyerabend, "Problems of Empiricism," p. 163.

36. Ibid., p. 164.

37. Ibid., p. 180.

38. Ibid., p. 213.

39. Ibid., p. 214.

40. Ibid., p. 150.
41. Ibid., p. 214.
42. Ibid., p. 151.
43. Ibid., p. 175.
44. Ibid., p. 176.
45. Ibid., p. 150.
46. Ibid., p. 149.
47. Ibid., p. 214.
48. Ibid., p. 254, n. 150.
49. Ibid., p. 254, n. 150.
50. Ibid., p. 199.
51. Ibid., p. 167.
52. Feyerabend, "Problems of Microphysics," p. 201.
53. Feyerabend, "Problems of Empiricism," p. 259, n. 163.
54. Ibid., p. 162.
55. Ibid., p. 180.
56. Ibid., p. 216; italics mine.
57. Ibid., p. 180; italics mine.
58. Ibid., p. 175.
59. An objection of this sort is raised by P. Achinstein, "On the Meaning of Scientific Terms," *J. of Philosophy*, 61 (1964), 497–509. Feyerabend's "On the 'Meaning' of Scientific Terms," discussed later, is a reply to Achinstein's paper.
60. Feyerabend, "Explanation, Reduction, and Empiricism," p. 29.
61. Feyerabend, "Problems of Empiricism," p. 219, n. 3.
62. Thus, as the positions of the new approach and the older logical empiricist movement are reversed with respect to the relations between theory and observation, so also are their difficulties. For logical empiricism, observation terms were basic and it was "theoretical terms" that had to be interpreted; and many of the difficulties of that movement have revolved around the question of what counts as an "observation term." For the "new philosophy of science," on the other hand, which takes the notion of "theory" (or, for other writers than Feyerabend, some corresponding notion like "paradigm") as basic, difficulties arise concerning what counts as a theory.
63. In a footnote to "Problems of Empiricism," Feyerabend gives a definition of "incommensurable": "Two theories will be called incommensurable when the meanings of their main descriptive terms depend on mutually inconsistent principles" (p. 277, n. 19). In what language are these "principles" themselves formulated? Presumably (as we have seen), in order for them to be inconsistent with one another, they must be formulated, or at least formulable, in a common language. But if they are formulable in a common language, then in what way are the "main descriptive terms" of the theories "dependent" on them in such a way that *those* terms are not even translatable into one another? The characterization of incommensurability given in "On the 'Meaning' of Scientific Terms" does not seem to differ from that given in "Problems of Empiricism," and so does not help answer these objections.
64. Feyerabend, "Problems of Empiricism," p. 202.
65. Ibid., p. 202.
66. Ibid., p. 216.
67. Ibid., pp. 216–17.
68. Ibid., p. 217.
69. Ibid., p. 217.
70. Ibid., p. 198.

71. Ibid., p. 212.
72. Ibid., pp. 214–15.
73. One is tempted now to go back and say that Feyerabend's references to the "overlapping" of theories are just slips of the pen—that it is not *theories* that, strictly speaking, have any overlap by virtue of which they can be compared, but only their domain of experiences. If this is a proper reinterpretation of Feyerabend's position, it only serves to emphasize how very radically (and peculiarly) he conceives of difference of meaning, as constituting a *complete* "incommensurability." This reinterpretation will in any case, however, not help Feyerabend, for reasons to be explained below; "experiences," in his sense, cannot provide a basis for comparison ("overlap") either.
74. Further possible questions about this facet of Feyerabend's philosophy of science appear—as we might expect—as revivals of old problems about traditional phenomenalism: whether, for example, it is possible to observe "in a straightforward manner," without any importation of theoretical presuppositions, the "causal context" in which a statement is uttered; whether the "order" which is to be "imitated" by the theory does not itself presuppose an interpretation of experience; and whether the judgment that a certain theory is successful in imitating experience is itself a product of interpretation—whether, that is, we cannot still, despite the pragmatic theory, so interpret our experience that it will always support our theory.
75. Perhaps one reason Feyerabend would object to making likeness of meaning a matter of degree is that, if relevance were to be established in terms of similarities, the conclusion might be drawn that two theories are more relevant to the testing of one another the more similar they are; and this would contradict his deep-rooted view that a theory is more relevant to the testing of another theory the more different the two are.
76. Feyerabend, "Problems of Empiricism," p. 149.
77. Feyerabend, "On the 'Meaning' of Scientific Terms," p. 267.
78. Ibid., p. 268. Feyerabend's criterion of change of meaning has some consequences that seem paradoxical, to say the least. If a new theory entails that *one* concept of the preceding theory has extension zero, apparently no meaning change has taken place. If *all but one* of the classes of the preceding theory have extension zero, again no meaning change has taken place. And if the extensions of all classes are changed radically, but not so much that the previous extensions are zero, again no meaning change has taken place.
79. Feyerabend, "On the 'Meaning' of Scientific Terms," p. 270.
80. Ibid., p. 268.
81. Feyerabend admits that his criteria require supplementation: "It is important to realize that these two criteria lead to unambiguous results only if some further decisions are first made. Theories can be subjected to a variety of interpretations . . ." (p. 268). But his ensuing discussion does nothing to take care of the difficulties raised here.
82. In any case, it is unclear how a new theory can "entail" that concepts of another theory have extension zero if the latter concepts do not even occur in the new theory.
83. See Note 34, above. The discussion of Kuhn's view which follows is based on that paper.
84. Kuhn, *Scientific Revolutions*, p. 23.
85. Ibid., p. 102.
86. Ibid., p. 105.

87. "The Structure of Scientific Revolutions." See also my "The Causal Efficacy of Space," *Philosophy of Science*, 31 (1964), 111–21.
88. Kuhn, *Scientific Revolutions*, p. 11.
89. Documents and commentary concerning the material to be discussed in what follows are found in M. Clagett, *The Science of Mechanics in the Middle Ages* (Madison: U. of Wisconsin Press, 1959). Excellent discussions are also found in Butterfield, *The Origins of Modern Science*; Dijksterhuis, *The Mechanization of the World Picture*; A. R. Hall, *The Scientific Revolution* (Boston: Beacon, 1954); Kuhn, *The Copernican Revolution* (Cambridge: Harvard U. Press, 1957).
90. E. J. Dijksterhuis, "The Origins of Classical Mechanics," *Critical Problems in the History of Science*, ed. M. Clagett (Madison: U. of Wisconsin Press, 1959), p. 167.
91. Quoted in *The Science of Mechanics in the Middle Ages*, p. 509.
92. J. Buridan, "Questions on the Eight Books of the Physics of Aristotle," in *The Science of Mechanics in the Middle Ages*, pp. 534–37.
93. Ibid., p. 536.
94. Other steps were necessary in addition to these two main ones—e.g., the notion of circular impetus had to be abandoned in favor of rectilinear. It is noteworthy that Buridan's example of a case of circular impetus, a rotating wheel, is repeated by Newton.
95. The tendency of the theory was not, however, always in the direction of unification: not only did the distinction between different kinds of impetus (circular, rectilinear) obstruct the unity of the impetus concept, but also, in at least one thinker (Thomas Bricot), impetus suffered the same sad fate as was dealt in the later Middle Ages to the doctrine of substantial forms: Every different kind of initial propellant produced a different kind of impetus.
96. Chiefly as a result of the critical work of Anneliese Maier.
97. Feyerabend, "Explanation, Reduction, and Empiricism," p. 59.
98. Correctly, that is, if Buridan really would have agreed to this quantitative measure of impetus; but this is not completely certain. Cf. Dijksterhuis, *The Mechanization of the World Picture*, pp. 182–83.
99. Feyerabend, "Explanation, Reduction, and Empiricism," p. 54. This statement holds only for the nonself-degenerative kind of impetus accepted by Buridan.
100. Feyerabend, "Explanation, Reduction, and Empiricism," p. 56.
101. Ibid.
102. Ibid.
103. Compare the discussion of Aristotelian physics and the Impetus Theory given here with the discussion of Newtonian mechanics in my "The Causal Efficacy of Space."
104. Dijksterhuis, "The Origins of Classical Mechanics," p. 182.

SYLVAIN BROMBERGER
Massachusetts Institute of Technology

Why-Questions

> As a result of my assiduous concern with this problem I arrived by a kind of internal necessity at a reflection of astounding import: there must be invented, I reflected, a kind of alphabet of human thoughts, and through the connection of its letters and the analysis of words which are composed out of them, everything else can be discovered and judged. This inspiration gave me then a very rare joy which was, of course, quite premature, for I did not yet then grasp the true significance of the matter.
> —Leibniz
> *Towards a Universal Characteristic* (1677)

IN THIS PAPER we seek to pin down the conditions that define correct answers to why-questions. The problem can be stated more precisely. We will mean by a *why-question* a question that can be put in English in the form of an interrogative sentence of which the following is true: (1) the sentence begins with the word *why;* (2) the remainder of the sentence has the (surface) structure of an interrogative sentence designed to ask a whether-question—i.e., a question whose right answer in English, if any, must be either "yes" or "no"; (3) the sentence contains no parenthetical verbs, in Urmson's sense.[1] A why-question put as an English sentence that satisfies (1), (2), and (3) will be said to be in *normal form.* By the *inner question* of a why-question we will mean the question alluded to in (2) above—i.e., the question reached by putting the why-question in normal form, then deleting the initial "why" and uttering the remaining string as a question. By the *presupposition* of a why-question we will mean that which one would be saying is the case if, upon being asked the inner question of the why-question through an affirmative interrogative

86

sentence, one were to reply "yes," or what one would be saying is the case if, upon being asked the inner question through a negative sentence, one were to reply "no." Thus, "Why does copper turn green when exposed to air?" is a why-question in normal form; its inner question is "Does copper turn green when exposed to air?"; and its presupposition is that copper turns green when exposed to air. The presupposition of "Why doesn't iron turn green when exposed to air?" is that iron does not turn green when exposed to air.[2]

We will not be concerned with every sort of why-question. We will ignore why-questions whose normal forms are not in the indicative. We will ignore why-questions whose presupposition refers to human acts or intentions or mental states. Finally, we will ignore why-questions whose correct answer cannot be put in the form "because p," where p indicates a position reserved for declarative sentences. Notice that this last stipulation affects not only why-questions whose correct answer must be put in some such form as "in order to . . ." or "to . . . ,"[3] but also why-questions that one might wish to say have no correct answer, and in particular why-questions with false presupposition and why-questions whose inner question itself has no answer—e.g., "Why doesn't iron form any compounds with oxygen?" and "Why does phlogiston combine with calx?" More may be ruled out, and we shall have to come back to this point.[4]

To simplify matters, we will disregard the fact that correct answers to the why-questions that do concern us can often be put in some other form than "because p" with a declarative sentence at the p. Furthermore, we will reserve the term *answer* to refer to what is conveyed by the sentence at p abstracted from the "because . . ." environment. Thus, if "Because the temperature is rising" is the correct answer to some why-question we will speak of "the temperature is rising" as the answer.

We can now put our problem very simply. Let a and b be any two true propositions; what necessary and sufficient conditions must they jointly satisfy if b is to be a correct answer to a why-question whose presupposition is a?[5]

II

So far we have relied on a characterization of why-questions in which features peculiar to the English lexicon and to English grammar play an essential role. We have carefully avoided identifying why-questions as a class of English interrogative sentences, but we have nevertheless defined them as questions that must be expressible in a certain way in English.

This may seem to detract from the interest of the problem. Philosophers of science in particular may feel wary of a typology of questions that rests squarely on the availability of certain forms in a specific natural language. There are good grounds for such suspicion. After all, scientific questions are for the most part only accidentally expressible in English. They can also be put in French, German, Russian, Japanese, etc., not to mention artificial languages. Furthermore, some of these questions may not be expressible in English at all, especially so if by "English" we mean contemporary, "ordinary" English. "Why is the emf induced in a coiled conductor a function of the rate of change of magnetic flux through it and of the resistance of the coil?" could probably not have been asked in seventeenth-century English, and a similar situation may hold for questions that have not yet arisen.

One could try to meet such reservations by providing at the outset a language-independent definition of why-questions, or rather of *Why*-questions, a class of questions that would include all why-questions but that would not be limited to questions expressible in English. However, it is not clear how one is to be guided in setting up such a definition. We propose to deal with the matter somewhat differently. We will set as one condition on the solution of our problem that it abstract completely from the peculiarities of English—i.e., that it be stated in terms that transcend linguistic idiosyncrasies and are applicable to expressions in any relevantly rich language. Having done this we should be able to give a definition of Why-questions that preserves whatever warrants an interest in the nature of why-questions on the part of philosophers of science.[6]

III

What we have just said commits us to two hypotheses. The first of these hypotheses is that the relation between presupposition and (correct) answer to a why-question can be analyzed in language-independent terms. This hypothesis may be false, in which case we will not be able to solve our problem within the restrictions that we have adopted. However, it should be clear that the hypothesis cannot prevent us from accepting as relevant intuitions about the presence or absence of the relation in specific cases available to us as speakers of English. When we say that the relation is language independent, we do *not* mean that it hinges only on extra-linguistic facts. We mean that insofar as it hinges on linguistic features it hinges only on syntactic and semantic properties that expressions from every language share. Thus, the properties of being true and of being mutually implied are properties that expressions may have whether they belong to English or Chinese or Beulemans. The property of being the result of a do-transformation (the transformation that inserts "do" in, e.g., "He did not eat" or in "Didn't he eat?" but not in "He will not eat" or in "Hasn't he eaten?") is a property shared only by English expressions. Our hypothesis is therefore compatible with the tenet that any speaker of English has the faculty to perceive whether the semantic and syntactic properties of two given English sentences meet (or fail to meet) the conditions that would make one of these sentences express the answer of a why-question whose presupposition is expressed by the other. He must, of course, understand the sentences, and he must also have certain relevant beliefs. On the other hand, to say that he has the faculty to perceive whether this sort of condition is satisfied in specific instances is not to say that he can describe them or analyze them. Nor is it to say that he will never or ought never to hesitate before pronouncing something to be a correct answer to a why-question. Hesitation is to be expected where the case at hand is complex and demands slow and careful scrutiny. It is also to be expected when the truth of the sentences or of the relevant beliefs are themselves objects of hesitation. But there are clear-cut cases and these constitute a corpus for which, as speakers of English, we must account.

IV

The second hypothesis is that there are issues in the philosophy of science that warrant an interest in the nature of why-questions. The most obvious of these issues are whether science (or some branch of science or some specific scientific doctrine or some approach) ought to, can, or does provide answers to why-questions, and if so, to which ones. In other words, when appraising critically the state of scientific knowledge (or of some branch of science or some doctrine or some approach), how much weight should we give to unanswered why-questions? Should we consider that some why-questions are beyond the reach of scientific methodology or rules of evidence? Should we refrain from accepting as final any doctrine that raises why-questions to which no answers are forthcoming? We will have little to say about these very complex issues here, but since they provide much of the motivation for our inquiry, a few words of caution are called for.

These issues are usually discussed in English with the word "explanation" used instead of "why-question" or "answer to why-question." Analogous substitutions occur in other languages. This way of putting things can be innocuous and is possibly justified by the awkwardness of using the more contrived locutions. But it is ambiguous and may be a source of confusion. To become aware of this we need but notice that "explanation" may refer to the answers of a huge variety of questions besides why-questions, the only requirement being that their *oratio obliqua* form fit as grammatical object of the verb "to explain" and its nominalization "explanation of," e.g., how-questions, what-is-the-cause-of-questions, what-corresponds-at-the-microscopic-level-questions, etc. Yet, the issues raised by these other types call for considerations peculiar to each type and different from those called for in the case of why-questions. Confusion is therefore likely to ensue and is apt to be further compounded if we allow ourselves to forget that "explanation" may also refer to things not readily specified as answers to a specific class of questions. To remain aware of the range of issues covered by a given analysis we must therefore keep sharp the differences among questions about (1) truth-conditions of sentences generated from "A explains B" and from "A is the explanation of B" by substituting any grammatically appropriate phrase for B, (2) truth-conditions of sentences obtained by substituting for B only *oratio obliqua* forms of grammatically appropriate questions, (3) truth-conditions of sentences obtained by substituting for B the *oratio obliqua* form of some more narrowly defined class of questions (e.g., why-questions, how-questions, what-corresponds-at-the-microscopic-level-questions, etc.), (4) conditions that are satisfied by answers and presupposition of all questions whose *oratio obliqua* form can be substituted for B, (5) conditions that are satisfied by answers and presupposition of some narrower class of questions whose *oratio obliqua* form can be substituted for B.[7] It should be clear that we will limit ourselves to a special case of (5) in this paper, the case of why-questions. In fact, our limits are even narrower since we have eliminated from consideration certain types of why-questions.

Offhand, it may seem that the above (1) to (5) enumeration is redundant and that we might have stopped after (3). Actually, subtle but important distinctions underlie the difference between "Explanation of Q" and "Answer to Q." We have discussed these at some length elsewhere[8] and will say just a few words about them here to suggest the sort of further problems involved.

Let us describe someone as in a *p-predicament* (*p* can be thought of as standing for "puzzled" or "perplexed" but for *mnemonic* purposes only) with regard to some question Q, if and only if on that person's views, the question Q admits of a right answer, yet the person can think of no answer, can make up no answer, can generate from his mental repertoire no answer to which, given that person's views, there are no decisive objections. For instance, a physicist committed to classical physics but aware of the photoelectric effect would be in a *p*-predicament with regard to the question "Why does a photoelectric current appear without delay as soon as light of frequency above the threshold frequency impinges on the target, and this no matter how low the frequency of the impinging light?" Let us also describe someone as in a *b-predicament* with regard to a question *Q* if and only if the question admits of a right answer, no matter what the views of the person, but that answer is beyond what that person can think of, can state, can generate from his mental repertoire. Thus, someone unacquainted with the kinetic-molecular theory of matter would be in a *b*-predicament with regard to the question "What is the mechanism by which water evaporates from uncovered dishes left in the open?" Let us say furthermore that a question *Q* is *unanswerable relative to a certain set of propositions and concepts C* if and only if anyone who subscribes to these propositions and limits himself to these concepts must be in either a *p*-predicament or *b*-predicament with regard to the question *Q*. The search for and discovery of scientific *explanations,* we think, is essentially the search for and discovery of answers to questions that are unanswerable relative to prevailing beliefs and concepts. It is not, therefore, merely a quest for evidence to settle which available answer is correct, it is a quest for the unthought-of.

The difference between "explanation" and "answer" just sketched transcends the distinction between why-questions and other questions. It should nevertheless be kept in mind when we deal with the issues described at the beginning of this section. These need not be resolved in the same way for why-questions that are unanswerable relative to the set under consideration and for those that are merely unanswered.

V

According to a very familiar theory, explaining a fact (an event, a phenomenon, a natural law) consists in deducing a statement describing the fact from the statement of a true law and additional true premises. Thus, according to this theory, the explanation of a fact is a valid and sound (i.e., all the premises are true) deduction, none of whose premises are superfluous, some of whose premises are empirical laws, and whose conclusion is a description of the fact explained. The premises of such a deduction are called the *explanans* and the conclusion, the *explanandum.* We will refer to such deductions as *deductive nomological explanations* and to the theory itself, whose most famous and competent exponent has been Carl Hempel, as the *Hempelian doctrine*.[9]

As a general characterization of the notion of explanation, i.e., as a description of the truth-conditions of statements of the form "A explains B" or "A is a correct explanation of B," or their non-English equivalents, the Hempelian doctrine obviously will not do, a fact that its proponents have always recognized. The evidence for this also shows that the doctrine does not describe necessary and sufficient conditions on the answers to all the sound questions whose *oratio obliqua* form may be substituted for B. Answers to, or explanations of, how cloud chambers work, of what the nature of light is, of what occurs at the molecular level when water freezes, etc. need not be explanans (nor even a pragmatically selected component of explanans). On the other hand, the doctrine no doubt does describe necessary and sufficient conditions on answers to *some* questions whose *oratio obliqua* form can be substituted for B. Thus, every deductive nomological explanation is an explanation or at least a sound answer to questions of the form "How could anyone knowing that . . . (here put the conjunction of all the premises in a deductive nomological explanans) . . . but not that . . . (here put the corresponding explanandum) . . . have predicted that . . . (here repeat the explanandum) . . . ?" and obviously the conjunction of the premises also constitutes a correct answer to questions of the form "From what laws and antecedent conditions can the fact that . . . (here put the explanandum) . . . be deduced?" But does the Hempelian doctrine tell us what we want to know about why-questions? Is a proposition *p* the correct answer of a why-question whose presupposition is *q* if and only if *p* is the conjunction of premises (or of some pragmatically selected subset of premises) of a deductive nomological explanation whose conclusion is *q*? The following counterexamples (and they are easily multiplied) strike us as settling the matter and this quite apart from some technical difficulties connected with the relevant notions of deducibility and law.

1. There is a point on Fifth Avenue, *M* feet away from the base of the Empire State Building, at which a ray of light coming from the tip of the building makes an angle of *θ* degrees with a line to the base of the building. From the laws of geometric optics, together with the "antecedent" condition that the distance is *M* feet, the angle *θ* degrees, it is possible to deduce that the Empire State Building has a height of *H* feet. Any high-school student could set up the deduction given actual numerical values. By doing so, he would not, however, have *explained* why the Empire State Building has a height of *H* feet, nor would he have

answered the question "Why does the Empire State Building have a height of H feet?" nor would an exposition of the deduction be the explanation of or answer to (either implicitly or explicitly) why the Empire State Building has a height of H feet.

2. From the Leavitt-Shapley Law, the inverse square law for light, the periods of Cepheid type variable stars in the Andromedan Galaxy, their apparent range of brightness, one can deduce that the Andromedan Galaxy is 1.5×10^6 light years away from the earth. The premises of the deduction, however, do not tell why or explain why the Andromedan Galaxy is 1.5×10^6 light years away from the earth.

3. Whenever the pointer of the water meter points to 5, and only the bathtub faucet is open, water flows at a rate of five gallons per minute into the bathtub. The pointer has been on 5 for the last three minutes, and no faucet except the bathtub one is open. Therefore, fifteen gallons of water must have flowed into the bathtub. The deduction does not explain or tell or reveal *why* fifteen gallons of water flowed into the bathtub during the last three minutes.

4. All of Cassandra's predictions always come true. (Cassandra is a computer.) Yesterday Cassandra predicted that it would rain today. But obviously that is not why it is raining today.

5. Only men who are more than six-feet tall leave footprints longer than fourteen inches. The footprints left by Gargantua on the beach are more than fourteen inches long. Therefore Gargantua is more than six-feet tall.

Again the reasoning fails to mention *why* Gargantua is more than six-feet tall.

These counterexamples are compatible with the thesis that answers and presuppositions of why-questions *must* be premises and conclusions of deductive nomological explanations. They do show, however, that this cannot be *sufficient*.

It has been suggested that these counterexamples and others like them are not really binding on philosophers of science, that they ultimately involve an appeal to ordinary usage and that such appeals are not appropriate when we deal with inquiries that are far removed from ordinary concerns. These objections can be construed in a number of ways.

1. They may mean that our refusal to call the explanans examples of *explanations*, or to look upon them as telling *why* something is the case, merely reflects allegiance to unscientific intellectual practices that scientists qua scientists have or should have abandoned. But this is hardly

plausible. In 1885, Balmer devised a formula from which the frequencies represented in the spectrum of a sample of excited hydrogen could be deduced. But any scientist worthy of the name would have refused to accept such a deduction as the answer to why these particular frequencies were represented. The case is far from unique, and we owe the birth of quantum mechanics and of modern astronomy to that sort of refusal.

2. They may mean that the verb "to explain" and its cognates have a technical meaning in scientific contexts, a status similar to that of "work," "action," "model," etc. But this is false. "To explain" does not belong to any technical jargon (except perhaps that of some philosophers), and anyhow the crucial words in our inquiry are "why" and "because."

3. They may mean that although we do not say of these inferences that they explain or tell why something is the case, we could, and that only an unscientific tradition prevents us from doing so. This would make sense if "ordinary use" merely demanded that we *refrain* from saying of the premises of the above inferences that they tell why something is the case, but words meaning what they do, we must also *deny* it. The deduction about Gargantua does *not* tell why Gargantua is more than six-feet tall; "because the footprints he left on the beach were more than fourteen inches long" is *not* the answer to "why was Gargantua more than six feet tall?" My typewriter is neither blind nor not blind. That is a state of affairs for which "ordinary language" is partly responsible and a case might be made for extending the meaning of "blind" so that my typewriter can be said to be blind. That horses are warm-blooded, however, is a fact about horses, not language. It would remain true even if "warm-blooded" meant "member of the Ku Klux Klan," although we would then have to put the matter differently. That the premises of the inference about Gargantua do not make up a correct answer to why Gargantua was so big is a fact about these premises. It would remain a fact even if "why" were to become a request-marker for premises of deductive nomological explanations, although we would then have to put the matter differently.

4. The relation between the explanans and the explanandum of a deductive nomological explanation—let us call it the *H*-relation—can be defined in language-independent terms, i.e., in terms applicable to the expressions of any language rich enough for science. On the basis of such a definition it is also possible to define, in *language-independent* terms, a class of questions very much like why-questions, whose answer and presupposition need only be *H*-related. Let us call them *H*-why-

questions. Their definition is a little complicated and we leave it for a footnote,[10] but anyone familiar with Hempel's doctrine will sense this possibility and will recognize it as one of the virtues of the doctrine. Those who reject the above counterexamples may simply doubt that why-questions can also be defined in language-independent terms and may believe that *H*-why-questions are the nearest possible language-independent approximation. Accepting the counterexamples as binding would then mean giving up the principle that scientific questions are essentially language independent. However, such qualms are premature if, as we believe, why-questions *can* be defined in language-independent terms.

5. The objection may finally mean that by insisting on the relevance of these examples we must not only be insisting on the importance of why-questions (which have their own interrogative in English), but must be denying the importance of *H*-why-questions (which do not have an interrogative in English). We do not.

VI

What is essential is not always easy to distinguish from what is accidental in the relation between why-questions and their answers. For instance, it is often assumed that besides being true, presuppositions of why-questions that have answers must also be something surprising, something that conflicts with what had been expected, or at least something unusual. Stated a little more precisely, the view amounts to this: We ask questions for all sorts of reasons and with many different purposes in mind—e.g., to test someone's knowledge, to offer someone the opportunity to show his erudition, to kill time, to attract attention; but questions have one basic function, the asking for information not already in our possession. On the view now considered, why-questions can fulfill that basic function only when asked by someone who finds the truth of the presupposition surprising and unexpected.

Why-questions no doubt are often asked by people to whom the presupposition comes as a surprise and the fact that they ask them is often related to their surprise. Furthermore, some why-questions whose presupposition is not surprising or unexpected seem to have no answer. Why does the earth have only one satellite? Why does every gram-molecular weight of matter contain 6×10^{23} molecules? Why can anything not move with a velocity greater than that of light? Why do bodies attract one another with a force that is directly proportional to their mass and inversely proportional to the square of their distance?

Why is *chien* the French word for dog? Why has there never been a President of the United States whose first name was Clovis? Why does anything exist at all? Anyone will feel about at least one of these questions that he cannot provide a "because . . ." answer, although not because he does not know or has forgotten but simply because there is no answer. The view is even compatible with the use of "why-should" questions that challenge one to show that a given why-question has an answer—e.g., "Why should there have been a President with the first name Clovis?" "Why shouldn't every gram-molecular weight contain 6×10^{23} molecules?"

If it were true that presuppositions of why-questions must be surprising, we would now have to seek out the relevant criteria for being surprising. Fortunately, it is not true. There is nothing unsound about the question "Why is the train late today?" asked by the harassed New Haven commuter who would be more surprised if the train were on time; nor is there anything unsound about why-questions raised by scientists about very familiar everyday phenomena. The same sort of considerations show that presuppositions need not be departures from regularities.

The view that we have just described is close to another view that is equally tempting and equally false. According to this second view, why-questions have answers only when there exists a plausible argument in behalf of a contrary of their presupposition. This could account for all the things accounted for by the previous view and for further things as well. If true, it would require us to analyze the relevant notion of plausible argument. But it is not true. There is no such plausible argument forthcoming in the case of "Why has there never been any President of the United States with the first name Clovis?" and yet the question is sound and has an answer: "Because no one by that name has ever been elected to the office or been the Vice-President when a President died in office." The example is deliberately chosen from the list of questions cited previously as seeming to have no answer. It suggests that one's attitude toward the presupposition and other "pragmatic" considerations play no crucial role.

VII

The solution that we are about to propose requires a few preliminary definitions. These definitions are stated with the help of predicate logic notation. The use of this notation introduces a number of theoretical problems that we will simply ignore. The problem of lawlikeness is but one of them. There are others that anyone familiar with the discussions of Hempelian doctrine will immediately detect.[11] We use the notation because it strikes us as providing the simplest way of exhibiting at present certain purely formal matters and we hope that our illustrations will bring out the intentions behind the schematisms. All these definitions must eventually be replaced by ones that make use of better representations. We think, however, that the heart of the analysis is essentially sound and that it may therefore be of some interest even in this temporary form. Each definition will be preceded by paradigms. This should make the formulae easier to read; it should, in fact, enable one to skip them altogether.

First Definition: General rule.

Paradigms: The level of a liquid in a cylindrical container on which a melting object is floating always rises. All French nouns form their plural by adding *s*. The velocity of an object never changes.

A general rule is a *lawlike* statement of the form

$$(x)(F_1x \cdot F_2x \ \ldots \ F_jx : \supset : S_1x \cdot S_2x \ \ldots \ S_kx) \qquad (j \geqslant 1, k \geqslant 1)$$

Note that the definition does *not* require that a general rule be true or even plausible.

Second Definition: General abnormic law.

Paradigms: 1. The level of liquid in a cylindrical container on which a melting object is floating at room temperature will rise unless the object is made of a substance whose density in liquid form is the same or is greater than that of the original liquid at room temperature. If the density is the same, the level will remain the same; if the density is greater, the level will go down.

2. The level of liquid in a cylindrical container on which a melting object is floating at room temperature will rise unless upon melting completely the floating object undergoes a decrease in volume equal to or greater than the volume originally above the surface of the water. In the former case, the level remains the same; in the latter case, the level goes down.

3. All French nouns form their plural by adding *s* unless they end in *al* (except *bal, cal, carnaval,* etc.) or in *eu,* or in *au,* or in *ou* (except *chou, genou,* etc.) or *x,* or *z,* or *s*. If and only if they end in *al* (except *bal,* etc.) they form the plural by dropping the last syllable and replacing it with *aux;* if and only if they end in *eu* or *ou* or *au* (except *chou,* etc.) they form their plural by adding *x;* if and only if they end in *x* or *z* or *s* they form their plural by adding nothing.

These are examples only if we are willing to assume that they are true as they stand.

A general abnormic law is a *true, lawlike* statement of the form

$$(x) \ (F_1x \cdot F_2x \ \ldots \ F_jx : \supset :. \ - Ex \ \equiv. \ A_1x \lor A_2x \ \ldots \lor A_nx \lor B_1x \ \ldots$$
$$\lor B_mx \ \ldots \lor R_ex$$
$$: A_1x \lor A_2x \ \ldots \ A_nx . \equiv S_Ax$$
$$: B_1x \lor B_2x \ \ldots \ B_mx . \equiv S_Bx$$
$$: \ldots \ldots \ldots \ldots \ldots$$
$$: R_1x \lor R_2x \ \ldots \ R_ex . \equiv S_Rx)$$
$$(n \geqslant 1, j \geqslant 1)$$

of which the corresponding following statements are also true:

(a) $(x) \ (F_1x \cdot F_2x \ \ldots \ F_jx : \supset. \ Ex \lor S_Ax \lor S_Bx \ \ldots \ S_Rx)$ $(R \geqslant 1)$

(b) $(x)(A_1x \supset: -A_2x \cdot -A_3x \ \ldots \ -A_nx \cdot -B_1x \ \ldots \ -B_mx \ \ldots \ -R_ex$
$$:. \ A_2x \supset: -A_1x \cdot -A_3x \ \ldots \ -A_nx \cdot -B_1x \ \ldots \ -B_mx \ldots \ -R_ex$$
$$:. \ \ldots \ \ldots \ \ldots \ \ldots \ \ldots \ \ldots \ \ldots \ \ldots \ \ldots \ \ldots \ \ldots$$
$$:. \ R_ex \supset: -A_1x \cdot -A_2x \ \ldots \ -R_{e-1}x)$$

(c) It does not remain a true, lawlike statement when one or more disjuncts in any of the internal biconditionals is dropped or when one or more of the conjuncts in the initial antecedent is dropped. (These three conditions are redundant, but we are obviously not after elegance in this sketch.)

(d) The closure of the main antecedent is not a logical truth or contradiction.

(e) The closure of none of the internal disjunctions is a logical truth or contradiction.

(We construe the "unless" in the paradigms as the exclusive disjunction.)

Third Definition: Special abnormic law.

Paradigms: 4. The velocity of an object does not change unless the net force on it is not equal to zero.

5. No sample of gas expands unless its temperature is kept constant but its pressure decreases, or its pressure is kept constant but its temperature increases, or its absolute temperature increases by a larger factor than its pressure, or its pressure decreases by a larger factor than its absolute temperature.

Again we must assume that these are true.

A special abnormic law is a true, lawlike statement of the form

$$(x)(F_1x \cdot F_2x \ \ldots \ F_jx : \supset :. \ -Ex \ \equiv. \ A_1x \lor A_2x \lor \ldots \lor A_nx)$$
$$(n \geqslant 1, j \geqslant 1)$$

that satisfies conditions (a) to (e) on general abnormic laws. (It is easy to show that every general abnormic law is equivalent to a conjunction of special abnormic laws but we will not make use of this fact.)[12]

Fourth Definition: Antonymic predicates of an abnormic law.

Paradigms: The antonymic predicates of (3) above are "Forms the plural by adding *s*," "Forms the plural by dropping the last syllable and replacing it with *aux*," "Forms the plural by adding *x*," "Forms the plural by adding nothing." Those of (4) are "Has a velocity that is changing," "Does not have a changing velocity."

The antonymic predicates of a general abnormic law are the predicates that appear in the consequent of (a). Those of a special abnormic law are the predicate substituted for *E* in the statement of that law, and the negation of that predicate.

Fifth Definition: The completion of a general rule by an abnormic law.

Paradigms: (1) and (2) are each a completion of the first paradigm of a general rule. (3) and (4) are the completion of the next two paradigms of a general rule.

An abnormic law is the completion of a general rule if and only if the general rule is false and is obtainable by dropping the "unless" qualifications—i.e., by closing the statement before the first exclusive disjunction. (With our representation of the exclusive disjunction this requires negating the predicate substituted for *E*—or dropping the negation if it is already negated—deleting the biconditional connective, and making the obvious bracketing adjustments.)

We can now describe what we believe to be the relation between presuppositions and answers to why-questions. Before doing so, we will briefly present an example that points out the relevant features. The example and those to follow will only involve monadic predicates and will therefore fit the formulae in the definitions given above. But the predicates of presuppositions and answers of why-questions will not always be monadic and these definitions are thus too narrow as they stand. The shortcoming is readily remedied. We can either replace the references to the various formulae by references to the closure of the formulae obtainable by substitution from those given, or we can replace the formulae by more abstract schemata that allow for polyadic and for "zero-adic" predicates.[13] We shall assume that some such correction has in fact been adopted without actually carrying it out. Doing so would not solve the deeper problems alluded to in the introductory paragraph of this section, and the apparent gain in rigor would only be deceptive.

Why is the plural of the French noun *cheval chevaux*, i.e. formed by dropping the last syllable and replacing it with *aux*? Answer: (Because) *cheval* ends in *al*.

The answer together with abnormic law (3) and the further premise that *cheval* is a French noun form an explanans whose conclusion is the presupposition. The further premise that is not part of the answer together with the general rule completed by the abnormic law constitute a valid (but not sound) deduction whose conclusion is a *contrary* of the presupposition.

Here then is the relation: *b* is the correct answer to the why-question whose presupposition is *a* if and only if (1) there is an abnormic law *L* (general or special) and *a* is an instantiation of one of *L*'s antonymic predicates; (2) *b* is a member of a set of premises that together with *L* constitute a deductive nomological explanation whose conclusion is *a;* (3) the remaining premises together with the general rule completed by *L* constitute a deduction in every respect like a deductive nomological explanation except for a false lawlike premise and false conclusion, whose conclusion is a contrary of *a;* (4) the general rule completed by *L* has the property that if one of the conjuncts in the antecedent is dropped the new general rule cannot be completed by an abnormic law.[14]

More examples may loosen up this jargon.

Why has there never been a President of the United States with the first name Clovis? We get the answer in the following way.

General rule: Every name is the name of some President of the United States.

Abnormic law that completes this general rule: Every name is the name of some President of the United States unless no one by that name has ever been elected to the Presidency and no one by that name has ever been Vice-President when a President died in office.

Premises that together with the law form a deductive nomological explanation whose conclusion is the presupposition: Clovis is a name; no one with the name Clovis has ever been elected to the Presidency of the United States, and no one by that name has ever been Vice-President when a President died in office.

Premises that together with the general rule lead to a contrary of the presupposition: Clovis is a name.

Remaining premise: the answer.

Next is an illustration of a why-question that has more than one correct answer. The case is adapted from a paper by Hempel: "In a beaker filled to the brim with water at room temperature there floats a chunk of ice which partly extends above the surface. As the ice gradually melts, one might expect the water in the beaker to overflow. Actually, however, the water level remains unchanged. How is this to be explained?" [15] We construe the last question as simply meaning, "Why did the level of water not rise?" Two relevant abnormic laws, (1) and (2) are available and both are completions of the same general rule—i.e., that given as our first example. The propositions that the contents of the beaker are a liquid on which a melting object is floating, that the liquid is water, that the object is ice, that ice upon melting becomes water—i.e., has the same density in liquid form as water, together with (1) form a deduction whose conclusion is the presupposition. The answer to the question: (Because) ice upon melting has the same density as water. The other premises together with the general rule lead to a contrary of the presupposition. We leave it to the reader to show that (2) leads in the same way to the answer: (Because) the ice undergoes a decrease in volume equal to the volume originally above the surface of the water.

It is instructive to read what Hempel wrote about this example:

The key to an answer is provided by Archimedes's principle, according to which a solid body floating in a liquid displaces a volume of liquid which is the same weight as the body itself. Hence the chunk of ice has the same weight as the volume of water its submerged portion displaces. Now since melting does not affect the weights involved, the water into which the ice turns has the same weight as the ice itself, and hence, the same weight as the water initially displaced by the submerged portion of ice. Having the same weight, it also has the same volume as the displaced water; hence the melting ice yields a volume of water that suffices exactly to fill the space initially occupied by the submerged part of the ice. Therefore the water level remains unchanged.

Insofar as there is an answer conveyed in all this, it seems to be roughly equivalent to our second one.

Hempel was undoubtedly right in holding that the key to the explanation is provided by Archimedes' principle. However, if we look upon the question as a why-question, the principle is no more crucial than the principle that melting does not affect weight. It is the key in the sense that it provides a clue, also in the sense that anyone in a *p*-predicament or *b*-predicament with regard to the why-question must in all likelihood be told or be reminded of the principle; it is also an essential piece of knowledge for establishing that the answers are true, but it is not essential to establish that the answers, granted that they are true, are also correct answers to the why-question.

Our last illustration was a why-question that has more than one correct answer. Most why-questions are probably like that—i.e., true presuppositions seldom if ever determine unique answers. According to our analysis, this is to be expected since more than one abnormic law is usually available from which a given presupposition can be derived. Our analysis, then, does not segregate good answers from poor ones, only correct ones from incorrect ones. We could, therefore, expect it even to account for the degenerate cases made famous by Molière: "Why does opium put people to sleep? Because it has dormitive power." One might as well have said, "Because it puts people to sleep." These cases almost go through because of the availability of such abnormic laws as "No substance puts people to sleep unless it puts people to sleep." Instances of the valid "$(x)(Fx \supset . -Ex \lor Ex)$" and of other schemata obtainable from "$p \supset .q \equiv q$" by substitution and generalization are always available. However, these cases do not quite go through insofar as (2) on page 100 together with the definition of "deductive nomological explanation" require that the abnormic law be *empirical*. Thus, we see why, on the one hand, one can assimilate such answers with correct answers and why, on the other hand, one knows that they ought to be rejected.

VIII

Our analysis accounts for some familiar facts about why-questions. In general, a question arises whenever there is reason to believe that it has an answer, although the answer is not known. This will happen in the case of why-questions when one believes that the presupposition is true, views it as a departure from a general rule, and thinks that the conditions under which departures from the general rule occur can be generalized by an abnormic law. One may be mistaken about this. One may, for instance, be mistaken in thinking that the presupposition is true. In that case, no answer (as we have defined the term, i.e., correct reply in the form of "because . . .") will be forthcoming. There will be, of course, appropriate replies. A statement to the effect that the presupposition is false will provide the relevant information.

One may, on the other hand, be mistaken in thinking that the presupposition represents a departure from a general rule. In that case, again, there will be no answer, although there will be other appropriate replies. "Why does this live oak keep its leaves during the winter?" "All live oaks do!" (Not however, "Because all live oaks do.") This sort of reply, like the previous one, has the force of a correction and entails that the question does not really arise.

One may, finally, be mistaken in thinking that the conditions under which departures from the general rule occur can be generalized. Here once more, no answer will be forthcoming: "Why is Johnny immune to poison ivy?" "Some people are and some people are not." However, an "answer" built from a degenerate abnormic law will also do, e.g., "No one is immune to poison ivy unless he is," and from that, "Because he is."

These everyday situations should not be taken too lightly by philosophers of science. Why-questions must sometimes be countered with a general rule rather than with an answer. This corresponds to the fact that scientific investigations of why something is the case often end not with the discovery of a "because . . ." answer, but with the establishment of a new general rule. And this poses a problem: When is such a substitution merely a *begging* of the why-question? When does our ignorance demand that we not trade a why-question for a *H*-why-question but find the limits of a general rule? Why-questions even in science must sometimes be dealt with by denying that a departure from a general rule can be nontrivially generalized, which also raises problems: What sort of evidence warrants such denials? Can any fact ever be *shown* to be ultimate and unexplainable?

We mentioned in section VI the view that why-questions can fulfill their basic function only if the presupposition is something surprising or if there is at least a plausible argument forthcoming in behalf of one of its contraries. It is easy to see how such a view might come to be accepted: many instances support it. This is no accident. One often guides one's expectations by general rules, rules that are sometimes explicitly and sometimes only implicitly acknowledged. Reliance on such rules entails belief that they work in most cases. But it also leads one to view certain facts as departures from general rules, a prerequisite for a why-question to arise. This prerequisite then is often satisfied under circumstances that surprise or that at least provide the grounds for a plausible argument for a contrary of a presupposition (the argument whose lawlike premise is the false general rule). As counterexamples show, such circumstances, although frequent, are not essential, and they do not provide the key to the nature of why-questions. Here too, an interesting problem for philosophers of science comes up. A clear mark of scientific genius is the ability to see certain well-known facts as departures from general rules that may have no actual instances, but that *could* have had some, and the germane ability to ask why-questions that occur to no one else. This way of looking at things can sometimes yield important insights, but it is also sometimes simply foolish. Is the difference analyzable in logical categories, or is it fundamentally a matter of psychology or perhaps theology?

Another view frequently held about why-questions—particularly about why-questions with negative presuppositions—is that the answer must describe the absence of a necessary condition for the contrary of the presupposition. This is not far from the truth for many cases to which these notions are easily applied, but it is an oversimplification, even for those cases. In the typical cases, the answer must describe the absence of (or at least something incompatible with) not merely *any* necessary condition for the contrary of the presupposition, but of a necessary condition belonging to a set (1) only one of whose members can be false, (2) each of whose members is necessary, and (3) all of whose members are jointly sufficient for that contrary. This follows from the definition of abnormic law. This is easily seen by looking at the propositional structure of instantiated special abnormic laws. A typical structure is

$$Ya \supset: Xa \equiv. Aa \lor Ba \lor Ca \tag{1}$$

where "$Ya \supset - Xa$" is the propositional structure of the instantiated general rule, "Xa" is the presupposition, and the answer must be one of the disjuncts to the right of the biconditional. Typically, when (1) is true, so is

$$Xa \equiv. Aa \lor Ba \lor Ca \tag{2}$$

("Ya" being the premise that together with the general rule leads to a contrary of the presupposition) and so then is

$$-Xa \equiv: -Aa \cdot -Ba \cdot -Ca \tag{3}$$

This shows that the answer ("Aa" or "Ba" or "Ca") describes the absence of a necessary condition("$-Aa$" or "$-Ba$" or "$-Ca$") for the contrary of the presupposition. (Throughout we follow the practice of using "contrary" to mean "contrary or contradictory.")

Condition (b) in the definition of an abnormic law requires that the disjuncts in (1) be mutually exclusive—i.e., that if one of the conjuncts in (3) is false, the others must be true. (3) by itself requires that these conjuncts be jointly sufficient for "$-Xa$."

We can test this consequence against an idealized, concrete instance. Two switches, A and B, are in series in a circuit so that current flows if and only if both switches are closed. Current is not flowing and both switches are open. Why is the current not flowing? Because both A and B are open. It would be misleading to say "Because A is open," although it is true and although it mentions the absence of a necessary condition for the contrary of the presupposition, and similarly for "Because B is open." Either of these replies *in this context* would imply that the other switch is closed. The possible answers, then, are: *A is open although B is closed;*

B is open although A is closed; A and B are both open. These are mutually exclusive. The negations are: *either A is closed or B is open; either B is closed or A is open; either A or B is closed.* But this is a set of conditions for the contrary of the presupposition (1) only one of whose members can be false, (2) each of whose members is necessary, (3) all of whose members are jointly sufficient.

We can now understand the function and form of the why-should questions mentioned in section VI. "Why is the current flowing?" "Why shouldn't it be flowing?" They are designed not only to bring out grounds for believing that the original why-question has an answer, but also to narrow down the area within which the answer is expected. They do this by asking what necessary conditions for the contrary of the presupposition *are satisfied,* what necessary conditions belong to a set of jointly sufficient conditions only one of which is presumably false.[16] The answer wanted for the original why-question is thereby defined since it must negate the one remaining condition. Why-should questions take on the force of a challenge when there is reason to doubt that only one condition is missing. On the other hand why-should questions need not have an answer when a necessary and sufficient condition for the presupposition of the why-question is expected—i.e., in cases where (1) has only one disjunct or (3) has only one conjunct.

We must now turn to the examples cited in section V against the Hempelian doctrine. How do they fail as answers to why-questions? Let us look at a simple but typical member of the family. The telephone post at the corner of Elm Street is forty-feet high. Its top is connected by a taut wire to a point thirty feet from its foot. The length of the wire is fifty feet. Why is the pole forty-feet high? According to one interpretation of the Hempelian doctrine, an answer should be available that is made up of the facts about the wire, since the height can be deduced from these facts and laws of physical geometry. There would be an answer made up that way according to our analysis if it were an abnormic law that no pole is forty-feet high unless a taut fifty-foot-long wire connects its top to a point thirty feet from its foot. But there is no such law. Fifty-foot-high poles may have no wires attached to them, and they may also have wires attached to them that are of a different length and connect to a different point on the ground. If we extend the clause after "unless" with disjunctions that include the cases with other wires and with no wires, we will still not end up with an abnormic law; some of the disjuncts will not be mutually exclusive and, furthermore, the law will remain a law if all the disjuncts except that pertaining to the case of no wires are dropped.

There would also be an answer made up of the facts about the wire according to our analysis if it were a law that no pole is forty-feet high unless, if there is a taut wire connecting the top to a point on the ground and the wire is fifty-feet long, then the point on the ground is thirty feet from the foot. But there is no such law. If there were, it would entail that every pole to which no wire is attached must be forty-feet high!

However, the following is a law: No pole whose top is connected to a point on the ground by a wire that is fifty-feet long is itself forty-feet high unless that point on the ground is thirty feet from the foot of the pole. Still, it does not meet the requirements of the analysis. According to (4) on p. 94, in the description of the relation, the general rule completed by the abnormic law must not be such that by dropping one or more of the conjuncts in the antecedent a new general rule is obtained that can also be completed by an abnormic law. But the above abnormic law violates that condition. We know enough about poles to be confident that there is an abnormic law of the form "No pole is forty-feet high unless. . . ."

All the cases cited against the Hempelian doctrine will fail for similar reasons. Just as we are confident that there are laws according to which poles will be forty-feet high regardless of whether wires are attached to them, so there must be laws according to which the Empire State Building will have the height it has even in total darkness, the distance to the Andromedan Galaxy would be what it is even if no light traveled to us from it, the rate of flow of water into the bathtub would be what it is whether or not measured, Gargantua would be more than six feet tall even if he had not gone to the beach.[17]

The very same sorts of considerations, it may be worth noting, will account for certain asymmetries that have puzzled some philosophers. From the laws of the simple pendulum and the length of a piece of string at the end of which a bob is hanging and local free-fall acceleration, one can deduce the period with which that bob is oscillating. From the same law and data about local free-fall acceleration and the period with which the bob is oscillating, one can deduce its length. Yet a statement of the length is an answer to "Why does the bob oscillate with such and such a period?" whereas a statement of the period of oscillation is not an answer to "Why is the length of the string at the end of which the bob is hanging so many inches long?" The asymmetry is traceable, in a manner exactly similar to the previous reasoning, to the fact that whereas the period would not have been what it is if the length had not been what it is, the length would have been what it is whether the bob had been oscillating or not.

Condition (4) may seem at first blush somewhat arbitrary. A little reflection will bring out, however, that it corresponds to a generally acknowledged and reasonable norm. It demands on the one hand that the answer be a consequence of the most general abnormic law [18] available, and it demands on the other hand that questions of the form "Why is this A a C?" not be given answers that are really designed for "Why is this AB a C?"

It may seem odd that abnormic laws should be associated with a special interrogative. But they are, after all, the form in which many common-sense generalizations that have been qualified through the ages are put. They are also a form of law appropriate to stages of exploratory theoretical developments when general rules are tried, then amended, until finally completely replaced. We are always at such a stage.

NOTES

This work was supported in part by the Joint Services Electronics Program under Contract DA36-039-AMC-03200(E); in part by the National Science Foundation (Grant GP-2495), the National Institutes of Health (Grant MH-04737-05), the National Aeronautics and Space Administration (Grant NsG-496), and the U.S. Air Force (ESD Contract AF19(628)-2487). This essay is dedicated to Carl G. Hempel and to Peter Hempel as a token of gratitude for the tough-mindedness of the one and the gentle-mindedness of the other.

1. J. O. Urmson, "Parenthetical Verbs," reprinted in *Essays in Conceptual Analysis*, ed. A. Flew (London, 1956), p. 192. (3) eliminates from our discussion questions designed to ask for an opinion rather than a fact. Thus, it eliminates, e.g., "Why do you think that nail biting is a symptom of anxiety neurosis?" in the sense of "Why, in your opinion, is nail biting a symptom of anxiety neurosis?" although not in the sense of "Why do you hold the belief that nail biting is a symptom of anxiety neurosis?"

2. A little care is needed in using the notions introduced here. A given why-question can often be put in more than one normal form, some of which will be ambiguous. This is particularly true of those that may be put in interrogative sentences with token reflexive expressions (e.g., "Why is your temperature above normal?" as put to Henry and "Why is Henry's temperature above normal?" as put to his doctor). Whenever this is the case, the inner question can also be ambiguous. We must therefore always think of the inner question as put under circumstances that give ambiguous expressions the same disambiguation given to them in the mother question.

We could have introduced the notion of presupposition by availing ourselves of some grammatical devices, e.g., the presupposition is what one would be saying is the case by asserting the sentence whose underlying structure pre-ceded by a Why morpheme yields the why-question (or at least the interrogative sentence) when subjected to the Question Transformation. But we wish to avoid complicating the exposition beyond necessity or involving ourselves in grammatical issues that are still in flux. See in this connection particularly section 4.2.4 of Jerrold J. Katz and Paul M. Postal, *An Integrated Theory of Linguistic Descriptions* (Cambridge: The Massachusetts Institute of Technology Press, 1964). Note that what we call the presupposition of a why-question does not turn out to be what they call the presupposition of a why-question.

3. It is not clear whether there are such questions—i.e., whether, for example, answers of the form "in order to . . ." cannot always be replaced without loss of meaning by answers of the form "because (subject) wished to . . . ," and similarly for the other types of answer. The issues involved here are extremely interesting but not central for this paper.

4. *Cf.* sec. VIII.

5. As should be clear by now, "correct answer" must be understood in a narrow sense. "Correct answer to Q" (where Q is a question) covers a possible reply to Q if and only if a statement of the form "A told B W" (where W indicates a position occupied by the *oratio obliqua* form of Q, and A and B indicate positions occupied by expressions through which persons are mentioned) would be true of any episode in which that reply had been given by A to B in response to Q. "Correct answer," therefore, does not cover such possibly warranted replies as "I don't know" or "The question involves a false presupposition."

6. See Note 14 below.

7. The literature abounds with discussions that are weakened by a failure to see all these possibilities. A classical example will be found in Pt. I of Pierre Duhem, *La Theorie Physique* (Paris, 1914) in which it is argued that the object of a physical theory is not to explain a set of empirical laws. However, "explain" is construed in effect to mean giving the answers to questions of the form "What fundamental entities involved in what processes and governed by what laws underlie . . . ?" As a consequence, Duhem did not examine a number of other types of explanations that one might plausibly assign to theoretical physics.

The notion of presupposition used in this section is broader than that defined in section I, since it also pertains to questions that are not why-questions. No analysis of this broader notion is needed for this paper. Note 14 may suggest the line that such an analysis might follow since it provides an instance of the schematisms to be generalized. It should be obvious to anyone who bothers to seek out the suggestion that it would be premature to attempt the analysis given the present state of our understanding of other types of questions. In this connection see again J. J. Katz and P. M. Postal, op. cit.

8. Some of the ideas in this section have been discussed in greater detail but at too great a length in my "An Approach to Explanation," in *Analytical Philosophy*, 2d Ser., ed. R. J. Butler (Oxford: Basil Blackwell, 1965) and in my "A Theory About the Theory of Theory and About the Theory of Theories" in *Philosophy of Science: The Delaware Seminar*, II, ed. Bernard Baumrin (New York: Interscience Publishers, 1963).

9. A complete bibliography on the subject probably appears in Carl G. Hempel, *Aspects of Scientific Explanation* (New York: The Free Press, 1965), which I have unfortunately not yet seen as this essay is being written. Otherwise, consult, e.g., the bibliography at the end of Hempel's magnificent "Deductive-Nomological vs. Statistical Explanation" in *Minnesota Studies in the Philosophy of Science*, III, eds. H. Feigl and G. Maxwell (Minneapolis: U. of Minnesota Press, 1962); Pt. I of Israel Scheffler, *The Anatomy of Inquiry* (New York: Knopf, 1963); Chap. 9 of Adolf Grünbaum, *Philosophical Problems of Space*

and Time (New York: Knopf, 1963); and *Philosophy of Science: The Delaware Seminar,* I, Pt. II; II, Pt. I.

10. See Note 14 below.

11. See particularly R. Eberle, D. Kaplan, and P. Montague, "Hempel and Oppenheim on Explanation," *Philosophy of Science,* 28 (1961), 418–28; D. Kaplan, "Explanation Revisited," *Philosophy of Science,* 28, 429–36; and J. Kim, "Discussion on the Logical Conditions of Deductive Explanation," *Philosophy of Science,* 30 (1963), 286–91.

12. Since every special abnormic law is also a general abnormic law, we could have dispensed with one of these two notions but not without complicating the exposition.

13. A "zero-adic" predicate will occur if, for instance, a position indicated in one of our schemata by a predicate letter and variable bound to an initial quantifier is replaced by a sentence with no free variables—i.e., with no variable bound to the initial quantifier. Abnormic laws with occurrences of such internal closed sentences are required for why-questions whose presupposition or answer are expressed by closed sentences, as is the case when they are laws.

14. We asked that this relation abstract from the peculiarities of English and be capable of serving as the basis of a definition of the notion of Why-questions, a type of question in every respect like why-questions except that they need not be expressed in English. To satisfy ourselves that it meets these demands we will sketch a more formal analysis that clearly uses only the vocabulary of predicate-cum-identity logic and language-independent predicates, and we will then use the relation to define the notion of Why-questions within the same limits. The analysis will be somewhat crude, its only function being to exhibit language independence. It will suffer in at least the following respects. (1) The second half of condition (1) and condition (4) are not incorporated on the ground that it seems obvious that their incorporation can be accomplished without introducing language-dependent concepts but would complicate matters beyond the point of diminishing returns. (2) We assume without argument that any language rich enough for the purposes of science includes sentences with the logical structure of abnormic laws. This, we believe, involves no more than the assumption that such a language must possess the equivalent of truth-functional connectives, quantifiers, and lawlikeness. (3) We assume without argument that if a set of sentences implies some conclusion in one language, then any set of sentences that expresses the same thing in another language must imply any sentence that expresses the same conclusion in that language—i.e., that although logic may be reflected by syntax, it is nevertheless independent of it. (4) We assume without argument—although not without qualms—that interrogative sentences of different languages may express the same question, that declarative sentences of different languages may express the same proposition, and that one may use a relational term to speak of a sentence and of what it expresses. It seems, however, that ontologically sounder rephrasings cannot introduce language-dependent elements. (5) We assume without argument that any language rich enough for the purposes of science will contain interrogative as well as declarative sentences; that it will also have methods for transforming declarative sentences into interrogative ones; that furthermore all the answers to all the questions generated by some of these methods must stand in a characteristic relation to the transformed sentence.

We will list a lexicon of language-independent predicates and will then define others in terms of these. Two things ought to be noted. First, we do not assume that being abnormic is a property of laws but assume rather that it is a property of certain sentences that express laws. Thus, certain laws may be expressible as abnormic lawlike statements in some languages but not in other languages, depending on the lexicon of each. Second, let us call the relation between presupposition and answer described above the W-relation. We do not assume that *any* question whose presupposition and correct answer, if any, stand in the W-relation is a why-question. Instead, we make allowance for the fact that the W-relation need not exclude relations characteristic of other questions (see particularly the definition of "TW" below in this connection).

To simplify the reading, we use numerals as free variables.

Initial lexicon:

$L1$ *1* is an empirical law.

$F1$ *1* is a fact.

$E123$ *1* expresses *2* in *3* and *3* is a language.

$A12$ *1* is an abnormic lawlike sentence of *2* and *2* is a language.

$G12$ *1* is a lawlike general rule in *2* and *2* is a language.

$C123$ *1* is a completion of *2*, both being sentences in *3* and *3* is a language.

$H1234$ *1* is a deduction whose conclusion is *3* and one of whose premises is *2*, all of whose premises are necessary for the conclusion, *2* is a lawlike sentence, all the premises and conclusion being in *4*, *4* is a language.

$P12$ *1* is an argument and *2* is a premise of *1*.

$T1234$ *1* is a method of generating (transformation) *2* from *3* in *4* and *2* is an interrogative sentence and *3* is a declarative sentence, *2* and *3* being sentences in *4* and *4* is a language.

$R123$ *1* is an interrogative sentence, *2* expresses a correct answer in *3* to the question expressed in *3* by *1* and *3* is a language.

$N123$ *1* expresses in *3* a contrary of what is expressed by *2* in *3* and *3* is a language.

Defined terms:

"$LA123$" = "$L1.A23.E213$"
(*1* is an empirical law expressed as an abnormic law by *2* in *3*)
"$GE123$" = "$-F1.G23.E213$"
(*2* is a false general rule expressing *1* in *3*)
"$FA123$" = "$F1.E213$"
(*1* is a fact expressed by *2* in *3*)
"$W123$" = "$(\exists s)(\exists t)(\exists u)(\exists v)(\exists w)(\exists x)(\exists y)$
$\qquad [LAst3.GEuv3.Ctv3.Hwvx3.Nx13.Hyt13.(p)(\exists z)(Pwp.$
$\qquad p \neq y : \supset : Pyp.Fzp3).(q)(Pyq. -Pwq.q \neq t : \equiv . q = 2)]$"
(*1* and *2* stand in *3* in the relation in which the presupposition and the answer of a why-question stand in English, i.e., the W-relation).
"$TW12$" = "$(x)(y) [(\exists z)(T1zx2.Ryz) \equiv Wxy2]$"
(*1* is a method in *2*—*2* being a language—of generating questions whose presupposition and answers are W-related.)
"$VY123$" = "$(\exists m)(TWm3.Tm123)$"
(*1* has been generated out of *2* by a method of generating Why-questions in *3*—i.e., *1* expresses a Why-question in *3* whose presupposition is expressed by *2* in *3*.)
"$WY12$" = "$(x)(y)(z)(Ey1x.Ez2x :\equiv VYyzx)$"
(*1* is a Why-question whose presupposition is *2*)
"$WHY1$" = "$(\quad x)WY1x$"
(*1* is a Why-question)

We can follow the same procedure to define H-Why-Questions—i.e., questions calling for deductive nomological explanations.

"$HW123$" = "$(\exists x)(z)(\neg y)(Gx3.H2x13{:}P2z \supset FAyz3)$"

(1 and 2 stand in the H-W-relation)

"$THW12$" = "$(x)(y)[(\neg z)(T1zx2.Ryz) \equiv HWxy2]$"

"$HVY123$" = "$(\exists m)(THWm3.Tm123)$"

"$HWY12$" = "$(x)(y)(z)(Ey1x.Ez2x{:} \equiv HVYyzx)$"

"$HWHY1$" = "$(\exists x) HWY1x$"

(1 calls for a Hempelian explanation.)

15. Carl G. Hempel, "The Logic of Functional Analysis," *Symposium on Sociological Theory*, ed. Llewellyn Gross (Evanston, Ill.: Peterson, 1959), p. 272.

16. Such a request obviously need not be met with an actual listing of conditions. The set can be indicated in many other ways—e.g., by pointing to other cases that seem in all relevant respects like those of the presupposition, but of which the predicate of the presupposition is not true.

17. We can cope with these cases in a different way. Instead of individuating why-questions by their presupposition, as we have done so far, we individuate them by an ordered pair consisting of their presupposition and a false general rule. Thus distinct why-questions can now share the same presupposition. We restate the characteristic relation of why-questions as follows: *b* is the correct answer to a why-question whose presupposition is *a* and whose general rule is *g* if and only if (1) there is an abnormic law *L* that is a completion of *g*, and *a* is an instantiation of one of *L's* antonymic predicates; (2) *b* is a member of a set of premises that together with *L* constitute a deductive nomological explanation whose conclusion is *a*; (3) the remaining premises together with *g* constitute a deduction in every respect like a deductive nomological explanation except for a false lawlike premise and false conclusion, whose conclusion is a contrary of *a*. We eliminate (4) on p. 100. Instead of appealing to it in analyzing the failure of the counter-examples to the Hempelian doctrine (when these examples are reconstructed to include true abnormic laws), we construe the failure as that of not containing the answer to the why-question most reasonably inferred from context and general background. This is compatible with the possibility that the examples contain the answer to *some* why-question with the given presupposition. The failure is nevertheless fatal. Note that this approach still allows for why-questions—even under this new individuation—that have more than one correct answer.

There is much to be said for this approach. It conforms to many of our practices. It does justice to our intuition that why-questions are governed not only by presuppositions but also by presumptions. It avoids certain difficulties with the argument in the text. However, it introduces certain pragmatic issues that we prefer to delay as long as possible.

18. For a discussion of a similar demand in connection with something the author calls "scientific understanding" (a notion whose relevance to the topic of why-questions, we confess, is not clear to us), cf. p. 310 of A. Grünbaum's *Philosophical Problems of Space and Time* or p. 93 of *Philosophy of Science: The Delaware Seminar*, I.

CARL G. HEMPEL

Princeton University

Recent Problems of Induction

> It is true that from truths we can conclude only truths; but
> there are certain falsehoods which are useful for finding the
> truth.
>
> —Leibniz, Letter to Canon Foucher (1692)

The Classical Problem of Induction

IN THE PHILOSOPHICAL DISCUSSION of induction, one problem has long
occupied the center of the stage—so much so, indeed, that it is usually
referred to as *the* problem of induction. That is the problem of justifying
the way in which, in scientific inquiry and in our everyday pursuits, we
base beliefs and assertions about empirical matters on logically inconclusive evidence.

This classical problem of justification, raised by Hume and made
famous by his skeptical solution, is indeed of great philosophical
importance. But more recent studies, most of which were carried out
during the past two or three decades, have given rise to new problems of
induction, no less perplexing and important than the classical one, which
are logically prior to it in the sense that the classical problem cannot even
be clearly stated—let alone solved—without some prior clarification of
the new puzzles.

In this paper, I propose to discuss some of these recent problems of
induction.

Induction may be regarded as effecting a transition from some body of
empirical information to a hypothesis which is not logically implied by it,
and for this reason it is often referred to as nondemonstrative *inference*.
This characterization has to be taken with a grain of salt; but it is
suggestive and convenient, and in accordance with it, I will therefore
sometimes refer to the sentences specifying the evidence as the *premises*

and to the hypothesis based on it as the *conclusion* of an *"inductive inference."*

Among the simplest types of inductive reasoning are those in which the evidence consists of a set of examined instances of a generalization, and the hypothesis is either the generalization itself or a statement about some unexamined instances of it. A standard example is the inference from the evidence statement that all ravens so far observed have been black to the generalization that all ravens are black or to the prediction that the birds now hatching in a given clutch of raven eggs will be black or to the retrodiction that a raven whose skeleton was found at an archeological site was black. As these examples show, induction does not always proceed from the particular to the general or from statements about the past or present to statements about the future.

The inductive procedures of science comprise many other, more complex and circumstantial, kinds of nondemonstrative reasoning, such as those used in making a medical diagnosis on the basis of observed symptoms, in basing statements about remote historical events on presently available evidence, or in establishing a theory on the basis of appropriate experimental data.

However, most of the problems to be considered here can be illustrated by inductions of the simple kind that proceed from instances of a generalization, and in general I will use these as examples.

The Narrow Inductivist View of Scientific Inquiry

It should be stressed at the outset that what we have called inductive inference must not be thought of as an effective method of discovery, which by a mechanical procedure leads from observational data to appropriate hypotheses or theories. This misconception underlies what might be called the narrow inductivist view of scientific inquiry, a view that is well illustrated by the following pronouncement:

If we try to imagine how a mind of superhuman power and reach, but normal so far as the logical processes of its thought are concerned . . . would use the scientific method, the process would be as follows: First, all facts would be observed and recorded, *without selection* or *a priori* guess as to their relative importance. Second, the observed and recorded facts would be analyzed, compared, and classified, *without hypothesis or postulates* other than those necessarily involved in the logic of thought. Third, from this analysis of the facts, generalization would be inductively drawn as to the relations, classificatory or causal, between them. Fourth, further research would be deductive as well as inductive, employing inferences from previously established generalizations.[1]

It need hardly be argued in detail that this conception of scientific procedure, and of the role induction plays in it, is untenable; the reasons have been set forth by many writers. Let us just note that an inquiry conforming to this idea would never go beyond the first stage, for—presumably to safeguard scientific objectivity—no initial hypotheses about the mutual relevance and interconnections of facts are to be entertained in this stage, and as a result, there would be no criteria for the selection of the facts to be recorded. The initial stage would therefore degenerate into an indiscriminate and interminable gathering of data from an unlimited range of observable facts, and the inquiry would be totally without aim or direction.

Similar difficulties would beset the second stage—if it could ever be reached—for the classification or comparison of data again requires criteria. These are normally suggested by hypotheses about the empirical connections between various features of the "facts" under study. But the conception just cited would prohibit the use of such hypotheses, and the second stage of inquiry as here envisaged would again lack aim and direction.

It might seem that the quoted account of inductive scientific procedure could be rectified by simply adding the observation that any particular scientific investigation is aimed at solving a specified problem, and that the initial selection of data should therefore be limited to facts that are relevant to that problem. But this will not do, for the statement of a problem does not generally determine what kinds of data are relevant to its solution. The question as to the causes of lung cancer does not by itself determine what sorts of data would be relevant—whether, for example, differences in age, occupation, sex, or dietary habits should be recorded and studied. The notion of "relevant" facts acquires a clear meaning only when some specific answer to the problem has been suggested, however tentatively, in the form of a hypothesis: an observed fact will then be favorably or unfavorably relevant to the hypothesis according as its occurrence is by implication affirmed or denied by the hypothesis. Thus, the conjecture that smoking is a potent causative factor in lung cancer affirms by implication a higher incidence of the disease among smokers than among nonsmokers. Data showing for a suitable group of subjects that this is the case or that it is not would therefore constitute favorably relevant (confirming) or unfavorably relevant (disconfirming) evidence for the hypothesis. Generally, then, those data are relevant and need to be gathered which can support or disconfirm the contemplated hypothesis and which thus provide a basis for testing it.

Contrary to the conception quoted above, therefore, hypotheses are put forward in science as tentative answers to the problem under investigation. And contrary to what is suggested by the description of the third stage of inquiry above, such answers in the form of hypotheses or theories cannot be inferred from empirical evidence by means of some set of mechanically applicable rules of induction. There is no generally applicable mechanical routine of "inductive inference" which leads from a given set of data to a corresponding hypothesis or theory somewhat in the way in which the familiar routine of multiplication leads from any two given integers, by a finite number of mechanically performable steps, to the corresponding product.

To be sure, mechanical induction routines can be specified for certain special kinds of cases, such as the construction of a curve, and of an analytic expression for the corresponding function, which will fit a finite set of points. Given a finite set of measurements of associated values of temperature and volume for a given body of gas under constant pressure, this kind of procedure could serve mechanically to produce a tentative general law connecting temperature and volume of the gas. But for generating scientific theories, no such procedure can be devised.

Consider, for example, a theory, such as the theory of gravitation or the atomic theory of matter, which is introduced to account for certain previously established empirical facts, such as regularities of planetary motion and free fall, or certain chemical findings such as those expressed by the laws of constant and of multiple proportions. Such a theory is formulated in terms of certain concepts (those of gravitational force, of atom, of molecule, etc.) which are novel in the sense that they had played no role in the description of the empirical facts which the theory is designed to explain. And surely, no set of induction rules could be devised which would be generally applicable to just any set of empirical data (physical, chemical, biological, etc.) and which, in a sequence of mechanically performable steps, would generate appropriate novel concepts, functioning in an explanatory theory, on the basis of a description of the data.[2]

Scientific hypotheses and theories, then, are not mechanically inferred from observed "facts": *They are invented by an exercise of creative imagination.* Einstein, among others, often emphasized this point, and more than a century ago William Whewell presented the same basic view of induction. Whewell speaks of scientific discovery as a "process of invention, trial, and acceptance or rejection" of hypotheses and refers to great scientific advances as achieved by "Happy *Guesses*," by "felicitous and inexplicable strokes of inventive talent," and he adds: "No rules can ensure to us similar success in new cases; or can enable men who do not possess similar endowments, to make like advances in knowledge."[3] Similarly, Karl Popper has characterized scientific hypotheses and theories as conjectures, which must then be subjected to test and possible falsification.[4] Such conjectures are often arrived at by anything but explicit and systematic reasoning. The chemist Kékulé, for example, reports that his ring formula for the benzene molecule occurred to him in a reverie into which he had fallen before his fireplace. Gazing into the flames, he seemed to see snakes dancing about; and suddenly one of them moved into the foreground and formed a ring by seizing hold of its own tail. Kékulé does not tell us whether the snake was forming a *hexagonal* ring, but that was the structure he promptly ascribed to the benzene molecule.

Although no restrictions are imposed upon the *invention* of theories, scientific objectivity is safeguarded by making their *acceptance* dependent upon the outcome of careful tests. These consist in deriving, from the theory, consequences that admit of observational or experimental investigation, and then checking them by suitable observations or experiments. If careful testing bears out the consequences, the hypothesis is accordingly supported. But normally a scientific hypothesis asserts more than (i.e., cannot be inferred from) some finite set of consequences that may have been put to test, so that even strong evidential support affords no conclusive proof. It is precisely this fact, of course, that makes inductive "inference" nondemonstrative and gives rise to the classical problem of induction.

Karl Popper, in his analysis of this problem, stresses that the inferences involved in testing a scientific theory always run deductively from the theory to implications about empirical facts, never in the opposite direction; and he argues that therefore "Induction, i.e., inference based on many observations, is a myth. It is neither a psychological fact, nor a fact of ordinary life, nor one of scientific procedure";[5] and it is essentially this observation which, he holds, "solves . . . Hume's problem of induction."[6] But this is surely too strong a claim, for although the procedure of empirical science is not inductive in the narrow sense we have discussed and rejected, it still may be said to be *inductive in a wider sense*, referred to at the beginning of this paper: While scientific hypotheses and theories are not *inferred* from empirical data by means of some effective inductive procedure, they are *accepted* on the basis of observational or experimental findings which afford no deductively conclusive evidence for their truth. Thus, the classical problem of induction retains its import: What justification is there for accepting hypotheses on the basis of incomplete evidence?

The search for an answer to this question will require a clearer specification of the procedure that is to be justified; for while the hypotheses and theories of empirical science are not deductively implied by the evidence, it evidently will not count as inductively sound reasoning to accept a hypothesis on the basis of just any inconclusive evidence. Thus, there arises the logically prior problem of giving a more explicit characterization and precise criteria of what counts as sound inductive reasoning in science.

It may be instructive briefly to consider the analogue to this problem for deductive reasoning.

Deduction and Induction; Discovery and Validation

Deductive soundness, of course, is tantamount to deductive validity. This notion can be suggestively although imprecisely characterized by saying that an argument is deductively valid if its premises and its conclusion are so related that if all the premises are true, then the conclusion cannot fail to be true as well.[7]

As for *criteria* of deductive validity, the theory of deductive logic specifies a variety of forms of inference which are deductively valid, such as, for example, *modus ponens:*

$$p \supset q$$
$$\underline{p \qquad\qquad}$$
$$q$$

or the inference rules of quantificational logic. Each of these represents a sufficient but not necessary condition of deductive validity. These criteria have the important characteristic of being expressible by reference to the syntactical structure of the argument, and thus without any reference to the meanings of the extralogical terms occurring in premises and conclusion. As we will see later, criteria of inductive soundness cannot be stated in purely syntactical terms.

We have already noted that whatever the rules of induction may be, they cannot be expected to specify mechanical routines leading from empirical evidence to appropriate hypotheses. Are the rules of deductive inference superior in this respect? Consider their role in logic and mathematics.

A moment's reflection shows that no interesting theorem in these fields is discovered by a mechanical application of the rules of deductive inference. Unless a putative theorem has first been put forward, such application would lack direction. Discovery in logic and mathematics, no less than in empirical science, *calls for imagination and invention;* it does not follow any mechanical rules.

Next, even when a putative theorem has been proposed, the rules of deduction do not, in general, provide a mechanical routine for proving or disproving it. This is illustrated by the famous arithmetical conjectures of Goldbach and of Fermat, which were proposed centuries ago but have remained undecided to this day. Mechanical routines for proving or disproving any given conjecture can be specified only for systems that admit of a decision procedure; and even for first-order quantificational logic and for elementary arithmetic, it is known that there can be no such procedure. In general, then, the construction of a proof or a disproof for a given logical or mathematical conjecture requires ingenuity.

But when a putative theorem has been proposed and a step-by-step argument has been offered as a presumptive proof for it, then the rules of deductive logic afford a means of establishing the validity of the argument: If each step conforms to one of those rules—a matter which can be decided by mechanical check—then the argument is a valid proof of the proposed theorem.

In sum, the formal rules of deductive inference are not rules of discovery leading mechanically to correct theorems or even to proofs for conjectured theorems which are in fact provable; rather, they provide criteria of soundness or of validity for proposed deductive proofs.

Analogously, rules of inductive inference will have to be conceived, not as canons of discovery, but as criteria of validation for proposed inductive arguments; far from generating a hypothesis from given evidence, they will *presuppose* that, in addition to a body of evidence, a hypothesis has been put forward, and they will then serve to appraise the soundness of the hypothesis on the basis of the evidence.

Broadly speaking, inductive arguments might be thought of as taking one of these forms:

$$\frac{e}{h} \quad \text{(i.e., evidence } e \text{ supports hypothesis } h)$$

$$\frac{e}{h} \, [r] \quad \text{(i.e., evidence } e \text{ supports hypothesis } h \text{ to degree } r)$$

Here, the double line is to indicate that the relation of e to h is not that of full deductive implication but that of partial inductive support.

The second of these schemata incorporates the construal of inductive support as a quantitative concept. Rules of induction pertaining to it would provide criteria determining the degree of support conferred on certain kinds of hypotheses by certain kinds of evidence sentences; these criteria might even amount to a general definition assigning a definite value of r to any given e and h; this is one objective of Carnap's inductive logic.[8]

The first schema treats inductive support or confirmation as a qualitative concept; the corresponding inference rules would specify conditions under which a given evidence sentence supports, or confirms, a given hypothesis.[9]

The formulation of rules of these or similar kinds will be required to explicate the concept of inductive inference in terms of which the classical problem of justification is formulated. And it is in this context of explication that the newer problems of induction arise. We now turn to one of those problems; it concerns the qualitative concept of confirmation.

The Paradoxes of Qualitative Confirmation

The most familiar rules of induction concern generalizations of the simple form "All F are G." According to one widely asserted rule, a hypothesis of this kind receives support from its positive instances—i.e., from cases of F that have been found also to be G. For example, the hypothesis "All ravens are black," or

$$(h) \qquad (x)(Rx \supset Bx)$$

is supported, or confirmed, by any object i such that

$$(I) \qquad Ri \cdot Bi$$

or, as we will say, by any evidence sentence of the form "$Ri \cdot Bi$." Let us refer to such instances as *positive instances of type I for h*. Similarly, h is disconfirmed (invalidated) by any evidence sentence of the form $Ri \cdot -Bi$. This criterion was explicitly discussed and advocated by Jean Nicod;[10] I will therefore call it Nicod's criterion.

Now, the hypothesis h is logically equivalent to, and thus makes exactly the same assertion as, the statement that all nonblack things are nonravens, or

$$(h') \qquad (x)(-Bx \supset -Rx)$$

According to Nicod's criterion, this generalization is confirmed by *its* instances—i.e., by any individual j such that

$$(II) \qquad -Bj \cdot -Rj$$

But since h' expresses exactly the same assertion as h, any such individual will also confirm h. Consequently, such things as a yellow rose, a green caterpillar, or a red herring confirm the generalization "All ravens are black," by virtue of being nonblack nonravens. I will call such objects *positive instances of type II for h.*

Next, the hypothesis h is logically equivalent also to the following statement:

(h'') $\qquad (x)[(Rx \lor -Rx) \supset (-Rx \lor Bx)]$

in words: Anything that is a raven or not a raven—i.e., anything at all— either is not a raven or is black. Confirmatory instances for this version, which I will call *positive instances of type III for h,* consist of individuals k such that

(III) $\qquad\qquad\qquad -Rk \lor Bk$

This condition is met by any object k that is not a raven (no matter whether it is black) and by any object k that is black (no matter whether it is a raven). Any such object, then, affords a confirmatory instance in support of the hypothesis that all ravens are black.

On the other hand, the hypothesis h can be equivalently expressed by the sentence

(h''') $\qquad\qquad (x)[(Rx \cdot -Bx) \supset (Rx \cdot -Rx)]$

for which nothing can possibly be a confirmatory instance in the sense of Nicod's criterion, since nothing can be both a raven and not a raven.

These peculiarities, and some related ones, of the notion of confirmatory instance of a generalization have come to be referred to as the *paradoxes of confirmation.*[11] And indeed, at first glance they appear to be implausible and perhaps even logically unsound. But on further reflection one has to conclude, I think, that they are perfectly sound, that it is our intuition in the matter which leads us astray, so that the startling results are paradoxical only in a psychological, but not in a logical sense.

To see this, let us note first that the results in question follow deductively from two simple basic principles, namely: (A) A generalization of the form "All F are G" is confirmed by its positive instances— i.e., by cases of F that have been found also to be cases of G. (B) Whatever confirms a hypothesis also confirms any logically equivalent one.

Principle (A) is, in effect, part of Nicod's criterion, of which Nicod himself remarks that it "cannot claim the force of an axiom. But it offers itself so naturally and introduces such great simplicity, that reason welcomes it without feeling any imposition." [12] We will encounter some surprising exceptions to it in Sections 5 and 6, but it does indeed seem very reasonable in cases of the kind we have considered so far—i.e., in reference to generalizations of universal conditional form containing exclusively property terms (one-place predicates).

Principle (B) may be called the equivalence condition. It simply reflects the idea that whether given evidence confirms a hypothesis must depend only on the content of the hypothesis and not on the way in which it happens to be formulated.

And once we accept these principles, we must also accept their surprising logical consequences.

Let us look at these consequences now from a different point of view, which will support the claim that they are sound. Suppose we are told that in the next room there is an object i which is a raven. Our hypothesis h then tells us about i that it is black, and if we find that this is indeed the case, so that we have $Ri \cdot Bi$, then this must surely count as bearing out, or confirming, the hypothesis.

Next, suppose we are told that in the adjoining room there is an object j that is not black. Again, our hypothesis tells us something more about it, namely, that it is not a raven. And if we find that this is indeed so—i.e., that $-Bj \cdot -Rj$, then this bears out, and thus supports, the hypothesis.

Finally, even if we are told only that in the next room there is an object k, the hypothesis still tells us something about it, namely, that either it is no raven or it is black—i.e., that $-Rk \lor Bk$; and if this is found to be the case, it again bears out the hypothesis.

Thus, our three types of positive instance must indeed be counted as confirmatory or supporting evidence for the generalization that all ravens are black.

Finally, the fact that the formulation h''' of our generalization admits of no confirming instances in the sense of Nicod's criterion presents no serious problem if, as here has been done, that criterion is stated as a sufficient but not necessary condition of confirmation.

But why does it seem implausible or paradoxical in the first place that positive instances of types II and III should be confirmatory for the generalizaton h? One important reason seems to lie in the assumption that the hypothesis "All ravens are black" is a statement about ravens and not about nonravens, let alone about all things in general. But surely, such a construal is untenable; anyone who accepts h would be bound to accept also the sentences h' and h'', which by the same token would have to be viewed as statements about nonravens and about all things, respectively. The use made of some statements of the form "All *F* are *G*" illustrates the same point. The Wassermann test, for example, is based, roughly speaking, on the generalization that any person infected with syphilis has a positive Wassermann reaction; but in view of its diagnostic implications for cases yielding a negative test result, this generalization surely cannot be said to be about syphilitically infected persons only.

To say that positive instances of types *I*, *II*, and *III* all confirm the hypothesis *h* is not to say, however, that they confirm the generalization to the same extent. Indeed, several writers have argued that the different types differ greatly in this respect and that, in particular, a positive instance of type *I*, i.e., a black raven, lends much stronger support to our generalization than a positive instance of type *II*, i.e., a nonblack object that is not a raven; and they have suggested that this is the objective basis for the first impression that instances of type *I* alone can count as confirmatory for our hypothesis.

This view can be made plausible by the following suggestive but imprecise consideration: Let *k* be the hypothesis "All marbles in this bag are red," and suppose that there are twenty marbles in the bag. Then the generalization *k* has twenty instances of type *I*, each being provided by one of the marbles. If we have checked each of the twenty objects that are marbles in the bag, we have exhaustively tested the hypothesis. And roughly speaking we might say that if we have examined one of the marbles and found it red, we have shown one twentieth of the total content of the hypothesis to be true.

Now consider the contrapositive of our generalization—i.e., the statement, "Any object that is not red is not a marble in this bag." Its instances are provided by all nonred objects. There are a large number of these in the world—perhaps infinitely many of them. Examining one of them and averring that it is not a marble in the bag is therefore to check, and corroborate, only a tiny portion of all that the hypothesis affirms. Hence, a positive finding of type *II* would indeed support our generalization, but only to a very small extent.

Analogously in the case of the ravens. If we may assume that there are vastly more nonblack things than there are ravens, then the observation of one nonblack thing that is not a raven would seem to lend vastly less support to the generalization that all ravens are black than would the observation of one raven that *is* black.

This argument might serve to mitigate the paradoxes of confirmation.[13] But I have stated it here only in an intuitive fashion. A precise formulation would require an explicit quantitative theory of degrees of confirmation or of inductive probability, such as Carnap's. Even within the framework of such a theory, the argument presupposes further assumptions, and the extent to which it can be sustained is not fully clear as yet.

Let us now turn to another perplexing aspect of induction. I will call it Goodman's riddle, because it was Nelson Goodman who first called attention to this problem and proposed a solution for it.[14]

Goodman's Riddle: A Failure of Confirmation by "Positive Instances"

One of the two basic principles from which we deduced the paradoxes of confirmation stated that a generalization of the form "All *F* are *G*" is confirmed, or supported, by its positive instances of type *I*—i.e., by objects which are *F* and also *G*. Although this principle seems entirely obvious, Goodman has shown that there are generalizations that derive no support at all from their observed instances. Take for example the hypothesis

(h) All ravens are blite

where an object is said to be blite if it is either examined before midnight tonight and is black or is not examined before midnight and is white.

Suppose now that all the ravens examined so far have been found to be black; then, by definition, all ravens so far examined are also blite. Yet this latter information does not support the generalization *h,* for that generalization implies that all ravens examined after midnight will be white—and surely our evidence must be held to militate against this forecast rather than to support it.

Thus, some generalizations do derive support from their positive instances of type *I;* for example, "All ravens are black," "All gases expand when heated," "In all cases of free fall from rest, the distance covered is proportional to the square of the elapsed time," and so forth; but other generalizations, of which "All ravens are blite" is an example, are not supported by their instances. Goodman expresses this idea by saying that the former generalizations can, whereas the latter cannot, be *projected* from examined instances to as yet unexamined ones.

The question then arises how to distinguish between projectible and nonprojectible generalizations. Goodman notes that the two differ in the character of the terms employed in their formulation. The term "black," for example, lends itself to projection; the term "blite" does not. He traces the difference between these two kinds of term to what he calls their *entrenchment*—i.e., the extent to which they have been used in previously projected hypotheses. The word "blite," for example, has never before been used in a projection, and is thus much less entrenched than such words as "black," "raven," "gas," "temperature," "velocity," and so on, all of which have served in many previous inductive projections— successful as well as unsuccessful ones. What Goodman thus suggests is that our generalizations are chosen not only in consideration of how well they accord with the available evidence, but also in consideration of how well entrenched are their constituent extralogical terms.

By reference to the relative entrenchment of those terms, Goodman then formulates criteria for the comparison of generalizations in regard to their projectibility, and he thus constructs the beginnings of a theory of inductive projection.

I cannot enter into the details of Goodman's theory here, but I do wish to point out one of its implications which is, I think, of great importance for the conception of inductive inference.

As we noted earlier, the standard rules of deductive inference make reference only to the syntactical form of the sentences involved; the inference rules of quantification theory, for example, apply to all premises and conclusions of the requisite form, no matter whether the extralogical predicates they contain are familiar or strange, well entrenched or poorly entrenched. Thus,

All ravens are blite

and

r is a raven

deductively implies

r is blite

no less than

All ravens are black

and

r is a raven

deductively implies

r is black

But on Goodman's conception of projectibility, even elementary rules of induction cannot be similarly stated in purely syntactical terms. For example, the rule that a positive instance confirms a generalization holds only for generalizations with adequately entrenched predicates; and entrenchment is neither a syntactical nor even a semantic property of terms, but a pragmatic one; it pertains to the actual use that has been made of a term in generalizations projected in the past.

A Further Failure of Confirmation by "Positive Instances"

Goodman's riddle shows that Nicod's criterion does not offer a generally adequate sufficient condition of confirmation: Positive instances do not confirm nonprojectible hypotheses.

But the criterion fails also in cases of a quite different kind, which do not hinge on the use of predicates such as "blite." Consider the hypothesis, "If for any two persons x,y it is not the case that each likes the other, then the first likes the second, but not vice versa"; in symbolic notation:

(h) $$(x)(y)[-(Lxy \cdot Lyx) \supset (Lxy \cdot -Lyx)]$$

Let e be the information that a,b are two persons such that a likes b but not vice versa, i.e. that

(e) $$Lab \cdot -Lba$$

This information can equivalently be stated as follows:

(e') $$-(Lab \cdot Lba) \text{ and } (Lab \cdot -Lba)$$

for the first of these two sentences is a logical consequence of the second one. The sentence e' then represents a positive instance of type I for h; hence, on Nicod's criterion, e' should confirm h.[15]

But e' is equivalent to

(e'') $$-(Lba \cdot Lab) \text{ and } (-Lba \cdot Lab)$$

and this, on Nicod's criterion, disconfirms h. In intuitive terms, the preceding argument is to this effect: If a is counted as the first person and b as the second, then the information provided by e shows that, as e' makes explicit, a and b satisfy both the antecedent and the consequent of h and thus confirm the hypothesis; but if b is counted as the first person and a as the second one, then by virtue of the same information, b and a satisfy the antecedent but not the consequent of h, as is made explicit in e''. Thus, on Nicod's criterion, e constitutes both confirming and invalidating evidence for h.

Incidentally, h can be thrown into the form

(h') $$(x)(y)(Lxy \cdot Lyx) \, ,$$

which makes it obvious that the evidence *e* logically contradicts the given hypothesis; hence, the same is true of *e′*, although Nicod's criterion qualifies *e′* as confirming *h*.[16]

Hypotheses of the form illustrated by *h* can be formulated in terms of well-entrenched predicate expressions, such as "*x* likes *y*" and "*x* is soluble in *y*"; the difficulty here illustrated does not, therefore, spring from the use of ill-behaved predicates of the Goodmanian variety.

The difficulty rather shows that the intuition which informs the Nicod criterion simply fails when the hypotheses under consideration include relational terms rather than only property terms. If one considers, in addition, that the Nicod criterion is limited to hypotheses of universal conditional form, then it becomes clear that it would be of great interest to develop a general characterization of qualitative confirmation which (1) affords a full definition rather than only partial criteria for the confirmation of a hypothesis *h* by an evidence sentence *e*, (2) is applicable to any hypothesis, of whatever logical form, that can be expressed within a specified language, and (3) avoids the difficulties of the Nicod criterion which have just been pointed out.

An explicit definition of this kind for the concept "*h* qualitatively confirms *e*" has in fact been constructed for the case where *h* and *e* are formulated in a formalized language that has the structure of a first-order functional calculus without identity; *h* may be any sentence whatsoever in such a language, and *e* may be any consistent sentence containing no quantifiers. The concept thus defined demonstrably avoids the difficulties encountered by the Nicod criterion in the case of hypotheses with relational predicates; and it implies the Nicod criterion in reference to those hypotheses of universal conditional form which contain only property terms. It has been argued, however, that the concept thus arrived at is not fully satisfactory as an explication of the vague idea of qualitative confirmation because it fails to capture certain characteristics which might plausibly be attributed to the relation of qualitative confirmation.[17]

The Ambiguity of Induction

I now turn to a further basic problem, which I will call the problem of inductive ambiguity. This facet of induction, unlike those we have considered so far, is not a recent discovery; both the problem and a possible solution of it have been recognized, if not always very explicitly, by several writers on probability, past as well as contemporary. But certain aspects of the problem are of special interest in the context of our discussion, and I will therefore consider them briefly.

Suppose that we have the following information:

(e_1)   Jones, a patient with a sound heart, has just had an appendectomy, and of all persons with sound hearts who underwent appendectomy in the past decade, 93% had an uneventful recovery.

This information, taken by itself, would clearly lend strong support to the hypothesis

(h_1)   Jones will have an uneventful recovery.

But suppose that we also have the information:

(e_2)   Jones is a nonagenarian with serious kidney failure; he just had an appendectomy after his appendix had ruptured; and in the past decade, of all cases of appendectomy after rupture of the appendix among nonagenarians with serious kidney failure only 8% had an uneventful recovery.

This information by itself lends strong support to the contradictory of h_1:

($-h_1$)   Jones will not have an uneventful recovery.

But e_1 and e_2 are logically compatible and may well both be part of the information available to us and accepted by us at the time when Jones' prognosis is being considered. In this case, our available evidence provides us with a basis for two rival arguments, both of them inductively sound, whose "conclusions" contradict each other. This is what I referred to above as the ambiguity of inductive reasoning: Inductively sound reasoning based on a consistent, and thus possibly true, set of "premises" may lead to contradictory "conclusions."

This possibility is without parallel in deductive reasoning: The consequences deducible from any premises selected from a consistent set of sentences form again a consistent set.

When two sound inductive arguments thus conflict, which conclusion, if any, is it reasonable to accept, and perhaps to act on? The answer, which has long been acknowledged, at least implicitly, is this: If the available evidence includes the premises of both arguments, it is irrational to base our expectations concerning the conclusions exclusively on the premises of one or the other of the arguments; the credence given to any contemplated hypothesis should always be determined by the support it receives from the *total* evidence available at the time. (Parts may be omitted if they are irrelevant in the sense that their omission leaves the inductive support of the contemplated hypothesis unchanged.) This is what Carnap has called the *requirement of total evidence*. According to it, an estimate of Jones' prospects of recovery should be based on all the relevant evidence at our disposal; and clearly, a physician trying to make a reasonable prognosis will try to meet this requirement as best he can.

What the requirement of total evidence demands, then, is that the credence given to a hypothesis h in a given knowledge situation should be determined by the inductive support, or confirmation, which h receives from the total evidence e available in that situation. Let us call this confirmation $c(h,e)$. Now for some brief comments on this maxim.

1. In the form just stated, the requirement presupposes a quantitative concept of the degree, $c(h,e)$, to which the evidence e confirms or supports the hypothesis h. This raises the question how such a concept might be defined and whether it can be characterized so generally that $c(h,e)$ is determined for *any* hypothesis h that might be proposed, relative to *any* body of evidence e that might be available. This issue has been much discussed in recent decades. Carnap, in his theory of inductive logic, has developed an explicit and completely general definition of the concept for the case where e and h are any two sentences expressible in one or another of certain formalized languages of relatively simple logical structure.[18] Others have argued that the concept in question can be satisfactorily defined at best for certain special types of hypotheses and of evidential information. For example, if the total relevant evidence consists just of the sentences e_1 and e_2 listed above, certain analysts would hold that no probability or degree of confirmation can be significantly assigned to the hypothesis, "Jones will have an uneventful recovery," since the evidence provides no information about the percentage of uneventful recoveries among nonagenarians with sound hearts but seriously defective kidneys who undergo appendectomy after rupture of the appendix.

2. Next, let us note that while the requirement of total evidence is a principle concerning induction, it is not a rule of inductive inference or, more precisely, of inductive support, for it does not concern the question whether, or how strongly, a given hypothesis is supported by given evidence. The requirement is concerned rather with the rational use, or

application, of inductive reasoning in the formation of empirical beliefs. This observation suggests a distinction between two kinds of rules pertaining to inductive reasoning:

a) *Rules of inductive support, or of valid inductive inference.* These would encompass, for example, all criteria concerning the qualitative confirmation or disconfirmation of generalizations by positive or negative instances; criteria determining degrees of confirmation; and also all general principles connecting degrees of confirmation with each other, such as the law, that the degrees of confirmation of a hypothesis and of its contradictory on the same evidence add up to unity.

b) *Rules of application.* These concern the use of rules of the former kind in the rational formation of empirical beliefs. The requirement of total evidence is one such rule of application, but not the only one, as will soon be seen.

The distinction between rules of inference and rules of application can be made also in reference to deductive reasoning. The rules of inference, as we noted earlier, provide criteria of deductive validity; but they qualify as deductively valid many particular arguments whose conclusions are false, and they do not concern the conditions under which it is reasonable to believe, or to accept, the conclusion of a deductively valid argument. To do so would be the task of rules for the rational application of deductive inference.

One such rule would stipulate, for example, that if we have accepted a set of statements as presumably true, then any logical consequence of that set (or, perhaps rather, any statement that is known to be such a consequence) should equally be accepted as presumably true.

The two kinds of rules for deduction call for quite different kinds of justification. An inference rule such as *modus ponens* might be justified by showing that when applied to true premises it will invariably yield a true conclusion—which is what is meant by the claim that an argument conforming to the rule is deductively valid.

But in order to justify a rule of application, we will have to consider what ends the acceptance or rejection of deductive conclusions is to serve. For example, if we are interested in a set of accepting statements, or of corresponding beliefs, which will afford us an emotionally reassuring or esthetically satisfying account of the world, then it will not always be reasonable to accept, or to believe, the logical consequences of what we have previously accepted. If, on the other hand, truth is what we value in our accepted statements, and if we are accordingly concerned to give credence to all statements that are true as far as our information enables us to tell, then indeed we have to accept all the consequences of previously accepted statements; thus, justification of our rule of application requires reference to the objectives, or the values, that our acceptance procedure is meant to achieve.

Induction and Valuation

Similarly, if we wish to devise rules for the rational application of valid inductive reasoning, or if we wish to appraise or justify such rules, we will have to take into account the objectives to be achieved by the inductive acceptance procedure, or the values or disvalues of the consequences that might result from correct or from incorrect acceptance decisions. In this sense, the construction and the justification of inductive acceptance rules for empirical statements presupposes judgments of value.

This is especially obvious when we wish to decide whether a given hypothesis is to be accepted in the strong sense of being relied on as a basis for practical action. Suppose, for example, that a new vaccine has been developed for immunization against a serious infectious disease that can afflict humans as well as chimpanzees. Let *h* be the hypothesis that the vaccine is both safe and effective in a sense specified by suitable operational criteria, and suppose that the hypothesis has been tested by examining a number of samples of the vaccine for safety and effectiveness. Let *e* be the evidence thus obtained.

Our rules of inductive support may then tell us how strongly the hypothesis is confirmed by the evidence; but in deciding whether to act on it we will have to consider, besides the strength of confirmation, also the kind of action that is contemplated, and what benefits might result from a correct decision, what harm from a mistaken one. For example, our standards of acceptance are likely to differ according as humans or chimpanzees are to be treated with the vaccine; and it may well happen that *on the same evidence* the given hypothesis is accepted as a basis of action in one case but rejected in the other.

Inductive decisions of this kind have been extensively studied in the mathematical theory of testing and decision-making. This theory deals in particular with the case where the values or disvalues attached to the possible consequences of the available decisions are expressible in numerical terms as so-called utilities. For such situations, the theory has developed a number of specific decision rules, which are rules of application in our sense. These rules—maximin, maximax, maximizing the expectable utility of the outcome, and others—make the acceptance or the rejection of the hypothesis contingent on the utilities assigned to the different possible consequences of acceptance or rejection; and when a measure for the evidential support of the hypothesis is available, that support is likewise taken into consideration.[19] In this fashion, the inductive decision rules combine empirical considerations with explicitly valuational ones.

That rules for the acceptance or rejection of empirical hypotheses thus presuppose valuational considerations has been emphasized by several writers. Some of these have made the stronger claim that the values in question are ethical values. Thus, Churchman asserts that "the simplest question of fact in science requires for even an approximation, a judgment of value," and that "the science of ethics . . . is *basic* to the meaning of any question the experimental scientist raises." [20] And in the context of a detailed study of the logic of testing statistical hypotheses, Braithwaite asserts, in a similar vein: "To say that it is 'practically certain' that the next 1000 births in Cambridge will include the birth of at least one boy includes a hedonic or ethical assessment." [21]

But while it is true that the justification of rules of acceptance for statements of fact requires reference to judgments of preference or of valuation, the claim that the values concerned are ethical values is, I think, open to question. Our argument about valuational presuppositions has so far been concerned only with the acceptance of hypotheses as a basis of specific *actions,* and in this case the underlying valuations may indeed be ethical in character. But what standards will govern the acceptance and rejection of hypotheses for which no practical application is contemplated? Braithwaite's statement about male births in Cambridge might well belong in that category, and surely so do the hypotheses examined in pure, or basic, scientific research; these might concern, for example, the rate of recession of distant galaxies or the spontaneous creation of hydrogen atoms in empty space. In such cases, it seems, we simply wish to decide, in consideration of the available evidence, whether to believe a proposed hypothesis; whether to record it, so to speak, in our book of tentative scientific knowledge, without envisaging any technological application. Here, we cannot relevantly base our decisions on any utilities or disutilities attached to practical consequences of acceptance or rejection and, in particular, ethical considerations play no part.

What will have to be taken into account in constructing or justifying inductive acceptance rules for pure scientific research are the objectives of such research or the importance attached in pure science to achieving certain kinds of results. What objectives does pure scientific research seek to achieve? Truth of the accepted statements might be held to be one of them. But surely not truth at all costs. For then, the only rational decision policy would be never to accept any hypothesis on inductive grounds since, however well supported, it might be false.

Scientific research is not even aimed at achieving very high probability of truth, or very strong inductive support, at all costs. Science is willing to take considerable chances on this score. It is willing to accept a theory that vastly outreaches its evidential basis if that theory promises to exhibit an underlying order, a system of deep and simple systematic connections among what had previously been a mass of disparate and multifarious facts.

It is an intriguing but as yet open question whether the objectives, or the values, that inform pure scientific inquiry can all be adequately characterized in terms of such theoretical desiderata as confirmation, explanatory power, and simplicity and, if so, whether these features admit of a satisfactory combination into a concept of purely theoretical or scientific utility that could be involved in the construction of acceptance rules for hypotheses and theories in pure science. Indeed, it is by no means clear whether the conception of basic scientific research as leading to the provisional acceptance or rejection of hypotheses is tenable at all. One of the problems here at issue is whether the notion of accepting a hypothesis independently of any contemplated action can be satisfactorily explicated within the framework of a purely logical and methodological analysis of scientific inquiry [22] or whether, if any illuminating construal of the idea is possible at all, it will have to be given in the context of a psychological, sociological, and historical study of scientific research. [23]

To conclude with a summary that centers about the classical problem of induction: For a clear statement of the classical problem of justification, two things are required. First, the procedure to be justified must be clearly characterized—this calls for an explication of the rules governing the inductive appraisal of hypotheses and theories; second, the intended objectives of the procedure must be indicated, for a justification of any procedure will have to be relative to the ends it is intended to serve. Concerning the first of these tasks, we noted that while there are no systematic mechanical rules of inductive discovery, two other kinds of rule have to be envisaged and distinguished, namely, rules of support and rules of application. And in our discussion of the objectives of inductive procedures we noted certain connections between rational belief on one hand and valuation on the other.

Whatever insights further inquiry may yield, the recognition and partial exploration of these basic problems has placed the classical problem of induction into a new and clearer perspective and has thereby advanced its philosophical clarification.

NOTES

1. A. B. Wolfe, "Functional Economics," *The Trend of Economics,* ed. R. G. Tugwell (New York: Knopf, 1924), p. 450 (author's italics).

2. This argument does not presuppose a fixed division of the vocabulary of empirical science into observational and theoretical terms; it is quite compatible with acknowledging that as a theory becomes increasingly well established and accepted, certain statements couched in terms of its characteristic concepts may come to be qualified as descriptions of "observed facts."

3. William Whewell, *The Philosophy of the Inductive Sciences,* 2d ed. (London: John W. Parker, 1847), II, 41 (author's italics).

4. See, for example, Popper's essay, "Science: Conjectures and Refutations," in his book, *Conjectures and Refutations* (New York and London: Basic Books, 1962).

5. Karl Popper, "Philosophy of Science: A Personal Report," *British Philosophy in the Mid-Century,* ed. C. A. Mace (London: Allen and Unwin, 1957), pp. 155–91, quotation from p. 181.

6. Popper, "Philosophy of Science," p. 183.

7. Precise general characterizations of deductive validity, for arguments in languages of certain specified forms, will be found, e.g., in W. V. O. Quine, *Methods of Logic,* rev. ed. (New York: Holt, Rinehart & Winston, 1959).

8. See especially the following publications by Rudolf Carnap: *Logical Foundations of Probability,* 2d ed. (Chicago: U. of Chicago Press, 1962); "The Aim of Inductive Logic," *Logic, Methodology and Philosophy of Science: Proceedings of the 1960 International Congress,* eds. E. Nagel, P. Suppes, and A. Tarski (Stanford: Stanford U. Press, 1962), pp. 303–18.

9. It seems to me, therefore, that Popper begs the question when he declares: "But it is obvious that this rule or craft of 'valid induction' . . . simply does not exist. No rule can ever guarantee that a generalization inferred from true observations, however often repeated, is true" ("Philosophy of Science," p. 181). That inductive reasoning is not *deductively* valid is granted at the outset; the problem is that of constructing a concept of *inductive* validity.

10. Jean Nicod, *Foundations of Geometry and Induction* (New York: Harcourt, Brace & World, 1930), p. 219. Nicod here speaks of "truths or facts," namely, "the presence or absence of *B* in a case of *A,*" as confirming or invalidating "the law *A* entails *B*" (author's italics). Such confirmatory and disconfirmatory facts can be thought of as described by corresponding evidence sentences. Nicod remarks about his criterion: "We have not seen it stated in any explicit manner. However, we do not think that anything ever written on induction is incompatible with it" (p. 220). Whether Nicod regards the specified conditions as necessary and sufficient or merely as sufficient for confirmation or invalidation is not entirely clear, although he does say: "It is conceivable that we have here the only two direct modes in which a fact can influence the probability of a law" (p. 219). We will construe his criteria simply as *sufficient* conditions of confirmation and invalidation.

11. These paradoxes were first noted in my essay "Le problème de la vérité," *Theoria* (Göteborg), 3 (1937), 206–46 (see especially p. 222) and were discussed in greater detail in my articles "Studies in the Logic of Confirmation," *Mind*, 54 (1945), 1–26, 97–121, and "A Purely Syntactical Definition of Confirmation," *The J. of Symbolic Logic*, 8 (1943), 122–43.

12. Nicod, *Geometry and Induction*, pp. 219–20.

13. It was first offered by Janina Hosiasson-Lindenbaum in her article "On Confirmation," *The J. of Symbolic Logic*, 5 (1940), 133–48. Similar ideas were proposed by, among others, D. Pears, "Hypotheticals," *Analysis*, 10 (1950), 49–63; I. J. Good, "The Paradoxes of Confirmation," Pts. I and II, *The British J. for the Philosophy of Science*, 11 (1960), 145–48; 12 (1961) 63–64. A detailed and illuminating study of qualitative confirmation and its paradoxes is offered in sec. 3, Pt. I of Israel Scheffler, *The Anatomy of Inquiry* (New York: Knopf, 1963).

14. Nelson Goodman, *Fact, Fiction, and Forecast* (Cambridge: Harvard U. Press, 1955); 2d, rev. ed. (Indianapolis: Bobbs-Merrill, 1965).

15. Nicod does not explicitly deal with hypotheses which, like h, contain relational terms rather than only property terms such as "raven" and "black"; but the application here suggested certainly seems to be in full accord with his basic conception.

16. This further paradox of qualitative confirmation was briefly noted in my article, "Studies in the Logic of Confirmation," p. 13.

17. The general definition is developed in "A Purely Syntactical Definition of Confirmation"; the gist of it is presented in sec. 9 of my article essay, "Studies in the Logic of Confirmation." The objections in question were raised especially by R. Carnap in *Logical Foundations of Probability*, secs. 86–88. Briefly, Carnap's principal objection is to the effect that under an adequate definition of qualitative confirmation, e should confirm h only if, in the sense of inductive probability theory, e raises the prior probability of h; and my definition of confirmation is not compatible with such a construal.

18. See especially the following publications: "On Inductive Logic," *Philosophy of Science*, 12 (1945), 72–97; *Logical Foundations of Probability; The Continuum of Inductive Methods* (Chicago: U. of Chicago Press, 1952).

19. A lucid account of these rules and of their theoretical use will be found in R. D. Luce and H. Raiffa, *Games and Decisions* (New York: Wiley, 1957).

20. C. W. Churchman, *Theory of Experimental Inference* (New York: Macmillan, 1948), pp. vii, viii (author's italics).

21. R. B. Braithwaite, *Scientific Explanation* (Cambridge: Cambridge U. Press, 1953), p. 251.

22. For a fuller discussion and bibliographic references concerning these issues, see, e.g., sec. 12 of C. G. Hempel, "Deductive-Nomological *vs.* Statistical Explanation" in *Scientific Explanation, Space, and Time*, eds. H. Feigl and G. Maxwell, Minnesota Studies in the Philosophy of Science, III (Minneapolis: U. of Minnesota Press, 1962), 98–169. Some of the basic issues are examined in R. B. Braithwaite's paper, "The Role of Values in Scientific Inference," and especially the discussion of that paper in *Induction: Some Current Issues*, eds. H. E. Kyburg, Jr., and E. Nagel (Middletown, Conn.: Wesleyan U. Press, 1963), pp. 180–204.

23. Such an alternative conception is represented, e.g., by T. S. Kuhn's work, *The Structure of Scientific Revolutions* (Chicago: U. of Chicago Press, 1962).

WESLEY C. SALMON

Indiana University

The Foundations of Scientific Inference

> The whole of science is nothing more than a refinement of everyday thinking. It is for this reason that the critical thinking of the physicist cannot possibly be restricted to the examination of the concepts of his own specific field. He cannot proceed without considering critically a much more difficult problem, the problem of analyzing the nature of everyday thinking.
>
> —Albert Einstein
> *Out of My Later Years*

ALTHOUGH PERHAPS BORN EARLIER, mathematical physics came of age in the seventeenth century through the work of such men as Descartes, Galileo, Kepler, and Newton. This development constituted one of the most far-reaching of all revolutions in human thought, and it did not go unnoticed by various philosophers, some of whom had made significant contributions to it. There were, consequently, serious philosophic efforts to understand the logic of the new science.

Mathematical physics has an abstract and formal side as well as an observational and experimental side, and it has never been easy to understand the relations between them. Philosophies arising early in the modern period tended to emphasize one aspect to the neglect of the other. Descartes and Leibniz, impressed by the power of the mathematics they had helped to create, developed rationalistic epistemologies which failed to account for the observational and experimental aspect. Bacon and Locke, in their determination to handle the observational and experimental side, developed empirical theories of knowledge which failed to do justice to the abstract and formal character of science.

Although Descartes unequivocally rejected medieval authoritarianism with its unquestioning appeal to Aristotle, his conception of the logic of scientific knowledge was similar in fundamentals to that of Aristotle. Aristotle regarded scientific reasoning as strictly syllogistic in character; the only nonsyllogistic part is the establishment of first principles, and this is accomplished by intuitive induction. Intuitive induction is very different from inductive generalization as we think of it nowadays; it is, instead, a kind of rational insight.[1] For Descartes also, scientific knowledge consists of deduction from first principles established by the natural light of reason.[2]

Some of the salient differences between the rationalistic and empirical attitudes are expressed by Descartes' comments on Galileo in a letter to Father Mersenne, written in 1638:

I find in general that he [Galileo] philosophizes much better than the average, in that he abandons as completely as he can the errors of the Schools, and attempts to examine physical matters by the methods of mathematics. In this I am in entire agreement with him, and I believe that there is absolutely no other way of discovering the truth. But it seems to me that he suffers greatly from continual digressions, and that he does not stop to explain all that is relevant to each point; which shows that he has not examined them in order, and that he has merely sought reasons for particular effects, without having considered the first causes of nature; and thus that he has built without a foundation. Indeed, because his fashion of philosophizing is so near to the truth, one can the more readily recognize his faults.[3]

While he applauds Galileo's use of mathematics, Descartes shows a complete lack of appreciation of the empirical approach. For Descartes, science is not an experimental enterprise in which one attempts to investigate clearly defined phenomena by observation of highly controlled situations. For him, the order is reversed. One understands the broadest aspects of nature by deduction from indubitable first principles; the details come at the end rather than the beginning. The first principles are grounded in pure reason. For the empiricist, on the other hand, the entire warrant for scientific theory rests upon its ability to explain precisely such details as can be handled experimentally.

It was Francis Bacon who first saw clearly that modern scientific method embodies a logic fundamentally different from that of Aristotle. In sharp contrast to Descartes, Bacon rejects rationalism and extols the method of careful observation and experimentation.

There are and can be only two ways of searching into and discovering truth. The one flies from the senses and particulars to the most general axioms, and from these principles, the truth of which it takes for settled and immovable, proceeds to judgment and to the discovery of middle axioms. And this way is now in fashion. The other derives axioms from the senses and particulars, rising by a gradual and unbroken ascent, so that it arrives at the most general axioms last of all. This is the true way, but as yet untried.[4]

Bacon realized that scientific knowledge must somehow be built upon inductive generalization from experience, and he tried to formulate the principles of this new logic—"a true induction." He confidently predicted that the assiduous application of this method would answer all important scientific questions. Looking back, we must regard his characterization as extremely primitive and wholly inadequate to the complexity of scientific method. His optimism for the future of science was charmingly naïve. He was, nevertheless, the enthusiastic herald of the new inductive method of science, and this in itself is an important contribution.

The seventeenth century could hardly imagine the foundational problems that were in store in connection with the methods of modern science. The spectacular successes of the newly developed methods led to an expansive attitude. The frontiers were pushed, but the foundations were seldom examined. Each of the previously noted aspects of mathematical physics had its foundational problems. The infinitesimal calculus was invented, and as an integral part of the mathematics of modern science it proved to be a powerful deductive tool. For about two centuries the foundations of calculus were in complete disorder.[5] The infinitesimal was a logical mystery; indeed, it was a logical absurdity. As a quantity smaller than any given positive quantity but greater than zero, it was a zero that was not really a zero—the ghost of a recently departed quantity! There was no clear understanding of mathematical functions, their values, or their limits. Illumination finally came early in the nineteenth century when Cauchy provided satisfactory explications of functions, limits, and derivatives. In the latter part of the century, further solidification resulted from the construction of the real number system and the arithmetization of calculus by Dedekind and Weierstrass. Moreover, even the logic of mathematical demonstration remained unexplicated until mathematical logic was invented and developed. Still, all was not well with the foundations. Logical analysis of mathematics pushed the notion of a class or set into greater and greater prominence, but even this apparently clear concept proved to be self-contradictory when defined in a natural way. At about the turn of the century, Russell derived his paradox of the class of all classes that do not belong to themselves from Cantor's theory of sets.[6]

Controversies and unsolved problems regarding the foundations of deductive inference still remain; foundations of mathematics is an active area of current research. Despite any remaining difficulties, however, there can be no question that our understanding of mathematics and deductive inference has been enormously enhanced by the investigations of the foundations. The foundations of inductive inference are far less fully understood, although they, too, are the object of considerable contemporary study. It is to the foundations of inductive inference in science that the present essay is devoted. I shall attempt to give a fairly well-rounded picture of the present state of investigations in this area, and in so doing I hope to present a convincing case for the desirability of continued study of these foundational questions.

The seventeenth century had even less basis for anticipating the foundational problems concerning inductive inference than it had for those of deductive inference. Although rationalists found various reasons for rejecting the empirical method, an awareness of the problem of induction cannot be counted as one of them. Ever since antiquity philosophers had been aware that the senses can deceive us, and this point was emphatically reiterated by Descartes. Those who were engaged in the quest for certainty found in this fact a basis for rejecting the empirical method. Some of the ancient skeptics even had been aware that inductive inference can sometimes lead to false conclusions; again, those engaged in the quest for certainty could reject inductive methods on this ground.[7] Philosophers who recognize that science cannot be expected to yield absolutely certain results can tolerate both of these shortcomings with equanimity. Hume's far more crushing critique of inductive inference came as a completely unanticipated development. It is notable that the most devastating criticism of empirical philosophy should come from a thoroughgoing empiricist. Hume's problem has proved astonishingly recalcitrant. Although there have been numerous efforts to solve or dissolve the difficulty, none is a satisfactory answer—at least, none is widely accepted as such.

Before turning to Hume, one other important seventeenth-century occurrence requires mention.[8] In 1654, the Chevalier de Méré, a gambler, asked Pascal to solve some problems relating to games of chance. One of these problems dealt with the fair division of stakes in a game not played through to completion; it is essentially the problem of calculating the probability that a player will win given a particular situation part way through the game. Another problem concerned the number of throws of two dice required to have at least a fifty-fifty chance of tossing a double six. Pascal communicated the problems to Fermat; in solving them, these two mathematicians founded the mathematical calculus of probability. Although originally applied only to gambling games, it was found to be applicable to wider and wider ranges of phenomena until today the concept of probability enjoys a fundamental position in all science. The development of probability theory provides still another example of foundational problems remaining long after the superstructure was well developed. For about two centuries it appears that the probability concept was regarded as easy to understand. To be sure, many authors presented definitions of the term, but this seems to have been a perfunctory gesture. The definitions were usually brief, and they were often quite out of harmony with the treatment of the subject when self-conscious definition was not under consideration. Nowhere can one find an appreciation of the severe difficulties encountered when detailed explication is undertaken. It is only with authors like Venn,[9] Peirce,[10] and Keynes [11] in the late nineteenth or early twentieth century that the problem of explicating the probability concept was taken seriously and treated at length. Furthermore, the relation between probability and induction was slow to be seen, and it is still widely misunderstood.

This, then, is the complex of problems I shall discuss: Hume's problem of induction, the problem of explicating the probability concept, and the problem of clarifying the relation between probability and inductive inference. Hume's critique of induction will constitute the historical as well as the logical point of departure.

The Problem of Induction

We all believe that we have knowledge of facts extending far beyond those we directly perceive. The scope of our senses is severely limited in space and time; our immediate perceptual knowledge does not reach to events that happened before we were born to events that are happening now in certain other places or to any future events. We believe, nevertheless, that we have some kind of indirect knowledge of such facts. We know that a glacier once covered a large part of North America, that the sun continues to exist at night, and that the tides will rise and fall tomorrow. Science and common sense have at least this one thing in common: Each embodies knowledge of matters of fact that are not open to our direct inspection. Indeed, science purports to establish general laws or theories that apply to all parts of space and time without restriction. A "science" that consisted of no more than a mere summary of the results of direct observation would not deserve the name.

Hume's profound critique of induction begins with a simple and apparently innocent question: How do we acquire knowledge of the unobserved? [12] This question, as posed, may seem to call for an empirical answer. We observe that human beings utilize what may be roughly characterized as inductive or scientific methods of extending knowledge from the observed to the unobserved. The sciences, in fact, embody the most powerful and highly developed methods known, and we may make an empirical investigation of scientific methods much as we might for any other sort of human behavior. We may consider the historical development of science. We may study the psychological, sociological, and political factors relevant to the pursuit of science. We may try to give an exact characterization of the behavior of scientists. In doing all these things, however, important and interesting as they are, we will have ignored the *philosophical* aspect of the problem Hume raised. Putting the matter very simply, these empirical investigations may enable us to describe the ways in which people arrive at *beliefs* about unobserved facts, but they leave open the question of whether beliefs arrived at in this way actually constitute *knowledge*. It is one thing to describe how people go about seeking to extend their knowledge; it is quite another to claim that the methods employed actually do yield knowledge.

One of the basic differences between knowledge and belief is that knowledge must be founded upon evidence—i.e., it must be belief founded upon some rational justification. To say that certain methods yield knowledge of the unobserved is to make a cognitive claim for them. Hume called into question the justification of such cognitive claims. The answer cannot be found entirely within an empirical study of human behavior, for a *logical* problem has been raised. It is the problem of understanding the logical relationship between evidence and conclusion in logically correct inferences. It is the problem of determining whether the inferences by which we attempt to make the transition from knowledge of the observed to knowledge of the unobserved are logically correct. The fact that people do or do not use a certain type of inference is irrelevant to its justifiability. Whether people have confidence in the correctness of a certain type of inference has nothing to do with whether such confidence is justified. If we should adopt a logically incorrect method for inferring one fact from others, these facts would not actually constitute evidence for the conclusion we have drawn. The problem of induction is the problem of explicating the very concept of *inductive evidence*.

There is another possibly misleading feature of the question as I have formulated it. When we ask how we can *acquire* knowledge of the unobserved, it sounds very much as if we are asking for a method for the *discovery* of new knowledge. This is, of course, a vital problem, but it is not the fundamental problem Hume raised. Whether there is or can be any sort of inductive logic of discovery is a controversial question I shall discuss in detail in a later section.[13] Leaving this question aside for now, there remains the problem of *justification* of conclusions concerning unobserved matters of fact. Given some conclusion, however arrived at, regarding unobserved facts, and given some alleged evidence to support that conclusion, the question remains whether that conclusion is, indeed, supported by the evidence offered in support of it.

Consider a simple and highly artificial situation. Suppose a number of balls have been drawn from an urn, and that all of the black ones that have been drawn are licorice-flavored. I am not now concerned with such psychological questions as what makes the observer note the color of these balls, what leads him to taste the black ones, what makes him take note of the fact that licorice flavor is associated with black color in his sample, or what makes him suppose that the black balls not yet drawn will also be licorice-flavored. The problem—Hume's basic *philosophical* problem—is this: Given that all of the observed black balls have been licorice-flavored, and given that somehow the conclusion has been entertained that the unobserved black balls in the urn are also licorice-flavored, do the observed facts constitute sound *evidence* for that conclusion? Would we be *justified* in accepting that conclusion on the basis of the facts alleged to be evidence for it?

As a first answer to this question we may point out that the inference does conform to an accepted inductive principle, a principle saying roughly that observed instances conforming to a generalization constitute evidence for it. It is, however, a very small step to the next question: What grounds have we for accepting this or any other inductive principle? Is there any reason or justification for placing confidence in the conclusions of inferences of this type? Given that the premises of this inference are true, and given that the inference conforms to a certain rule, can we provide any rational justification for accepting its conclusion rather than, for instance, the conclusion that black balls yet to be drawn will taste like quinine?

It is well known that Hume's answer to this problem was essentially skeptical. It was his great merit to have shown that a justification of induction, if possible at all, is by no means easy to provide. In order to appreciate the force of his argument it is first necessary to clarify some terminological points. This is particularly important because the word *induction* has been used in a wide variety of ways.

For purposes of systematic discussion one distinction is fundamental, namely, the distinction between demonstrative and nondemonstrative inference. A *demonstrative* inference is one whose premises necessitate its conclusion; the conclusion cannot be false if the premises are true. All valid deductions are demonstrative inferences. A *nondemonstrative* inference is simply one that fails to be demonstrative. Its conclusion is not necessitated by its premises; the conclusion could be false even if the premises are true. A demonstrative inference is *necessarily truth-preserving;* a nondemonstrative inference is not.

The category of nondemonstrative inferences, as I have characterized it, contains, among other things perhaps, all kinds of fallacious inferences. If, however, there is any kind of inference whose premises, although not necessitating the conclusion, do lend it weight, support it, or make it probable, then such inferences possess a certain kind of logical rectitude. It is not deductive validity, but it is important anyway. Inferences possessing it are *correct inductive inferences.*

Since demonstrative inferences have been characterized in terms of their basic property of necessary truth preservation, it is natural to ask how they achieve this very desirable trait. For a large group of demonstrative inferences, including those discussed under "valid deduction" in most logic texts, the answer is rather easy. Inferences of this type purchase necessary truth preservation by sacrificing any extension of content. The conclusion of such an inference says no more than do the premises—often less.[14] The conclusion cannot be false if the premises are true *because* the conclusion says nothing that was not already stated in the premises. The conclusion is a mere reformulation of all or part of the content of the premises. In some cases the reformulation is unanticipated and therefore psychologically surprising, but the conclusion cannot augment the content of the premises. Such inferences are *nonampliative;* an ampliative inference, then, has a conclusion with content not present either explicitly or implicitly in the premises.

While it is easy to understand why nonampliative inferences are necessarily truth-preserving, the further question arises whether there are any necessarily truth-preserving inferences that are also ampliative. Is there any type of inference whose conclusion must, of necessity, be true if the premises are true, but whose conclusion says something not stated by the premises? Hume believed that the answer is negative and so do I, but it is not easy to produce an adequate defense of this answer. Let us see, however, what an affirmative answer would amount to.

Suppose there were an ampliative inference that is also necessarily truth-preserving. Consider the implication from its premises, P_1,

. . . , P_k, to its conclusion C. If the inference were an ordinary nonampliative deduction, this implication would be analytic and empty; but since the argument is supposed to be ampliative, the implication must be synthetic. At the same time, because the argument is supposed to be necessarily truth-preserving, this implication must be not only true but necessarily true. Thus, to maintain that there are inferences that are both ampliative and necessarily truth-preserving is tantamount to asserting that there are synthetic a priori truths.[15] This may be seen in another way. Any ampliative inference can be made into a nonampliative one by adding a premise. In particular, if we add to the foregoing ampliative inference the synthetic a priori premise, "If P_1 and P_2 and . . . and P_k, then C," the resulting inference will be an ordinary valid nonampliative deduction. Consider our example once more; this time let us set it out more formally:

1. Some black balls from this urn have been observed.
   All observed black balls from this urn are licorice-flavored.

   ———————————————————————————————

   All black balls in this urn are licorice-flavored.

This argument is clearly ampliative, for the premise makes a statement about observed balls only, while the conclusion makes a statement about the unobserved as well as the observed balls. It appears to be nondemonstrative as well, for it seems perfectly possible for the conclusion to be false even if the premises are true. We see no reason why someone might not have dropped a black marble in the urn which, when it is drawn, will be found to be tasteless. We could, however, rule out this sort of possibility by adding another premise:

2. Some black balls from this urn have been observed.
   All observed black balls in this urn are licorice-flavored.
   Any two balls in this urn that have the same color also have the same flavor.

   ———————————————————————————————

   All black balls in this urn are licorice-flavored.

The additional premise has transformed the former nondemonstrative inference into a demonstrative inference, but we must also admit that we have transformed it into a nonampliative inference. If, however, the third premise of 2 were a synthetic a priori truth, the original inference, although ampliative, would have been necessarily truth-preserving and, hence, demonstrative. If the premise that transformed inference 1 into inference 2 were necessarily true, then it would be impossible for the

conclusion of inference 1 to be false if the premises were true, for that
would contradict the third premise of inference 2.

Hardly anyone would be tempted to say that the statement, "Any two
balls in this urn that have the same color also have the same flavor,"
expresses a synthetic a priori truth. Other propositions have, however,
been taken to be synthetic a priori. Hume and many of his successors
noticed that typical inductive inferences, such as our example concerning
licorice-flavored black balls, would seem perfectly sound if we could
have recourse to some sort of principle of uniformity of nature. If we
could only prove that the course of nature is uniform, that the future will
be like the past, or that uniformities that have existed thus far will
continue to hold in the future, then we would seem to be justified in
generalizing from past cases to future cases—from the observed to the
unobserved. Indeed, Hume suggests that we presuppose in our inductive
reasoning a principle from which the third premise of 2 would follow as a
special case: "We always presume, when we see like sensible qualities,
that they have like secret powers, and expect that effects, similar to those
which we have experienced, will follow from them." [16] Again, "From
causes which appear *similar* we expect similar effects. This is the sum of
all our experimental conclusions." [17]

Hume's searching examination of the principle of uniformity of nature
revealed no ground on which it could be taken as a synthetic a priori
principle. For all we can know a priori, Hume argued, the course of
nature might change, the future might be radically unlike the past, and
regularities that have obtained in respect to observed events might prove
completely inapplicable to unobserved cases. We have found by experience, of course, that nature has exhibited a high degree of uniformity and
regularity so far, and we infer inductively that this will continue, but to
use an inductively inferred generalization as a justification for induction,
as Hume emphasized, would be flagrantly circular. He concluded, in fact,
that there are no synthetic a priori principles in virtue of which we could
have demonstrative inferences that are ampliative. Hume recognized two
kinds of reasonings: reasoning concerning relations of ideas and reasoning concerning matters of fact and existence. The former is demonstrative
but nonampliative while the latter is ampliative but not necessarily truth-
preserving.

If we agree that there are no synthetic a priori truths, then we must
identify necessarily truth-preserving inference with nonampliative inference. All ampliative inference is nondemonstrative. This leads to an
exhaustive trichotomy of inferences: valid deductive inference, correct

inductive inference, and assorted fallacies. The first question is, however, whether the second category is empty or whether there are such things as correct inductive inferences. This is Hume's problem of induction. Can we show that any particular type of ampliative inference can be justified in any way? If so, it will qualify as correct induction.

Consider, then, any ampliative inference whatever. The example of the licorice-flavored black balls illustrates the point. We cannot show *deductively* that this inference will have a true conclusion given true premises. If we could, we would have proved that the conclusion must be true if the premises are. That would make it necessarily truth-preserving, hence, demonstrative. This, in turn, would mean that it was nonampliative, contrary to our hypothesis. Thus, if an ampliative inference could be justified deductively it would not be ampliative. It follows that ampliative inference cannot be justified deductively.

At the same time, we cannot justify any sort of ampliative inference *inductively*. To do so would require the use of some sort of nondemonstrative inference. But the question at issue is the justification of nondemonstrative inference, so the procedure would be question begging. Before we can properly employ a nondemonstrative inference in a justifying argument, we must already have justified that nondemonstrative inference.

Hume's position can be summarized succinctly: We cannot justify any kind of ampliative inference. If it could be justified deductively it would not be ampliative. It cannot be justified nondemonstratively because that would be viciously circular. It seems, then, that there is no way in which we can extend our knowledge to the unobserved. We have, to be sure, many beliefs about the unobserved, and in some of them we place great confidence. Nevertheless, they are without rational justification of any kind!

This is a harsh conclusion, yet it seems to be supported by impeccable arguments. It might be called "Hume's paradox," for the conclusion, although ingeniously argued, is utterly repugnant to common sense and our deepest convictions. We *know* ("in our hearts") that we have knowledge of unobserved fact. The challenge is to show how this is possible.

Attempted Solutions

It hardly needs remarking that philosophers have attempted to meet Hume's intriguing challenge in a wide variety of ways. There have been direct attacks upon some of Hume's arguments. Attempts to provide inductive arguments to support induction and attempts to supply a synthetic a priori principle of uniformity of nature belong in this category. Some authors have claimed that the whole problem arises out of linguistic confusion, and that careful analysis shows it to be a pseudoproblem. Some have even denied that inductive inference is needed, either in science or in everyday affairs. In this section I shall survey what seem to me to be the most important efforts to deal with the problem.

1. Inductive Justification. If Hume's arguments had never been propounded and we were asked why we accept the methods of science, the most natural answer would be, I think, that these methods have proved themselves by their results. We can point to astonishing technological advances, to vastly increased comprehension, and to impressive predictions. Science has provided us with foresight, control, and understanding. No other method can claim a comparable record of successful accomplishment. If methods are to be judged by their fruits, there is no doubt that the scientific method will come out on top.

Unfortunately, Hume examined this argument and showed that it is viciously circular. It is an example of an attempt to justify inductive methods inductively. From the premise that science has had considerable predictive success in the past, we conclude that it will continue to have substantial predictive success in the future. Observed cases of the application of scientific method have yielded successful prediction; therefore, as yet unobserved cases of the application of scientific method will yield successful predictions. This argument has the same structure as our black-balls-in-the-urn example; it is precisely the sort of ampliative inference from the observed to the unobserved whose justifiability is in question.

Consider the parallel case for a radically different sort of method. A crystal gazer claims that his method is the appropriate method for making predictions. When we question his claim he says, "Wait a moment; I will find out whether the method of crystal gazing is the best method for making predictions." He looks into his crystal ball and announces that future cases of crystal gazing will yield predictive success. If we should protest that his method has not been especially successful in the past, he might well make certain remarks about parity of reasoning. "Since you have used your method to justify your method, why shouldn't I use my method to justify my method? If you insist upon judging my method by using your method, why shouldn't I use my method to evaluate your method? By the way, I note by gazing into my crystal ball that the scientific method is now in for a very bad run of luck."

The trouble with circular arguments is obvious: with an appropriate circular argument you can prove anything. In recent years, nevertheless, there have been several notable attempts to show how inductive rules can be supported inductively. The authors of such attempts try to show, of course, that their arguments are not circular. Although they argue persuasively, it seems to me that they do not succeed in escaping circularity.

One of the most widely discussed attempts to show that self-supporting inductive inferences are possible without circularity is due to Max Black.[18] Black correctly observes that the traditional fallacy of circular argument (*petitio principii*) involves assuming as a premise, often unwittingly, the conclusion that is to be proved. Thus, for example, a variety of "proofs" of Euclid's fifth postulate offered by mathematicians for about two millenia before the discovery of non-Euclidean geometry are circular in the standard fashion. They fail to show that the fifth postulate follows from the first four postulates alone; instead, they require in addition the assumption of a proposition equivalent to the proposition being demonstrated. The situation is quite different for self-supporting inductive arguments. The conclusion to be proved does not appear as one of the premises. Consider one of Black's examples: [19]

3. In most instances of the use of R_2 in arguments with true premises examined in a wide variety of conditions, R_2 has usually been successful.

   Hence (*probably*):

   In the next instance to be encountered of the use of R_2 in an argument with true premises, R_2 will be successful.

To say that an argument with true premises is successful is merely to say that it has a true conclusion. The rule R_2 is

   To argue from *Most instances of A's examined in a wide variety of conditions have been B* to (probably) *The next A to be encountered will be B*.

Inference 3 can be paraphrased suggestively, although somewhat inaccurately, as:

4. R_2 has usually been successful in the past.

   Hence (*probably*):

   R_2 will be successful in the next instance.

Inference 3 is governed by R_2, that is, it conforms to the stipulation laid down by R_2. R_2 is *not* a premise, however, nor is any statement to the effect that all, some, or any future instances of R_2 will be successful. As Lewis Carroll showed decisively, there is a fundamental distinction between premises and rules of inference.[20] Any inference, inductive or deductive, must conform to some rule, but neither the rule nor any statement about the rule is to be incorporated into the inference as an additional premise. If such additional premises were required, inference would be impossible. Thus, inference 3 is not a standard *petitio principii*.

What, then, are the requirements for a self-supporting argument? At least three are immediately apparent: (1) The argument must have true premises. (2) The argument must conform to a certain rule. (3) The conclusion of that argument must say something about the success or reliability of that rule in unexamined instances of its application. Inference 3 has these characteristics.

It is not difficult to find examples of deductive inferences with the foregoing characteristics.

5. If snow is white, then *modus ponens* is valid.
   Snow is white.

   Modus ponens is valid.

Inference 5 may seem innocuous enough, but the same cannot be said for the following inference:

6. If affirming the consequent is valid, then coal is black.
   Coal is black.

   Affirming the consequent is valid.

Like inference 5, inference 6 has true premises, it conforms to a certain rule, and its conclusion asserts the validity of that rule. Inference 5 did nothing to enhance our confidence in the validity of *modus ponens,* for we have far better grounds for believing it to be valid. Inference 6 does nothing to convince us that affirming the consequent is valid, for we know on other grounds that it is invalid. Arguments like 5 and 6 are, nevertheless, instructive. Both are circular in some sense, though neither assumes *as a premise* the conclusion it purports to establish. In deductive logic the situation is quite straightforward. A deductive inference establishes its conclusion if it has true premises and has a valid form. If either of these features is lacking the conclusion is not established by that argument. If the argument is valid but the premises are not true we need not accept the conclusion. If the premises are true but the argument is invalid we need not accept the conclusion. One way in which an argument can be circular is by adopting as a premise the very conclusion that is to be proved; this is the fallacy of *petitio principii* which I shall call "premise-circularity." Another way in which an argument can be circular is by exhibiting a form whose validity is asserted by the very conclusion that is to be proved; let us call this type of circularity "rule-circularity." Neither type of circular argument establishes its conclusion in any interesting fashion, for in each case the conclusiveness of the argument depends upon the assumption of the conclusion of that argument. Inferences 5 and 6 are not premise-circular; each is rule-circular. They are, nevertheless, completely question begging.

The situation in induction is somewhat more complicated, but basically the same.[21] Consider the following argument:

7. In most instances of the use of R_3 in arguments with true premises examined in a wide variety of conditions, R_3 has usually been *un*successful.

Hence (probably):

In the next instance to be encountered of the use of R_3 in an argument with true premises, R_3 will be successful.

The rule R_3 is

To argue from *Most instances of A's examined in a wide variety of conditions have been non-B* to (probably) *The next A to be encountered will be B.*

Inference 7 can be paraphrased as follows:

8. R_3 has usually been unsuccessful in the past.

Hence (probably):

R_3 will be successful in the next instance.

Notice that there is a perfect parallel between R_2, 3, 4 on the one hand and R_3, 7, 8 on the other. Since those instances in which R_2 would be successful are those in which R_3 would be unsuccessful, the premises of 3 and 4 describe the same state of affairs as do the premises of 7 and 8. Thus, the use of R_3 in the next instance seems to be supported in the same manner and to the same extent as the use of R_2 in the next instance. However, R_2 and R_3 conflict directly with each other. On the evidence that most Italians examined in a wide variety of conditions have been dark-eyed, R_2 allows us to infer that the next Italian to be encountered will be dark-eyed, while R_3 permits us to infer from the same evidence that he will have light-colored eyes. It appears then that we can construct self-supporting arguments for correct and incorrect inductive rules just as we can for valid and invalid deductive rules.

Black would reject self-supporting arguments for the fallacy of affirming the consequent and for a counterinductive rule like R_3, because we know on independent grounds that such rules are faulty. Affirming the consequent is known to be fallacious, and the counterinductive method can be shown to be self-defeating. An additional requirement for a self-supporting argument is that the rule thus supported be one we have no independent reason to reject. Nevertheless, the fact that we can construct self-supporting arguments for such rules should give us pause. What if we had never realized that affirming the consequent is fallacious? What if we had never noticed anything wrong with the counterinductive method? Would arguments like 6, 7, and 8 have to be considered cogent? What about the standard inductive method? Is it as incorrect as the counterinductive method, but for reasons most of us have not yet realized?

It sounds as if a self-supporting argument is applicable only to rules we already know to be correct; as a matter of fact, this is the view Black holds. He has argued in various places that induction is in no need of a general justification.[22] He holds that calling into question of all inductive methods simultaneously results in a hopelessly skeptical position. He is careful to state explicitly at the outset of his discussion of self-supporting inductive arguments that he is not dealing with the view "that *no* inductive argument ought to be regarded as correct until a philosophical justification of induction has been provided."[23] At the conclusion he acknowledges, moreover, that "anybody who thinks he has good grounds for condemning all inductive arguments will also condemn inductive arguments in support of inductive rules."[24] Black is careful to state explicitly that self-supporting inductive arguments provide no answer to the problem of justification of induction as raised by Hume. What good, then, are self-supporting inductive arguments?

In deductive logic, correctness is an all-or-nothing affair. Deductive inferences are either totally valid or totally invalid; there cannot be such a thing as degree of validity. In inductive logic the situation is quite different. Inductive correctness does admit of degrees; one inductive conclusion may be more strongly supported than another. In this situation it is possible, Black claims, to have an inductive rule we know to be correct to some degree, but whose status can be enhanced by self-supporting arguments. We might think a rather standard inductive rule akin to Black's R_2 is pretty good, but through inductive investigation of its application we might find that it is extremely good—much better than we originally thought. Moreover, the inductive inferences we use to draw that conclusion might be governed by precisely the sort of rule we are investigating. It is also possible, of course, to find by inductive investigation that the rule is not as good as we believed beforehand.

It is actually irrelevant to the present discussion to attempt to evaluate Black's view concerning the possibility of increasing the justification of inductive rules by self-supporting arguments. The important point is to emphasize, because of the possibility of constructing self-supporting arguments for counterinductive rules, that the attempt to provide inductive support of inductive rules cannot, without vicious circularity, be applied to the problem of justifying induction from scratch. If there is any way of providing the beginnings of a justification, or if we could show that some inductive rule stands in no need of justification in the first instance, then it would be suitable to return to Black's argument concerning the increase of support. I am not convinced, however, that Black has successfully shown that there is a satisfactory starting place.

I have treated the problem of inductive justification of induction at some length, partly because other authors have not been as cautious as Black in circumscribing the limits of inductive justification of induction.[25] More important, perhaps, is the fact that it is extremely difficult, psychologically speaking, to shake the view that past success of the inductive method constitutes a genuine justification of induction. Nevertheless, the basic fact remains: Hume showed that inductive justifications of induction are fallacious, and no one has since proved him wrong.

2. *The Complexity of Scientific Inference.* The idea of a philosopher discussing inductive inference in science is apt to arouse grotesque images in many minds. People are likely to imagine someone earnestly attempting to explain why it is reasonable to conclude that the sun will rise tomorrow morning because it always has done so in the past. There may have been a time when primitive man anticipated the dawn with assurance based only upon the fact that he had seen dawn follow the blackness of night as long as he could remember, but this primitive state of knowledge, if it ever existed, was unquestionably *prescientific*. This kind of reasoning bears no resemblance to science; in fact, the crude induction exhibits a complete absence of scientific understanding. Our scientific reasons for believing that the sun will rise tomorrow are of an entirely different kind. We understand the functioning of the solar system in terms of the laws of physics. We predict particular astronomical

occurrences by means of these laws in conjunction with a knowledge of particular initial conditions that prevail. Scientific laws and theories have the logical form of general statements, but they are seldom, if ever, simple generalizations from experience.

Consider Newton's gravitational theory: Any two bodies are mutually attracted by a force proportional to the product of their masses and inversely proportional to the square of the distance between their centers. Although general in form, this kind of statement is not established by generalization from instances. We do not go around saying, "Here are two bodies—the force between them is such and such; here are two more bodies—the force between them is such and such; etc." Scientific theories are taken quite literally as hypotheses. They are entertained in order that their consequences may be drawn and examined. Their acceptability is judged in terms of these consequences. The consequences are extremely diverse—the greater the variety the better. For Newtonian theory, we look to such consequences as the behavior of Mars, the tides, falling bodies, the pendulum, and the torsion balance. These consequences have no apparent unity among themselves; they do not constitute a basis for inductive generalization. They achieve a kind of unity only by virtue of the fact that they are consequences of a single physical theory.

The type of inference I have been characterizing is very familiar; it is known as the *hypothetico-deductive method*.[26] It stands in sharp contrast to *induction by enumeration*, which consists in simple inductive generalization from instances. Schematically, the hypothetico-deductive method works as follows: From a general hypothesis and particular statements of initial conditions, a particular predictive statement is deduced. The statements of initial conditions, at least for the time, are accepted as true; the hypothesis is the statement whose truth is at issue. By observation we determine whether the predictive statement turned out to be true. If the predictive consequence is false, the hypothesis is disconfirmed. If observation reveals that the predictive statement is true, we say that the hypothesis is confirmed to some extent. A hypothesis is not, of course, conclusively proved by any one or more positively confirming instances, but it may become highly confirmed. A hypothesis that is sufficiently confirmed is accepted, at least tentatively.

It seems undeniable that science uses a type of inference at least loosely akin to the hypothetico-deductive method.[27] This has led some people to conclude that the logic of science is thoroughly deductive in character. According to this view, the only nondeductive aspect of the situation consists in thinking up hypotheses, but this is not a matter of logic and therefore requires no justification. It is a matter of psychological ingenuity of discovery. Once the hypothesis has been discovered, by some entirely nonlogical process, it remains only to *deduce* consequences and check them against observation.

It is, of course, a fallacy to conclude that the premises of an argument must be true if its conclusion is true. This fact seems to be the basis for the quip that a logic text is a book that consists of two parts; in the first part (on deduction) the fallacies are explained, in the second part (on induction) they are committed. The whole trouble with saying that the hypothetico-deductive method renders the logic of science entirely deductive is that we are attempting to establish a *premise* of the deduction, not the conclusion. Deduction is an indispensible part of the logic of the hypothetico-deductive method, but it is not the only part. There is a fundamental and important sense in which the hypothesis must be regarded as a conclusion instead of a premise. Hypotheses (later perhaps called "theories" or "laws") are among the *results* of scientific investigation; science aims at establishing general statements about the world. Scientific prediction and explanation require such generalizations. While we are concerned with the status of the general hypothesis— whether we should accept it or reject it—the hypothesis must be treated as a conclusion to be supported by evidence, not as a premise lending support to other conclusions. The inference *from* observational evidence *to* hypothesis is surely not deductive. If this point is not already obvious it becomes clear the moment we recall that for any given body of observational data there is, in general, more than one hypothesis compatible with it. These alternative hypotheses differ in factual content and are incompatible with each other. Therefore, they cannot be deductive consequences of any consistent body of observational evidence.

We must grant, then, that science embodies a type of inference resembling the hypothetico-deductive method and fundamentally different from induction by enumeration. Hume, on the other hand, has sometimes been charged with a conception of science according to which the only kind of reasoning is induction by enumeration. His typical examples are cases of simple generalization of observed regularities, something like our example of the licorice-flavored black balls. In the past, water has quenched thirst; in the future, it will as well. In the past, fires have been hot; in the future, they will be hot. In the past, bread has nourished; in the future, it will do so likewise. It might be said that Hume, in failing to see the essential role of the hypothetico-deductive method, was unable to appreciate the complexity of the theoretical science of his own time, to say nothing of subsequent developments. This is typical, some might say, of the misunderstandings engendered by philosophers who undertake to discuss the logic of science without being thoroughly conversant with mathematics and natural science.

This charge against Hume (and other philosophers of induction) is ill-founded. It was part of Hume's genius to have recognized that the arguments he applied to simple enumerative induction apply equally to any kind of ampliative or nondemonstrative inference whatever. Consider the most complex kind of scientific reasoning—the most elaborate example of hypothetico-deductive inference you can imagine. Regardless of subtle features or complications, it is ampliative overall. The conclusion is a statement whose content exceeds the observational evidence upon which it is based. A scientific theory that merely summarized what had already been observed would not deserve to be called a theory. If scientific inference were not ampliative, science would be useless for prediction, postdiction, and explanation. The highly general results that are the pride of theoretical science would be impossible if scientific inference were not ampliative.

In presenting Hume's argument, I was careful to set it up so that it would apply to any kind of ampliative or nondemonstrative inference, no matter how simple or how complex. Furthermore, the distinction between valid deduction and nondemonstrative inference is completely exhaustive. Take any inference whatsoever. It must be deductive or nondemonstrative. Suppose it is nondemonstrative. If we could justify it deductively it would cease to be nondemonstrative. To justify it nondemonstratively would presuppose an already justified type of nondemonstrative inference, which is precisely the problem at issue. Hume's argument does *not* break down when we consider forms more complex than simple enumeration. Although the word "induction" is sometimes used as a synonym for "induction by simple enumeration," I am not using it in that way. Any type of logically correct ampliative inference is induction; the problem of induction is to show that some particular form of ampliative inference is justifiable. It is in this sense that we are concerned with the problem of the justification of inductive inference.

A further misunderstanding is often involved in this type of criticism of Hume. There is a strong inclination to suppose that induction is regarded as the method by which scientific results are discovered.[28] Hume and other philosophers of induction are charged with the view that science has developed historically through patient collection of facts and generalization from them. I know of no philosopher—not even Francis Bacon!—who has held this view, although it is frequently attacked in the contemporary literature.[29] The term "generalization" has an unfortunate ambiguity which fosters the confusion. In one meaning, "generalization" refers to an inferential process in which one makes a sort of mental transition from particulars to a universal proposition; in this sense, generalization is an act of generalizing—a process that yields general results. In another meaning, "generalization" simply refers to a universal type of proposition, without any reference to its source or how it was thought of. It is entirely possible for science to contain many generalizations (in the latter sense) without embodying any generalizations (in the former sense). As I said explicitly at the outset, the problem of induction I am discussing is a problem concerning justification, not discovery. The thesis I am defending—that science does embody induction in a logically indispensable fashion—has nothing to do with the history of science or the psychology of particular scientists. It is simply the claim that scientific inference is ampliative.

3. *Deductivism.* One of the most interesting and controversial contemporary attempts to provide an account of the logic of science is Karl Popper's deductivism.[30] In the preceding section I discussed the view that the presence of the hypothetico-deductive method in the logic of science makes it possible to dispense with induction in science and, thereby, to avoid the problem of induction. I argued that the hypothetico-deductive method, since it is ampliative and nondemonstrative, is not strictly deductive; it is, in fact, inductive in the relevant sense. As long as the hypothetico-deductive method is regarded as a method for supporting scientific hypotheses, it cannot succeed in making science thoroughly deductive. Popper realizes this, so in arguing that deduction is the sole mode of inference in science he rejects the hypothetico-deductive method as a means for confirming scientific hypotheses. He asserts that induction plays no role whatever in science; indeed, he maintains that there is no such thing as correct inductive inference. Inductive logic is, according to Popper, a complete delusion. He admits the psychological fact that people (including himself) have faith in the uniformity of nature, but he holds, with Hume, that this can be no more than a matter of psychological fact. He holds, with Hume, that there can be no rational justification of induction, and he thinks Hume proved this point conclusively.

Popper's fundamental thesis is that falsifiability is the mark by which statements of empirical science are distinguished from metaphysical statements and from tautologies. The choice of falsifiability over verifiability as the criterion of demarcation is motivated by a long familiar fact— namely, it is possible to falsify a universal generalization by means of one negative instance, while it is impossible to verify a universal generalization by any limited number of positive instances. This, incidentally, is the meaning of the old saw which is so often made into complete nonsense: "The exception proves the rule." In this context, a rule is a universal generalization, and the term "to prove" means archaically "to test." The exception (i.e., the negative instance) proves (i.e., tests) the rule (i.e., the universal generalization), not by showing it to be true, but by showing it to be false. There is no kind of positive instance to prove (i.e., test) the rule, for positive instances are completely indecisive. Scientific hypotheses, as already noted, are general in form, so they are amenable to falsification but not verification.

Popper thus holds that falsifiability is the hallmark of empirical science. The aim of empirical science is to set forth theories to stand the test of every possible serious attempt at falsification. Scientific theories are hypotheses or conjectures; they are general statements designed to explain the world and make it intelligible, but they are never to be regarded as final truths. Their status is always that of tentative conjecture, and they must continually face the severest possible criticism. The function of the theoretician is to propose scientific conjectures; the function of the experimentalist is to devise every possible way of falsifying these theoretical hypotheses. The attempt to confirm hypotheses is no part of the aim of science.[31]

General hypotheses by themselves do not entail any predictions of particular events, but they do in conjunction with statements of initial conditions. The laws of planetary motion in conjunction with statements about the relative positions and velocities of the earth, sun, moon, and planets enable us to predict a solar eclipse. The mode of inference is deduction. We have a high degree of intersubjective agreement concerning the initial conditions, and we likewise can obtain intersubjective agreement as to whether the sun's disc was obscured at the predicted time and place. If the predicted fact fails to occur, the theory has suffered falsification. Again, the mode of inference is deduction. If the theory were true, then, given the truth of the statements of initial conditions, the prediction would have to be true. The prediction, as it happens, is false; therefore, the theory is false. This is the familiar principle of *modus tollens;* it is, according to Popper, the only kind of inference available for the acceptance or rejection of hypotheses, and it is clearly suitable for rejection only.

Hypothetico-deductive theorists maintain that we have a confirming instance for the theory if the eclipse occurs as predicted. Confirming instances, they claim, tend to enhance the probability of the hypothesis or give it inductive support. With enough confirming instances of appropriate kinds, the probability of the hypothesis becomes great enough to warrant accepting it as true—not, of course, with finality and certainty, but provisionally. With sufficient inductive support of this kind we are justified in regarding it as well established. Popper, however, rejects the positive account, involving as it does the notion of inductive support. If a hypothesis is tested and the result is negative, we can reject it. If the test is positive, all we can say is that we have failed to falsify it. We cannot say that it has been confirmed or that it is, because of the positive test result, more probable. Popper does admit a notion of *corroboration* of hypotheses, but that is quite distinct from confirmation. We shall come to corroboration presently. For the moment, all we have are successful or unsuccessful attempts at falsification; all we can say about our hypotheses is that they are falsified or unfalsified. This is as far as inference takes us; according to Popper, this is the limit of logic. Popper therefore rejects the hypothetico-deductive method as it is usually characterized and accepts only the completely deductive *modus tollens*.

Popper—quite correctly I believe—denies that there are absolutely basic and incorrigible protocol statements that provide the empirical foundation for all of science. He does believe that there are relatively basic observation statements about macroscopic physical occurrences concerning which we have a high degree of intersubjective agreement. Normally, we can accept as unproblematic such statements as, "There is a wooden table in this room," "The pointer on this meter stands between 325 and 350," and "The rope just broke and the weight fell to the floor." Relatively basic statements of this kind provide the observation base for empirical science. This is the stuff of which empirical tests of scientific theories are made.

Although Popper's basic statements must in the last analysis be considered hypotheses, falsifiable and subject to test like other scientific hypotheses, it is obvious that the kinds of hypotheses that constitute theoretical science are far more general than the basic statements. But now we must face the grim fact that valid deductive inference, although necessarily truth-preserving, is nonampliative.[32] It is impossible to deduce from accepted basic statements any conclusion whose content exceeds that of the basic statements themselves. Observation statements and deductive inference yield nothing that was not stated by the observation statements themselves. If science consists solely of observation statements and deductive inferences, then talk about theories, their falsifiability, and their tests is empty. The content of science is coextensive with the content of the statements used to describe what we directly observe. There are no general theories, there is no predictive content, there are no inferences to the remote past. Science is barren.

Consider a few simple time-honored examples. Suppose that the statement "All ravens are black" has been entertained critically and subjected to every attempt at falsification we can think of. Suppose it has survived all attempts at falsification. What is the scientific content of all this? We can say that "All ravens are black" has not been falsified, which is equivalent to saying that we have not observed a nonblack raven. This statement is even poorer in content than a simple recital of our color observations of ravens. To say that the hypothesis has not been falsified is to say less than is given in a list of our relevant observation statements. Or, consider the generalization, "All swans are white." What have we said when we say that this hypothesis has been falsified? We have said only that a nonwhite swan has been found. Again, the information conveyed by this remark is less than we would get from a simple account of our observations of swans.

Popper has never claimed that falsification by itself can establish scientific hypotheses. When one particular hypothesis has been falsified, many alternative hypotheses remain unfalsified. Likewise, there is nothing unique about a hypothesis that survives without being falsified. Many other unfalsified hypotheses remain to explain the same facts. Popper readily admits all of this. If science is to amount to more than a mere collection of our observations and various reformulations thereof, it must embody some other methods besides observation and deduction. Popper supplies that additional factor: *corroboration*.[33]

When a hypothesis has been falsified, it is discarded and replaced by another hypothesis which has not yet experienced falsification. Not all unfalsified hypotheses are on a par. There are principles of selection among unfalsified hypotheses. Again, falsifiability is the key. Hypotheses differ from one another with respect to the ease with which they can be falsified, and we can often compare them with respect to degree of falsifiability. Popper directs us to seek hypotheses that are as highly falsifiable as possible. Science, he says, is interested in bold conjectures.

These conjectures must be consistent with the known facts, but they must run as great a risk as possible of being controverted by the facts still to be accumulated. Furthermore, the search for additional facts should be guided by the effort to find facts that will falsify the hypothesis.

As Popper characterizes falsifiability, the greater the degree of falsifiability of a hypothesis, the greater its content. Tautologies lack empirical content because they do not exclude any possible state of affairs; they are compatible with any possible world. Empirical statements are not compatible with every possible state of affairs; they are compatible with some and incompatible with others. The greater the number of possible states of affairs excluded by a statement, the greater its content, for the more it does to pin down our actual world by ruling out possible but nonactual states of affairs. At the same time, the greater the range of facts excluded by a statement—the greater the number of situations with which the statement is incompatible—the greater the risk it runs of being false. A statement with high content has more *potential falsifiers* than a statement with low content. For this reason, high content means high falsifiability. At the same time, content varies inversely with probability. The logical probability of a hypothesis is defined in terms of its range—that is, the possible states of affairs with which it is compatible. The greater the logical probability of a hypothesis, the fewer are its potential falsifiers. Thus, high probability means low falsifiability.

Hypothetico-deductive theorists usually recommend selecting, from among those hypotheses that are compatible with the available facts, the most probable hypothesis. Popper recommends the opposite; he suggests selecting the most falsifiable hypothesis. Thus, he recommends selecting a hypothesis with low probability. According to Popper, a highly falsifiable hypothesis which is severely tested becomes highly corroborated. The greater the severity of the tests—the greater their number and variety—the greater the corroboration of the hypothesis that survives them.

Popper makes it very clear that hypotheses are not regarded as true because they are highly corroborated. Hypotheses cannot be firmly and finally established in this or any other way. Furthermore, because of the inverse relation between falsifiability and probability, we cannot regard highly corroborated hypotheses as probable. To be sure, a serious attempt to falsify a hypothesis which fails does add to the corroboration of this hypothesis, so there is some similarity between corroboration and confirmation as hypothetico-deductive theorists think of it, but it would be a misinterpretation to suppose that increasing corroboration is a process of accumulating positive instances to increase the probability of the hypothesis.[34]

Nevertheless, Popper does acknowledge the need for a method of selecting among unfalsified hypotheses. He has been unequivocal in his emphasis upon the indispensability of far-reaching theory in science. Empirical science is not an activity of merely accumulating experiences; it is theoretical through and through. Although we do not regard any hypotheses as certainly true, we do accept them tentatively and provisionally. Highly corroborated hypotheses are required for prediction and explanation. From among the ever-present multiplicity of hypotheses compatible with the available evidence, we select and accept.

There is just one point I wish to make here regarding Popper's theory. It is not properly characterized as *deductivism*. Popper has not succeeded in purging the logic of science of all inductive elements. My reason for saying this is very simple. Popper furnishes a method for selecting hypotheses whose content exceeds that of the relevant available basic statements. Demonstrative inference cannot accomplish this task alone, for valid deductions are nonampliative and their conclusions cannot exceed their premises in content. Furthermore, Popper's theory does not pretend that basic statements plus deduction can give us scientific theory; instead, corroboration is introduced. Corroboration is a nondemonstrative form of inference. It is a way of providing for the acceptance of hypotheses even though the content of these hypotheses goes beyond the content of the basic statements. *Modus tollens* without corroboration is empty; *modus tollens* with corroboration is induction.

When we ask, "Why should we reject a hypothesis when we have accepted one of its potential falsifiers?" the answer is easy. The potential falsifier contradicts the hypothesis, so the hypothesis is false if the potential falsifier holds. That is simple deduction. When we ask, "Why should we accept from among all the unfalsified hypotheses one that is highly corroborated?" we have a right to expect an answer. The answer is some kind of justification for the methodological rule—for the method of corroboration. Popper attempts to answer this question.

Popper makes it clear that his conception of scientific method differs in important respects from the conceptions of many inductivists. I do not want to quibble over a word in claiming that Popper is, himself, a kind of inductivist. The point is not a trivial verbal one. Popper has claimed that scientific inference is exclusively deductive. We have seen, however, that demonstrative inference is not sufficient to the task of providing a reconstruction of the logic of the acceptance—albeit tentative and provisional—of hypotheses. Popper himself realizes this and introduces a mode of nondemonstrative inference. It does not matter whether we call this kind of inference "induction"; whatever we call it, it is ampliative and not necessarily truth preserving. Using the same force and logic with which Hume raised problems about the justification of induction, we may raise problems about the justification of any kind of nondemonstrative inference. As I argued in the preceding section, Hume's arguments are not peculiar to induction by enumeration or any other special kind of inductive inference; they apply with equal force to any inference whose conclusion can be false, even though it has true premises. Thus, it will not do to dismiss induction by enumeration on grounds of Hume's argument and then accept some other mode of nondemonstrative inference without even considering how Hume's argument might apply to it. I am not arguing that Popper's method is incorrect.[35] I am not even arguing that Popper has failed in his attempt to justify this method. I do claim that Popper is engaged in the same task as many inductivists—namely, the task of providing some sort of justification for a mode of nondemonstrative inference. This enterprise, if successful, *is* a justification of induction.

4. Synthetic a priori Principles. A long philosophical tradition, dating back to antiquity, denies the empiricist claim that knowledge of the world rests solely upon observational evidence—that factual knowledge is limited to what we can observe and what we can infer therefrom. In the modern period, this rationalistic tradition is represented by men like Descartes and Leibniz who took their inspiration from the abstract aspect of modern physics. After Hume's devastating criticism of induction, Kant provided a more precise formulation, a fuller elaboration, and a more subtle defense of rationalism than any that had been given earlier (or, quite possibly, subsequently). As Kant himself testified, it was Hume who awakened him from his "dogmatic slumbers" and thereupon stimulated the *Critique of Pure Reason.*

The doctrine that there are synthetic a priori truths is, as I explained above, tantamount to the view that there are necessarily truth-preserving ampliative inferences. If we could find a *bona fide* demonstrative ampliative inference we would have a solution to Hume's problem of the ground of inference from the observed to the unobserved. This solution could be presented in either of two ways. First, one could assert that there are factual propositions that can be established by pure reason— without the aid of empirical evidence—and that these synthetic a priori propositions, in conjunction with premises established by observation, make it possible to deduce (nonampliatively) conclusions pertaining to unobserved matters of fact. Second, one could claim that these synthetic a priori propositions, although not added as premises to ampliative inferences to render them nonampliative, do instead provide a warrant for genuinely ampliative inferences from the observed to the unobserved. These alternatives are illustrated by inferences 2 and 1, respectively. Inference 2 has been made out of 1 by the addition of a premise; 2 has been rendered nonampliative. If the premise added in 2 were synthetic a priori it would provide the ground for saying that 1, although ampliative, is necessarily truth-preserving and, hence, demonstrative. The synthetic a priori principle would constitute, in current parlance, an "inference ticket."

In order to appreciate the philosophical issues involved in the attempt to justify induction by means of a synthetic a priori principle, we must introduce some reasonably precise definitions of key terms. Two pairs of concepts are involved: first, the distinction between *analytic* and *synthetic* statements, and second, the distinction between *a priori* and *a posteriori* statements. I shall begin by discussing logical systems and defining some basic concepts relating to them. This will be a useful preliminary to the explications that are of primary concern.

A standard logical system contains clearly specified kinds of symbols that can be combined and manipulated according to certain explicit rules. The symbols will include logical constants such as "$\cdot$," "$\vee$," "$\sim$," "$\supset$," "(x)," and "$(\exists x)$" (which have, respectively, the following rough translations into English: "and," "or," "not," "if . . . then . . . ," "for all x," and "for some x"). Often the system includes variables for statements, "p," "q," "r,". . . . In addition, there are variables for individuals, "x," "y," "z,". . . , as well as predicate variables, "F," "G," "H,". . . , which stand for properties of individuals and relations among them. Some systems contain constants or proper names for individuals or predicates, but these are not necessary for our discussion. Formation rules specify the ways in which symbols may be combined; they define the concept of a well-formed-formula. For instance, "$(x)(Fx \vee Gx)$" is well-formed, while "$Fy \vee \supset (x)$" is not. The well-formed-formulas may be regarded as the meaningful formulas of the system in the sense that they are susceptible of meaningful interpretation. Formulas that are not well-formed are like nonsense strings of symbols. They are ungrammatical with regard to the rules of logical grammar in the way that "Edgar heaven unwise from without" is ungrammatical with regard to the rules of English grammar. Transformation rules, or rules of inference, provide means of deriving some formulas from others. They are the rules for manipulating formulas, and they define the concept of logical demonstration or proof.[36]

The formulas of a logical system can be interpreted by choosing some nonempty domain of individuals (concrete or abstract) and assigning meanings to the logical symbols with reference to the individuals of the chosen domain.[37] The logical constants are given their usual meanings, as indicated above; the statement connectives, for example, are interpreted in the usual truth table manner. The individual variables range over the individuals in the domain of interpretation, and the predicate variables refer to properties of and relations among these individuals. The truth values, truth and falsehood, are the values of the statement variables. Giving an interpretation consists in specifying the domain of individuals and assigning meanings to the symbols; the interpretation itself is the domain and the meanings assigned. When an interpretation is given, the well-formed-formulas of the logical system become true or false statements about the individuals of the domain. A logical system normally has many interpretations within any given domain of individuals, for there are various ways of assigning meanings to the nonlogical symbols.

Suppose, for instance, that we choose as the domain of interpretation the set of numbers $\{2, 4, 6, 8, 10\}$, and we let "F" stand for the property of being divisible by three. With this interpretation, the formula "$(x)Fx$," which means "every member of the domain is divisible by three," is false, while "$(\exists x)Fx$," which means "at least one member of the domain is divisible by three," is true. If, in a different interpretation within the same domain of individuals, we let "F" stand for the property of being even, the formula "$(x)Fx$," which now means "every member of the domain is even," becomes a true statement. On the other hand, if we choose a new domain consisting of all the integers from one to ten, retaining the same meaning "even" for "F," "$(x)Fx$" is rendered false.

We say that a given well-formed formula is *satisfied* in a given interpretation if it has become a true statement about the individuals of the domain as a result of that interpretation. We say that the formula is *satisfiable in that domain* if there is some interpretation in that domain in which it becomes a true statement. We say that a formula is *satisfiable* if there is some nonempty domain of individuals with respect to which the formula can be interpreted so as to become a true statement. A formula is *consistent* if and only if it is satisfiable; it is *inconsistent* if there is no interpretation in any nonempty domain within which it is satisfied. The denial of an inconsistent formula is a *valid* formula; a valid formula is one that is satisfied in every interpretation in every nonempty domain. A consistent formula whose denial is also consistent is *logically contingent.*

A valid formula is one that comes out true on every interpretation in every nonempty domain. While we know that it is impossible to have an axiomatic system of logic in which every valid formula is a provable theorem, we earnestly desire that only valid formulas shall be provable. If we find that a nonvalid formula can be deduced in a logical system, we modify or abandon the system. We shall say that any interpretation of a valid formula is a *logical truth.* A logical truth is any statement that results from any assignment of meanings to the symbols of a valid formula (provided this assignment does not violate the conditions demanded of all interpretations). For example,

$$(x)(Fx \supset Gx) \cdot (x)(Gx \supset Hx) \supset (x)(Fx \supset Hx)$$
$$\sim(p \lor q) \supset (\sim p \cdot \sim q)$$

are valid formulas; consequently, the following interpretations of them are logical truths:

If all cows are mammals and all mammals are warm-blooded, then all cows are warm-blooded.

If one can neither escape death nor escape taxes, then one cannot escape death and one cannot escape taxes.

This explication captures, I think, the intent of the traditional view that logical truths are propositions that hold in all possible worlds. Domains of interpretation play a role analogous to the notion of a possible world, and a valid formula is one that holds no matter how it is interpreted in any of these domains. A logical truth is any instance of a valid formula. Notice, however, that the definition of "valid formula" makes no reference to possible domains; it refers only to domains—i.e., actual domains. The reason that the qualification "possible" is not needed is that there are no impossible domains—to say that a domain is impossible would mean that it could not exist—so "impossible domains" are not available to be chosen as domains of interpretation.

Although it is reasonable to maintain, I think, that all logical truths are analytic, there seem to be analytic statements that are not logical truths. For instance,

All bachelors are unmarried

is not an interpretation of any valid formula. However, given the definition,

Bachelor $=_{df}$ unmarried adult male,

the foregoing statement can be transformed into a logical truth, for the definition gives license to substitute the *definiens,* "unmarried adult male," for the *definiendum* "bachelor." This substitution yields,

All unmarried adult males are unmarried,

which is an interpretation of the valid formula,

$$(x)(Fx \cdot Gx \cdot Hx \supset Fx) .$$

To incorporate cases of this sort, we may define an *analytic statement* as one that is a logical truth or can be transformed into a logical truth by definitional substitution of *definiens* for *definiendum*. The negation of an analytic truth is a *self-contradiction.* Any statement that is neither analytic nor self-contradictory is *synthetic.* More technically, we may define an *analytic statement* as one whose truth can be established solely by reference to the syntactic and semantic rules of the language, a *self-contradictory statement* as one whose falsity can be established solely by reference to the syntactic and semantic rules of the language, and a *synthetic statement* as one whose truth value is, in relation to the syntactic and semantic rules alone, indeterminate.[38]

Analytic statements, like logical truths, have been characterized as statements that are true in all possible worlds. I have already explained how I think this characterization applies to logical truths. When the class of analytic statements is constructed by augmenting logical truths with statements that can be reduced to logical truths by definitional substitution, it is evident that these additional statements are true in all possible worlds in just the same manner as are logical truths. A definitional substitution cannot, after all, alter the truth value of any statement.

Analytic statements have sometimes been characterized as statements that are true by definition.[39] The general idea behind this formulation is sound in the sense I have been trying to explicate, but it is also misleading. We do not give a direct definition of a sentence as true; rather, when we provide definitions and other linguistic conventions for our language, certain statements have to be true in consequence. Analytic statements have often been characterized as statements whose truth depends upon the definitions of the terms occurring in them. Again, the idea is fundamentally correct, but the formulation is faulty. In a certain trivial sense, the truth of any statement depends upon the definitions of the terms in it. On a cloudy day, the statement, "The sky is blue," is false, but it can be transformed into a true statement if we are willing to redefine the word "blue" so that it means what we usually mean by "gray." On either meaning, however, the truth or falsity of the statement depends not only upon the definition of "blue" and the other words in it, but also upon some nonlinguistic meteorological facts. Every statement depends for its truth or falsity partly upon linguistic conventions; the truth values of analytic and self-contradictory statements depend entirely upon linguistic considerations.[40]

Analytic statements are often said, moreover, to be devoid of any factual content. Although there are difficulties in giving an adequate account of the concept of factual content, enough can be said to illuminate its relation to analytic statements. The basic feature seems to be that factual content of a statement is a measure of the capacity of that statement to *rule out* possibilities. In this respect, it is a negative concept. In a state of total ignorance all possible states of affairs are live possibilities; any possible state of affairs might, for all we know, be the actual state of things. As knowledge accumulates, we realize that some of the possibilities are not actualized. The statements expressing our knowledge are incompatible with descriptions of various possible worlds, so we know that these possibilities are ruled out—our actual world does not coincide with any of these possibilities that are incompatible with what we know. Generally speaking, moreover, the greater our knowledge —the greater the factual content of the statements we know—the more possibilities are disqualified from being actual. Imagine, for instance, the inhabitants of Plato's famous cave, who are totally ignorant of the nature of the external world. They can imagine birds of all sorts, including ravens of various colors. When the emissary to the outer world returns and reports that all ravens are black, those who remained in the cave can rule out all possibilities that had room for ravens of other colors. The statement, "All ravens are black," has factual content because of the descriptions of possible worlds with which it is incompatible. If, however, the emissary should return and remark that every raven is either black or nonblack, his statement would be totally lacking in content, and the permanent inhabitants of the cave—anxious for knowledge of the external world—would be justly furious with him for his empty report. His statement would lack content because it is compatible with every possibility. It is an interpretation of a valid formula, so it is a logical truth. It is an interpretation of a formula that cannot have a false interpretation—a formula that is true under any interpretation in any nonempty domain. Since it is true under any possible circumstances and is not incompatible with any description of a possible world, its content is zero. Any analytic statement will, as we have seen above, share this characteristic. We are, therefore, entitled to assert that analytic statements have no factual content. Synthetic statements, on the other hand, are interpretations of logically contingent formulas. Since the denial of a logically contingent formula has true interpretations in nonempty domains, knowledge that a synthetic statement holds does rule out some possibilities, so the synthetic statement does have factual content.

It is worth noting that the nonampliative nature of valid deduction is a consequence of the foregoing characterization of factual content. Take any valid deduction from premises P_1, P_2, . . . , P_n and conclusion C. The conditional statement, $P_1 \cdot P_2. \ldots \cdot P_n \supset C$, formed by taking the conjunction of the premises of the deduction as antecedent and the conclusion of the deduction as consequent, is analytic. This conditional statement, therefore, holds in all possible worlds; consequently, the set of possible worlds in which the antecedent is true is a subset of the set of possible worlds in which the consequent is true. It follows that the set of all possible worlds *excluded* by the conclusion is contained within the set of all possible worlds *excluded* by the premises. The factual content of the premises is, therefore, at least as great as that of the conclusion, and the factual content of the premises includes the factual content of the conclusion. Moreover, the content of the premises is equal to the combined factual content of all valid deductive conclusions of these premises, for any set of premises follows deductively from the conjunction of all conclusions that can be validly deduced from them. These considerations establish the claim that valid deductions are nonampliative, and the claim that the deductive consequences of a statement reveal its factual content.

Let us now turn to the other distinction required for our discussion. A statement is a priori if its truth or falsity can be established without recourse to observational evidence; it is a posteriori if observational evidence is needed to establish its truth or falsity. The distinction between a priori and a posteriori statements refers exclusively to the justification of statements and has nothing to do with discovery. The statements of arithmetic, for example, are regarded by most philosophers as a priori; the fact that children may learn arithmetic by counting physical objects (e.g., fingers) has nothing to do with the issue. Arithmetic statements can be established formally, without the aid of empirical observation or experiment, and this qualifies them as a priori. It is evident, moreover, that analytic statements, as they have been described above, are a priori. Since their truth follows from logical truths and definitions alone—that is, from syntactical and semantical considerations alone—observation and experiment are not required for their proof.

Most philosophers would acknowledge that many synthetic statements are a posteriori. It would seem that no amount of pure ratiocination would reveal whether I had eggs for breakfast this morning or whether there is a typewriter on the desk in the next office. Some sort of observation would seem to be indispensable. However, it is not nearly as evident that *all* synthetic statements are a posteriori. The doctrine that there are synthetic a priori statements is, I take it, the thesis of rationalism. It was maintained by Kant, as well as by many other philosophers both before and after him. The doctrine that all a priori statements are either analytic or self-contradictory is the thesis of empiricism as I understand it.

I know of no easy way to argue the question of whether there are any synthetic a priori statements. The history of human thought has provided many attempts to establish synthetic a priori truths, with a notable lack of success in my opinion. It is interesting to note some of the more important statements that have been alleged to enjoy this status. From antiquity, the proposition that nothing can be created out of nothing—*ex nihilo nihil fit*—has been taken as a self-evident truth of reason. It was accepted by the ancient atomist Lucretius,[41] although it is denied by contemporary steady-state cosmologists who are prepared to maintain that hydrogen atoms are created *ex nihilo*.[42] These cosmologists are sometimes ridiculed by cosmologists of other persuasions because of their rejection of the ancient principle. A closely related principle that has a long history as a putative synthetic a priori truth is the principle of sufficient reason. Although formulated in a variety of ways, it says roughly that nothing happens unless there is a sufficient reason for it. Lucretius, however, rejected the principle of sufficient reason, for he maintained that his atoms swerved *for no reason of any kind.*[43] He has often been disparaged for this doctrine by those who maintain the principle of sufficient reason, and typical college sophomores today still find the concept of a genuinely undetermined event unintelligible. There *must* be *some* reason for the swerving, they say. At the same time, modern physical theory appears to proceed in violation of the principle of sufficient reason. Quantum theory denies, for example, that there is a sufficient reason for the radioactive decay of one particular atom rather than another at some particular time. Quantum theory may be false, but if so its falsity must be shown empirically. Attempts to provide a priori demonstrations of the falsity of indeterministic quantum mechanics are, I believe, entirely unsuccessful.

Descartes provides an especially clear example of the use of synthetic a priori principles to justify ampliative inference. Starting from his famous *cogito,* he set out to deduce a complete account of the real world. He never supposed that nonampliative deduction would be equal to the task; instead, he appealed to principles he considered evident to the natural light of reason: "Now it is manifest by the natural light that there must at least be as much reality in the efficient and total cause as in its effect. For, pray, whence can the effect derive its reality, if not from its cause?" [44] The man who thought he could not be certain that $2 + 2 = 4$ or that he had hands unless he could prove that God is not a deceiver found the foregoing principle so clear and distinct that it is impossible to conceive its falsity!

Contemporary philosophy has not been lacking in claims for the synthetic a priori status of a variety of statements, although frequently they seem to be far less fancy than those for which the traditional claim was made. A recent important text in the philosophy of science argues that the statement,

No event [temporally] precedes itself

qualifies for the position.[45] However, the author fails to consider the empirical hypothesis that the history of the universe is a closed cycle. If this were true, events would precede themselves.[46] Since the statement in question is incompatible with an empirical hypothesis, it could be falsified empirically, and this means that it cannot be an a priori truth. Another currently famous example is the statement,

Anything colored is extended.[47]

Again, it seems to me, the statement turns out on close examination to be a posteriori. It is a physical fact, established empirically, that the stimulus that normally gives rise to color sensations is a very short wave. We find, by experience, that short waves provide rather reliable indications of the surface characteristics of objects from which they are emitted or reflected. If our visual sensations were elicited by long waves, like radio waves, they would be found not to provide much useful information about surfaces from which they emanate; in particular, they would be rather uninformative about size. Under these circumstances, I seriously doubt that we would closely associate the qualities of color and extensiveness, for we do not as a matter of fact make a close association between auditory qualities and extension. These considerations provide grounds, I believe, for denying that the foregoing statement is actually synthetic a priori.

Although Kant's attempt to supply a synthetic a priori grounding for ampliative inference was by no means the first nor the last, it is, in many respects, the most notable. According to his view, the statements of geometry and arithmetic are synthetic a priori. The case of geometric proposititions is clearest.[48]

Since Euclid at least, geometry had been an a priori science, and until the seventeenth century it was the only well-developed science we had. There was, consequently, a tradition of more than two millenia in which geometry was *the* science—the model for all scientific knowledge. Geometry had existed throughout all this time in an axiomatic form; the theorems of the system were thought to be purely deductive conse-quences of a small number of postulates. Moreover, there was one unique set of postulates. It was not until the discovery of non-Euclidean geometry by Bolyai and Lobachewsky early in the nineteenth century that anyone thought very seriously about alternatives. Until the advent of non-Euclidean geometry, the postulates of Euclidean geometry were regarded as self-evident truths—as propositions whose denials could not be reasonably entertained. Thus, until the early part of the nineteenth century at least, the a priori status of geometry seemed completely secure.[49]

Long before the discovery of non-Euclidean geometries it was widely recognized that experience with physical objects has substantial heuristic value. As we all know, the Egyptians discovered a number of important geometric truths in dealing with practical problems of surveying and engineering. Even Plato—a rationalist of the first order—recognized that experience in dealing with physical objects that approximate ideal geometrical figures is an indispensable part of the education of a geometer. But these heuristic considerations have nothing to do with the question of whether geometry is a priori or a posteriori. Empirical observations fulfill much the same function as the diagrams in the geometry text; they help the student to understand the subject, but they have no logical place in the proofs as such.

The synthetic status of geometry also seemed well assured during the long reign of Euclidean geometry. The postulates and theorems appeared to have real factual content; they seemed to provide indispensable aid in making ampliative inferences regarding the spatial characteristics of actual physical objects. Consider an example. A farmer has a flat rectangular field with one side 90 yards long and another side 120 yards long. He wants to divide the field diagonally with a wire fence, so using the Pythagorean Theorem he calculates the required length of fence wire to be 150 yards. He goes to town and buys that much wire, and finds that it does, indeed, just reach across the diagonal distance he wants to fence. There is no doubt that he has made an ampliative inference, for there is no logical contradiction in supposing that the wire would be too long or too short. He has made a successful ampliative inference from the observed to the unobserved; because of the propositions of geometry it was a necessary inference as well. Thus, so it seemed, geometry did embody truly synthetic a priori propositions.

Non-Euclidean geometry was discovered a bare twenty years after Kant's death, and it was later proved that Euclidean and non-Euclidean geometries are equally consistent. If non-Euclidean geometry contains a contradiction, so does Euclidean geometry, and if Euclidean geometry contains a contradiction, so does non-Euclidean geometry. All these geometries are on a par from the standpoint of logical consistency. This is sometimes taken to be a refutation of Kant's doctrine of the synthetic a priori character of geometry, but to do so is a mistake. To be sure, the existence of non-Euclidean geometries provides an impetus for the careful examination of the Kantian thesis, but it does not by itself disprove it. Kant himself entertained the possibility of logically consistent alternatives to Euclidean geometry. After all, Kant was *not* trying to show that geometrical propositions are logically necessary; if they were, they would be analytic, not synthetic. Kant was attempting to establish a different sort of necessity for them.

According to Kant, geometry constitutes a necessary form into which our experience of objective physical reality must fit. It is a necessary form of visualization. Kant admitted the possibility of alternative types of geometry as formal toys for mathematicians to play with, but they were epistemologically unsuitable as forms for experience of the objective world. Kant claims, therefore, that Euclidean geometry, although equal to the non-Euclidean geometries from the purely logical aspect, held a privileged position from an *epistemological* standpoint. This view seems widely held today, for one often hears remarks to the effect that it is impossible to visualize non-Euclidean geometries and that Euclidean geometry is the only one that can be visualized. Kant held it to be a necessary characteristic of the human mind that it must organize sense experiences according to the forms established by Euclidean geometry.

Subsequent philosophical analysis, primarily by Helmholtz and Reichenbach,[50] has shown two things, I believe. First, the alleged inability of people to visualize non-Euclidean geometries, if such inability does obtain, is a fact of empirical psychology; it is not a necessary aspect of the human intellect that can be demonstrated philosophically. Second, the supposition that we cannot visualize non-Euclidean geometries is probably false. This false supposition is based partly upon the lack of clarity about what we mean by "visualize" and partly upon the accident of being born into a world in which Euclidean relations are frequently exemplified by physical objects (at least to a high degree of approximation) and non-Euclidean relations are not.

The net outcome of the analysis of geometry is a rejection of the doctrine that geometry is synthetic a priori. To see this, it is useful to distinguish pure and applied geometry. Pure geometry is a strictly formal discipline concerned solely with what theorems follow deductively from what postulates. No attempt is made to elevate any particular set of postulates to a privileged position. *Pure geometry is a priori, but it is* not *synthetic.* Within the domain of pure geometry as such, there is no room for the question of which of the various geometries actually describes the spatial relations among real physical objects. To raise this question we must move to the domain of applied geometry. This question is empirical. From the logical standpoint of consistency, all the geometries are on a par. From the epistemological standpoint of visualizability, they are also on a par. The choice of a geometry to describe the world depends upon the behavior of physical objects, and that can be determined only by observation. Thus, *applied geometry is synthetic, but it is* not *a priori.*

Kant maintained that arithmetic, as well as geometry, embodies synthetic a priori truths. In their monumental work, *Principia Mathematica*, Russell and Whitehead attempt to refute this doctrine by showing that arithmetic can be reduced to logic; from this it would follow that the statements of arithmetic, although a priori, are analytic rather than synthetic. Full agreement has not yet been reached regarding the final success of the Russell-Whitehead program, but nothing emerges from it to give any aid or comfort to the defenders of the synthetic a priori in arithmetic. A more satisfactory account will, perhaps, distinguish pure from applied arithmetic just as we distinguish pure from applied geometry. In that case, the result would parallel that of geometry: Pure arithmetic is a priori but not synthetic, while applied arithmetic is synthetic but not a priori.[51]

Kant's approach to the question of synthetic a priori principles is profoundly instructive. So convinced was he that geometry provided examples of synthetic a priori propositions that he did not need to tarry long over the question of whether there are any such things. Instead, he moved on the question of how they are possible. Synthetic a priori knowledge (if there is such) does exhibit a genuine epistemological mystery. After some exposure to formal logic one can see without much difficulty how linguistic stipulations can yield analytic statements that hold in any possible world. It is easy to see that "Snow is white or snow is not white" is true simply because of the meanings we attach to "or" and "not." Analytic a priori statements are no great mystery. Likewise, it is not too difficult to see how our senses can provide clues to the nature of physical reality, helping us to establish propositions that are true in some but not all possible worlds. Although there are epistemological problems of perception, like illusion, that must not be ignored, we can still understand in very general terms how there can be a posteriori knowledge of synthetic propositions. But how could we conceivably establish by pure thought that some logically consistent picture of the real world is false? How could we, without any aid of experience whatever, find out anything about our world in contradistinction to other possible worlds? Given a logically contingent formula—one that admits of true as well as false interpretations—how could we hope to decide on a completely a priori basis which of its interpretations are true and which false? The empiricist says it is impossible to do so, and in this I think he is correct. Nevertheless, it is tempting to endow various principles with the status of synthetic a priori truths. It was to Kant's great credit that he saw the urgency of the question: *How is this possible?*

Various causal principles, as we have seen, have been accorded the status of synthetic a priori truths—for example, the traditional *ex nihilo* principle, the principle of sufficient reason, and Descartes' principle that the cause must be as great as the effect. Kant also, in addition to claiming that the propositions of arithmetic and geometry are synthetic a priori, maintained that the principle of universal causation—everything that happens presupposes something from which it follows according to a rule —is synthetic a priori.[52] It is by means of this principle that he hoped to dispose of the problem of induction. However, Kant's attempt to explain the possibility of synthetic a priori propositions is unsatisfactory. The propositions of Euclidean geometry do not enjoy epistemological primacy; the propositions of arithmetic lack synthetic content, and the physical world can be made intelligible in nondeterministic terms. Human powers of conception and visualization far exceed the limits Kant saw as necessary constraints upon the human intellect and as the source of synthetic a priori truths.

It is unfortunate that subsequent philosophers have paid little attention to Kant's central question: How are synthetic a priori propositions possible? Instead, the category of synthetic a priori propositions has too often become a convenient wastebasket for statements not readily classifiable as analytic or a posteriori. The contents of this wastebasket may, of course, turn out to be very handy in dealing with tough philosophical problems, but the crucial point is whether the wastebasket is really empty. It seems to me that all such statements can be shown, on careful examination, to be analytic or a posteriori, and that no convincing example of a synthetic a priori proposition has yet been produced. Even if this is so, of course, it does not prove that there are no synthetic a priori statements. It should, however, give us pause, and it does relieve us of **any obligation to** accept the positive rationalistic thesis that there are synthetic a priori propositions. It does place the burden of proof upon those who hope to escape Hume's problem of induction by way of a synthetic a priori principle. Moreover, even if a recalcitrant example were given—one that seemed to defy all analysis as either analytic or a posteriori—it might still be reasonable to suppose that we had not exercised sufficient penetration in dealing with it. If we are left with a total epistemological mystery on the question of how synthetic a priori propositions are possible, it might be wise to suppose it more likely that our analytic acumen is deficient than that an epistemological miracle has occurred.

5. *The Principle of Uniformity of Nature.* A substantial part of Hume's critique of induction rested upon his attack on the principle of the uniformity of nature. He argued definitively that the customary forms of inductive inference cannot be expected to yield correct predictions if nature fails to be uniform—if the future is not like the past—if like sensible qualities are not accompanied by like results.

All inferences from experience suppose, as their foundation, that the future will resemble the past, and that similar powers will be conjoined with similar sensible qualities. If there be any suspicion that the course of nature may change, and that the past may be no rule for the future, all experience becomes useless, and can give rise to no inference or conclusion.[53]

He argued, moreover, that there is no logical contradiction in the supposition that nature is not uniform—that the regularities we have observed up to the present will fail in wholesale fashion in the future.

It implies no contradiction that the course of nature may change, and that an object, seemingly like those which we have experienced, may be attended with different or contrary effects. May I not clearly and distinctly conceive that a body, falling from the clouds, and which, in all other respects, resembles snow, has yet the taste of salt or feeling of fire? Is there any more intelligible proposition than to affirm, that all the trees will flourish in December and January, and decay in May and June? Now whatever is intelligible, and can be distinctly conceived, implies no contradiction, and can never be proved false by any demonstrative argument . . .[54]

He argues, in addition, that the principle of uniformity of nature cannot be established by an inference from experience: "It is impossible, therefore, that any arguments from experience can prove this resemblance of the past to the future; since all these arguments are founded on the supposition of that resemblance."[55] Throughout Hume's discussion there is, however, a strong suggestion that we might have full confidence in the customary inductive methods if nature were known to be uniform.

Kant attempted to deal with the problem of induction in just this way, by establishing a principle of uniformity of nature, in the form of the principle of universal causation, as a synthetic a priori truth. Kant claimed, in other words, that every occurrence is governed by causal regularities, and this general characteristic of the universe can be established by pure reason, without the aid of any empirical evidence. He did not try to show that the principle of universal causation is a principle of logic, for to do so would have been to show that it was analytic—not synthetic—and thus lacking in factual content. He did not reject Hume's claim that there is no logical contradiction in the statement that nature is not uniform; he did not try to prove his principle of universal causation by deducing a contradiction from its denial. He did believe, however, that this principle, while not a proposition of pure logic, is necessarily true nevertheless. Hume, of course, argued against this alternative as well. He maintained not only that the uniformity of nature is not a logical or analytic truth, but also that it cannot be any other kind of a priori truth either. Even before Kant had enunciated the doctrine of synthetic a priori principles, Hume had offered strong arguments against them:

I shall venture to affirm, as a general proposition, which admits of no exception, that the knowledge of this relation [of cause and effect] is not, in any instance, attained by reasonings a priori.[56]

Adam, though his rational faculties be supposed, at the very first, entirely perfect, could not have inferred from the fluidity and transparency of water that it would suffocate him, or from the light and warmth of fire that it would consume him.[57]

When we reason a priori, and consider merely any object or cause, as it appears to the mind, independent of all observation, it never could suggest to us the notion of any distinct object, such as its effect; much less, show us the inseparable and inviolable connexion between them. A man must be very sagacious who could discover by reasoning that crystal is the effect of heat, and ice of cold, without being previously acquainted with the operation of these qualities.[58]

Now whatever is intelligible, and can be distinctly conceived . . . can never be proved false by any . . . abstract reasoning *a priori.*[59]

Hume argues, by persuasive example and general principle, that nothing about the causal structure of reality can be established by pure reason. He poses an incisive challenge to those who would claim the ability to establish a priori knowledge of a particular causal relation or of the principle of universal causation. In the foregoing discussion of synthetic a priori statements, I have given reasons for believing that Kant failed to overcome Hume's previous objections.

There is, however, another interesting issue that arises in connection with the principle of uniformity of nature. Suppose it could be established—never mind how—prior to a justification of induction. Would it then provide an adequate basis for a justification of induction? The answer is, I think, negative.[60]

Even if nature is uniform to some extent, it is not absolutely uniform. The future is something like the past, but it is somewhat different as well. Total and complete uniformity would mean that the state of the universe at any given moment is the same as its state at any other moment. Such a universe would be a changeless, Parmenidean world. Change obviously does occur, so the future is not exactly like the past. There are some uniformities, it appears, but not a complete absence of change. The problem is how to ferret out the genuine uniformities. As a matter of actual fact, there are many uniformities *within experience* that we take to be mere coincidences, and there are others that seem to represent genuine causal regularities. For instance, in every election someone finds a precinct, say in Maryland, which has always voted in favor of the winning presidential candidate. Given enough precincts, one expects this sort of thing by sheer chance, and we classify such regularities as mere coincidences. By contrast, the fact that glass windowpanes break when bricks are hurled at them is more than mere coincidence. Causal regularities provide a foundation for inference from the observed to the unobserved; coincidences do not. We can predict with some confidence that the next glass window pane at which a brick is hurled will break; we take with a grain of salt the prediction of the outcome of a presidential election early on election night when returns from the above-mentioned precinct are in. The most that a principle of uniformity of nature could say is that there are some uniformities that persist into the future; if it stated that every regularity observed to hold within the scope of our experience also holds universally, it would be patently false. We are left with the problem of finding a sound basis for distinguishing between mere coincidence and genuine causal regularity.

Kant's principle of universal causation makes a rather weak and guarded statement. It asserts only that there exist causal regularities: "Everything that happens presupposes something from which it follows according to some rule." For each occurrence it claims only the existence of *some* prior cause and *some* causal regularity. It gives no hint as to how we are to find the prior cause or how we are to identify the causal regularity. It therefore provides no basis upon which to determine whether the inductive inferences we make are correct or incorrect. It would be entirely consistent with Kant's principle for us always to generalize on the basis of observed coincidences and always to fail to generalize on the basis of actual causal relations. It would be entirely consistent with Kant's principle, moreover, for us always to cite a coincidentally preceding event as the cause instead of the event that is the genuine cause. Kant's principle, even if it could be established, would not help us to justify the assertion that our inductive inferences would always or usually be correct. It would provide no criterion to distinguish sound from unsound inductions. Even if Kant's program had succeeded in establishing a synthetic a priori principle of universal causation, it would have failed to produce a justification of induction.

6. The Postulational Approach. Some philosophers, chary of synthetic a priori principles and pessimistic about the possibility of overcoming Hume's skeptical arguments concerning induction, have turned to the elaboration of postulates for scientific inference. They have sought, sometimes with great skill and ingenuity, for the kinds of assumptions which, if accepted, would render scientific method acceptable. They have assiduously tried to avoid both extremes observed in the preceding section: principles too strong to be true or too weak to be useful.

One notable recent attempt to provide a postulational foundation for scientific inference is due to Bertrand Russell.[61] After analyzing and rejecting J. M. Keynes' famous "postulate of limited independent variety,"[62] Russell goes on to propound a relatively complex set of five postulates of his own. He maintains that without some synthetic assumptions about the world it is impossible to infer from the observed to the unobserved. The alternative to adopting postulates of scientific inference is solipsism of the moment. "If anyone chooses to maintain solipsism of the moment, I shall admit that he cannot be refuted, but shall be profoundly skeptical of his sincerity." [63] The only tenable approach is to find assumptions that are "logically necessary if any occurrence or set of occurrences is ever to afford evidence in favor of any other occurrence." [64]

Owing to the world being such as it is, certain occurrences are sometimes, in fact, evidence for certain others; and owing to animals being adapted to their environment, occurrences which are, in fact, evidence of others tend to arouse expectation of those others. By reflecting on this process and refining it, we arrive at the canons of inductive inference. These canons are valid if the world has certain characteristics which we all believe it to have. [65]

Russell offers the following five postulates to serve the intended function: [66]

1. The postulate of quasi-permanence: *"Given any event A, it happens very frequently that, at any neighboring time, there is at some neighboring place an event very similar to A."*

2. The postulate of separable causal lines: *"It is frequently possible to form a series of events such that from one or two members of the series something can be inferred as to all the other members."*

3. The postulate of spatio-temporal continuity in causal lines: "This postulate is concerned to deny 'action at a distance,' and to assert that when there is a causal connection between two events that are not contiguous, there must be intermediate links in the causal chain such that each is contiguous to the next."

4. The structural postulate: *"When a number of structurally similar complex events are ranged about a center in regions not widely separated, it is usually the case that all belong to causal lines having their origin in an event of the same structure at the center."*

5. The postulate of analogy: *"Given two classes of events A and B, and given that, whenever both A and B can be observed, there is reason to believe that A causes B, then if, in a given case, A is observed, but there is no way of observing whether B occurs or not, it is probable that B occurs; and similarly if B is observed, but the presence or absence of A cannot be observed."*

Russell discusses in detail the function he claims for these postulates in inference from the observed to the unobserved. Each of the postulates asserts that something happens frequently, but not invariably, so the postulates support inferences whose conclusions can be accepted with a degree of confidence but not with certainty. This does not mean, of course, that such inferences are useless. There is no reason to regard the fallibility of scientific inference as a devastating criticism of it.

While Russell argues that some synthetic postulates are *necessary* for scientific inference, he does not wish to maintain that those he has stated enjoy that status.

The above postulates are probably not stated in their logically simplest form, and it it likely that further investigation would show that they are not all necessary for scientific inference. I hope and believe, however, that they are sufficient. . . .

The postulates, in the form in which I have enunciated them, are intended to justify the first steps toward science, and as much of common sense as can be justified. My main problem in this Part has been epistemological: What must we be supposed to know, in addition to particular observed facts, if scientific inferences are to be valid?[67]

The first task that demands attention, if we are to evaluate this postulational approach, is to straighten out the relations of implication that are being asserted. There is considerable vagueness on this score. For one thing, there seems to be a certain amount of vacillation between the search for necessary conditions and for sufficient conditions, and for another, Russell is not unequivocal regarding the question of what the condition, be it necessary or sufficient, is to be a *condition of.* Consider the second point first. As the foregoing quotations reveal, Russell sometimes speaks as if he is seeking a condition for the possibility of any kind of inference whatsoever from one matter of fact to another—for the possibility that any fact could constitute evidence of any sort for any other fact. At other times he appears to be looking for a condition for the general correctness of the sorts of inference from the observed to the unobserved we usually regard as correct within science and common sense. Enough has been said already to show that these two desiderata are by no means identical, for we have made reference above to a variety of alternative methods: induction by enumeration, crystal gazing, the hypothetico-deductive method, the counterinductive method, and the method of corroboration. We shall see below that there is no trouble at all in describing an infinite array of distinct, conflicting methods of ampliative inference. To say merely that ampliative inference is possible would mean only that some of these methods are correct; to say merely that one occurrence can constitute evidence for another is to say the same. Neither of these claims goes far toward handling the problem of induction, which is, basically, the problem of choosing the appropriate method or methods from among the infinity of available candidates. Moreover, the whole spirit of Russell's discussion indicates that he is assuming the soundness by and large of scientific knowledge as presently constituted. This is, of course, much stronger than the assumption that knowledge is possible at all. To assume the fundamental correctness of the methods of empirical science is, obviously, to assume an answer to Hume's problem of the justification of induction. To make such an assumption is not to provide a solution of the problem.

Granting for the moment, however, that we are looking for a condition of the validity of scientific inference as generally practiced, is it a necessary or a sufficient condition we seek? One common way of putting the question is to ask: What are the *presuppositions* of induction or scientific inference? To answer this question we must first be clear about the meaning of the term "presuppose." Consider a simple and typical example: Receiving a scholarship *presupposes* being admitted as a student; likewise, being a student *is a presupposition of* the receipt of a scholarship. In the foregoing statement, the term "presupposes" can be translated "implies." Receiving a scholarship implies being a student, but being a student does not imply receiving a scholarship, for many students pay their tuition. In general, "*A* presupposes *B*" can be translated "*A* implies *B*," which means, in turn, "*A* is a *sufficient condition* of *B*." Moreover, "*A* presupposes *B*" means "*B* is presupposed by *A*" or "*B* is a presupposition of *A*." Thus, a presupposition of *A* is a *necessary condition* of *A*, that is, it is anything that *A* implies. A presupposition of induction would be any statement *implied by* the assertion, "Induction is a correct method of inference from the observed to the unobserved." A presupposition of the validity of scientific inference would be any statement *implied by* the assertion, "Scientific knowledge is, by and large, well founded." We cannot conclude from any presupposition of induction or scientific method that such methods are correct, for the implication goes in the opposite direction. To justify scientific inference we need a postulate that is a *sufficient condition* of the correctness of induction. This is, after all, what Russell claims for his postulates. But not just any sufficient condition will do; the search is for sufficient conditions that are both minimal and plausible. We should not assume more than necessary, and we should not assume postulates that are obviously false. It appears, then, that Russell is seeking a condition that is both necessary and sufficient to the suitability of scientific modes of inference—that is, a statement to fill the blank in "Induction is an acceptable inferential tool if and only if . . ." "Induction is an acceptable inferential tool" obviously works, but we hope to find a more interesting statement.

When we realize that there are many alternative modes of ampliative inference, we are naturally led to ask in what sorts of circumstances different ones will work better than their fellows. There is no way, as we have learned from Hume, to prove that any one of them will work successfully in all conceivable circumstances, so we might reasonably attempt to characterize the kinds of universes in which each is most suitable. Thus, instead of looking for postulates to justify *the* inductive method, we seek different sets of postulates, each set being sufficient to justify a different inductive method. Since the alternative inductive methods are in mutual conflict, we expect to find sets of postulates that are mutually incompatible. Arthur Burks has pursued this line of inquiry in some detail, and he has exhibited, by way of example, three radically different and conflicting inductive methods, each of which would require a distinct set of postulates.[68] If we could find some ground for holding one such postulate set in preference to all competing sets, that would constitute a justification of induction, for we would have justified acceptance of those postulates and *ipso facto* of the consequence that a certain method works. Such a justification is, of course, precisely the sort that Hume's arguments rule out.

Russell writes as if we have a simple choice between accepting his postulates (or some suitable modification thereof) and embracing solipsism of the moment. The situation is not that simple. We have a choice between accepting Russell's postulates and a wide variety of other conflicting postulates. We cannot pretend to know, except by inductive reasoning, which ones are true. We cannot use inductive inference to establish one set of postulates in preference to the others on pain of circularity. The most we can hope to establish is a series of conditional statements of the form, "If postulate set P holds, then inductive method M will work (at least decently often)." We cannot hope to show the unconditional utility of any method. Such a result can hardly be said to do justice to the method of science. In astronomy we predict an eclipse unconditionally. We do not say, either explicitly or implicitly, "If Russell's five postulates hold, then the sun's disc will be obscured by the moon at a specified time from a particular vantage point." From the postulational standpoint, however, the most we can assert is the conditional. Science, as a result, would be empty.

If a philosopher embraces the postulational approach to induction, he must not boggle at frankly making factual assumptions without attempting any justification of them. This is clearly an admission of defeat regarding Hume's problem, but it may be an interesting way to give up on the problem. The search for the weakest and most plausible assumptions sufficient to justify various alternative inductive methods may cast considerable light upon the logical structure of scientific inference. But, it seems to me, admission of unjustified and unjustifiable postulates to deal with the problem is tantamount to making scientific method a matter of faith. I shall have more to say on that subject while discussing the significance of the problem of induction.[69]

7. A Probabilistic Approach. It may seem strange in the extreme that this discussion of the problem of induction has proceeded at such great length without seriously bringing in the concept of probability. It is very tempting to react immediately to Hume's argument with the admission that we do not have *knowledge* of the unobserved. Scientific results are not established with absolute certainty. At best we can make probabilistic statements about unobserved matters of fact, and at best we can claim that scientific generalizations and theories are highly confirmed. We who live in an age of scientific empiricism can accept with perfect equanimity the fact that the quest for certainty is futile; indeed, our thanks go to Hume for helping to destroy false hopes for certainty in science.

Hume's search for a justification of induction, it might be continued, was fundamentally misconceived. He tried to find a way of proving that inductive inferences with true premises would have *true* conclusions. He properly failed to find any such justification precisely because it is the function of *deduction* to prove the truth of conclusions, given true premises. Induction has a different function. An inductive inference with true premises establishes its conclusions as *probable*. No wonder Hume failed to find a justification of induction. He was trying to make induction into deduction, and he succeeded only in proving the platitude that induction is not deduction.[70] If we want to justify induction, we must show that inductive inferences establish their conclusions as probable, not as true.

The foregoing sort of criticism of Hume's arguments is extremely appealing, and it has given rise to the most popular sort of attempt, currently, to deal with the problem.[71] In order to examine this approach, we must consider, at least superficially, the meaning of the concept of probability. Two basic meanings must be taken into account at present.

One leading probability concept identifies probability with frequency —roughly, the probable is that which happens often, and the improbable is that which happens seldom. Let us see what becomes of Hume's argument under this interpretation of probability. If we were to claim that inductive conclusions are probable in this sense, we would be claiming that inductive inferences with true premises often have true conclusions, although not always. Hume's argument shows, unhappily, that this claim cannot be substantiated. It was recognized long before Hume that inductive inferences cannot be expected always to lead to the truth. Hume's argument shows, not only that we cannot justify the claim that *every* inductive inference with true premises will have a true conclusion, but also, that we cannot justify the claim that *any* inductive inference with true premises will have a true conclusion. Hume's argument shows that, for all we can know, every inductive inference made from now on might have a false conclusion despite true premises. Thus, Hume has proved, we can show neither that inductive inferences establish their conclusions as true nor that they establish their conclusions as probable in the frequency sense. The introduction of the frequency concept of probability gives no help whatever in circumventing the problem of induction, but this is no surprise, for we should not have expected it to be suitable for this purpose.

A more promising probability concept identifies probability with degree of rational belief. To say that a statement is probable in this sense means that one would be rationally justified in believing it; the degree of probability is the degree of assent a person would be rationally justified in giving. We are not, of course, referring to the degree to which anyone *actually* believes in the statement, but rather to the degree to which one could *rationally* believe it. Degree of actual belief is a purely psychological concept, but degree of rational belief is determined objectively by the evidence. To say that a statement is probable in this sense means that it is supported by evidence. But, so the argument goes, if a statement is the conclusion of an inductive inference with true premises, it *is* supported by evidence—by inductive evidence—this is part of what it *means* to be supported by evidence. The very concept of evidence depends upon the nature of induction, and it becomes incoherent if we try to divorce the two. Trivially, then, the conclusion of an inductive inference is probable under this concept of probability. To ask, with Hume, if we should accept inductive conclusions is tantamount to asking if we should fashion our beliefs in terms of the evidence, and this, in turn, is tantamount to asking whether we should be rational. In this way we arrive at an "ordinary language dissolution" of the problem of induction. Once we understand clearly the meanings of such key terms as "rational," "probable," and "evidence," we see that the problem arose out of linguistic confusion and evaporates into the question of whether it is rational to be rational. Such tautological questions, if meaningful at all, demand affirmative answers.

Unfortunately, the dissolution is not satisfactory.[72] Its inadequacy can be exhibited by focusing upon the concept of inductive evidence and seeing how it figures in the foregoing argument. The fundamental difficulty arises from the fact that the very notion of inductive evidence is determined by the rules of inductive inference. If a conclusion is to be supported by inductive evidence, it must be the conclusion of a correct inductive inference with true premises. Whether the inductive inference is correct depends upon whether the rule governing that inference is correct. The relation of inductive evidential support is, therefore, inseparably bound to the correctness of rules of inductive inference. In order to be able to say whether a given statement is supported by inductive evidence we must be able to say which inductive rules are correct.

For example, suppose that a die has been thrown a large number of times, and we have observed that the side two came up in one sixth of the tosses. This is our "evidence" *e*. Let *h* be the conclusion that, "in the long run," side two will come up one sixth of the times. Consider the following three rules:

1. (Induction by enumeration) Given m/n of observed *A* are *B*, to infer that the "long run" relative frequency of *B* among *A* is m/n.
2. (A priori rule) Regardless of observed frequencies, to infer that the "long run" relative frequency of *B* among *A* is $1/k$, where *k* is the number of possible outcomes—six in the case of the die.
3. (Counterinductive rule) Given m/n of observed *A* are *B*, to infer that the "long run" relative frequency of *B* among *A* is $(n-m)/n$.

Under Rule 1, *e* is positive evidence for *h;* under Rule 2, *e* is irrelevant to *h;* and under Rule 3, *e* is negative evidence for *h*. In order to say which conclusions are supported by what evidence, it is necessary to arrive at a decision as to what inductive rules are acceptable. If Rule 1 is correct, the evidence *e* supports the conclusion *h*. If Rule 2 is correct, we are justified in drawing the conclusion *h*, but this is entirely independent of the observational evidence *e;* the same conclusions would have been sanctioned by Rule 2 regardless of observational evidence. If Rule 3 is correct, we are not only prohibited from drawing the conclusion *h*, but also we are permitted to draw a conclusion *h'* which is logically incompatible with *h*. Whether a given conclusion is *supported by evidence*—whether it would be *rational to believe* it on the basis of given evidence—whether it is *made probable* by virtue of its relation to given evidence—depends upon selection of the correct rule or rules from among the infinitely many rules we might conceivably adopt.

The problem of induction can now be reformulated as a problem about evidence. What rules ought we to adopt to determine the nature of inductive evidence? What rules provide suitable concepts of inductive evidence? If we take the customary inductive rules to define the concept of inductive evidence, have we adopted a proper concept of evidence? Would the adoption of some alternative inductive rules provide a more suitable concept of evidence? These are genuine questions which need to be answered.[73]

We find, moreover, that what appeared earlier as a pointless question now becomes significant and difficult. If we take the customary rules of inductive inference to provide a suitable definition of the relation of inductive evidential support, it makes considerable sense to ask whether it is rational to believe on the basis of evidence as thus defined rather than to believe on the basis of evidence as defined according to other rules. For instance, I believe that the a priori rule and the counterinductive rule mentioned above are demonstrably unsatisfactory, and hence, they demonstrably fail to provide a suitable concept of inductive evidence. The important point is that something concerning the selection from among possible rules needs demonstration and is amenable to demonstration.

There is danger of being taken in by an easy equivocation. One meaning we may assign to the concept of inductive evidence is, roughly, the basis on which we ought to fashion our beliefs. Another meaning results from the relation of evidential support determined by whatever rule of inductive inference we adopt. It is only by supposing that these two concepts are the same that we suppose the problem of induction to have vanished. The problem of induction is still there; it is the problem of providing adequate grounds for the selection of inductive rules. We want the relation of evidential support determined by these rules to yield a concept of inductive evidence which is, in fact, the basis on which we ought to fashion our beliefs.[74]

We began this initially promising approach to the problem of the justification of induction by introducing the notion of probability, but we end with a dilemma. If we take "probability" in the frequency sense, it is easy to see why it is advisable to accept probable conclusions in preference to improbable ones. In so doing we shall be right more often. Unfortunately, we cannot show that inferences conducted according to any particular rule establish conclusions that are probable in this sense. If we take "probability" in a nonfrequency sense it may be easy to show that inferences which conform to our accepted inductive rules establish their conclusions as probable. Unfortunately, we can find no reason to prefer conclusions which are probable in this sense to those that are improbable. As Hume has shown, we have no reason to suppose that probable conclusions will often be true and improbable ones will seldom be true. This dilemma is Hume's problem of induction all over again. We have been led to an interesting reformulation, but it is only a reformulation and not a solution.

8. *Pragmatic Justification.* Of all the solutions and dissolutions proposed to deal with Hume's problem of induction, Hans Reichenbach's attempt to provide a pragmatic justification seems to me the most fruitful and promising.[75] This approach accepts Hume's arguments up to the point of agreeing that it is impossible to establish, either deductively or inductively, that any inductive inferences will ever again have true conclusions. Nevertheless, Reichenbach claims, the standard method of inductive generalization can be justified. Although its *success* as a method of prediction cannot be established in advance, it can be shown to be superior to any alternative method of prediction.

The argument can be put rather simply. Nature may be sufficiently uniform in suitable respects for us to make successful inductive inferences from the observed to the unobserved. On the other hand, for all we know, she may not. Hume has shown that we cannot prove in advance which case holds. All we can say is that nature may or may not be uniform—if she is, induction works; if she is not, induction fails. Even in the face of our ignorance about the uniformity of nature, we can ask what would happen if we adopted some radically different method of inference. Consider, for instance, the method of the crystal gazer. Since we do not know whether nature is uniform or not, we must consider both possibilities. If nature is uniform, the method of crystal gazing might work successfully, or it might fail. We cannot prove a priori that it will not work. At the same time, we cannot prove a priori that it will work, even if nature exhibits a high degree of uniformity. Thus, in case nature is reasonably uniform, the standard inductive method *must* work while the alternative method of crystal gazing *may or may not* work. In this case, the superiority of the standard inductive method is evident. Now, suppose nature lacks uniformity to such a degree that the standard inductive method is a complete failure. In this case, Reichenbach argues, the alternative method must likewise fail. Suppose it did not fail—

suppose, for instance, that the method of crystal gazing worked consistently. This would constitute an important relevant uniformity that could be exploited inductively. If a crystal gazer had consistently predicted future occurrences, we could infer inductively that he has a method of prediction that will enjoy continued success. The inductive method would, in this way, share the success of the method of crystal gazing, and would therefore be, contrary to hypothesis, successful. Hence, Reichenbach concludes, the standard inductive method will be successful *if any other method could succeed.* As a result, we have everything to gain and nothing to lose by adopting the inductive method. If any method works, induction works. If we adopt the inductive method and it fails, we have lost nothing, for any other method we might have adopted would likewise have failed. Reichenbach does not claim to prove that nature is uniform, or that the standard inductive method will be successful. He does not postulate the uniformity of nature. He tries to show that the inductive method is the best method for ampliative inference, whether it turns out to be successful or not.

This ingenious argument, although extremely suggestive, is ultimately unsatisfactory. As I have just presented it, it is impossibly vague. I have not specified the nature of the standard inductive method. I have not stated with any exactness what constitutes success for the inductive method or any other. Moreover, the uniformity of nature is not an all-or-none affair. Nature appears to be uniform to some extent and also to be lacking in uniformity to some degree. As we have already seen, it is not easy to state a principle of uniformity that is strong enough to assure the success of inductive inference and weak enough to be plausible. The vagueness of the foregoing argument is not, however, its fundamental drawback. It can be made precise, and I shall do so below in connection with the discussion of the frequency interpretation of probabililty.[76] When it is made precise, as we shall see, it suffers the serious defect of equally justifying too wide a variety of rules for ampliative inference.

I have presented Reichenbach's argument rather loosely in order to make intuitively clear its basic strategy. The sense in which it is a pragmatic justification should be clear. Unlike many authors who have sought a justification of induction, Reichenbach does not try to prove the truth of any synthetic proposition. He recognizes that the problem concerns the justification of a rule, and rules are neither true nor false. Hence, he tries to show that the adoption of a standard inductive rule is practically useful in the attempt to learn about and deal with the unobserved. He maintains that this can be shown even though we cannot prove the truth of the assertion that inductive methods will lead to predictive success. This pragmatic aspect is, it seems to me, the source of the fertility of Reichenbach's approach. Even though his argument does not constitute an adequate justification of induction, it seems to me to provide a valid core from which we may attempt to develop a more satisfactory justification.

Significance of the Problem

Hume's problem of induction evokes, understandably, a wide variety of reactions. It is not difficult to appreciate the response of the man engaged in active scientific research or practical affairs who says, in effect, "Don't bother me with these silly puzzles; I'm too busy doing science, building bridges, or managing affairs of state." No one, including Hume, seriously suggests any suspension of scientific investigation or practical decision pending a solution of the problem of induction. The problem concerns the *foundations* of science. As Hume eloquently remarks:

Let the course of things be allowed hitherto ever so regular; that alone, without some new argument or inference, proves not that, for the future, it will continue so. In vain do you pretend to have learned the nature of bodies from your past experience. Their secret nature, and consequently all their effects and influence, may change, without any change in their sensible qualities. This happens sometimes, and with regard to some objects: Why may it not happen always, and with regard to all objects? What logic, what process of argument secures you against this supposition? My practice, you say, refutes my doubts. But you mistake the purport of my question. As an agent, I am quite satisfied in the point; but as a philosopher, who has some share of curiosity, I will not say scepticism, I want to learn the foundation of this inference.

We should know by now that the foundations of a subject are usually established long after the subject has been well developed, not before. To suppose otherwise would be a glaring example of "naïve first-things-firstism." [77]

Nevertheless, there is something intellectually disquieting about a serious gap in the foundations of a discipline, and it is especially disquieting when the discipline in question is so broad as to include the whole of empirical science, all of its applications, and indeed, all of common sense. As human beings we pride ourselves on rationality—so much so that for centuries rationality was enshrined as the very essence of humanity and the characteristic that distinguishes man from the lower brutes. Questionable as such pride may be, our intellectual consciences should be troubled by a gaping lacuna in the structure of our knowledge and the foundations of scientific inference. I do not mean to suggest that the structure of empirical science is teetering because of foundational difficulties; the architectural metaphor is really quite inappropriate. I do suggest that intellectural integrity requires that foundational problems not be ignored.

Each of two opposing attitudes has its own immediate appeal. One of these claims that the scientific method is so obviously the correct method that there is no need to waste our time trying to show that this is so. There are two difficulties. First, we have enough painful experience to know that the appeal to obviousness is dangerously likely to be an appeal to prejudice and superstition. What is obvious to one age or culture may well turn out, on closer examination, to be just plain false. Second, if the method of science is so obviously superior to other methods we might adopt, then I should think we ought to be able to point to those characteristics of the method by which it gains its obvious superiority.

The second tempting attitude is one of pessimism. In the face of Hume's arguments and the failure of many attempts to solve the problem, it is easy to conclude that the problem is hopeless. Whether motivated by Hume's arguments or, as is probably more often the case, by simple impatience with foundational problems, this attitude seems quite widespread. It is often expressed by the formula that science is, at bottom, a matter of faith. While it is no part of my purpose to launch a wholesale attack on faith as such, this attitude toward the foundations of scientific inference is unsatisfactory. The crucial fact is that science makes a *cognitive claim,* and this cognitive claim is a fundamental part of the rationale for doing science at all. Hume has presented us with a serious challenge to that cognitive claim. If we cannot legitimize the cognitive claim, it is difficult to see what reason remains for doing science. Why not turn to voodoo, which would be simpler, cheaper, less time consuming, and more fun?

If science is basically a matter of faith, then the scientific faith exists on a par with other faiths. Although we may be culturally conditioned to accept this faith, others are not. Science has no ground on which to maintain its *cognitive* superiority to any form of irrationalism, however repugnant. This situation is, it seems to me, intellectually and socially undesirable. We have had enough experience with various forms of irrationalism to recognize the importance of being able to distinguish them logically from genuine science. I find it intolerable to suppose that a theory of biological evolution, supported as it is by extensive scientific evidence, has no more rational foundation than has its rejection by ignorant fundamentalists. I, too, have faith that the scientific method is especially well suited for establishing knowledge of the unobserved, but I believe this faith should be justified. It seems to me extremely important that some people should earnestly seek a solution to this problem concerning the foundations of scientific inference.

One cannot say in advance what consequences will follow from a solution to a foundational problem. It would seem to depend largely upon the nature of the solution. But a discipline with well-laid foundations is surely far more satisfactory than one whose foundations are in doubt. We have only to compare the foundationally insecure calculus of the seventeenth and eighteenth centuries with the calculus of the late nineteenth century to appreciate the gains in elegance, simplicity, and rigor. Furthermore, the foundations of calculus provided a basis for a number of other developments, interesting in their own right and *greatly extending the power and fertility of the original theory.* Whether similar extensions will occur as a result of a statisfactory resolution of Hume's problem is a point on which it would be rash to hazard any prediction, but we know from experience that important consequences result from the most unexpected sources. The subsequent discussion of the foundations of probability will indicate directions in which some significant consequences may be found, but for the moment it will suffice to note that a serious concern for the solution of Hume's problem cannot fail to deepen our understanding of the nature of scientific inference. This, after all, is the ultimate goal of the whole enterprise.

The Philosophical Problem of Probability

The foregoing lengthy discussion of the problem of induction has been presented, not only for its own sake, but also for its crucial bearing upon the problem of explicating the concept of probability. Although I cannot claim to have provided an exhaustive discussion of the whole variety of ways in which philosophers have tried to solve or dissolve Hume's problem, I do maintain that no such attempt has yet proved completely satisfactory. At the very least, there is nothing approaching universal agreement that any has succeeded. I have attempted to show, moreover, that the problem of induction does not immediately dissolve when the concept of probability is brought into the discussion. In the remaining sections I shall pursue the relation between probability and induction and try to show that the problem of induction not only does not vanish in the face of the probability concept, but rather poses the most fundamental problem that plagues our attempts to provide an intelligible explication of it. In order to elaborate this thesis, I shall present three general criteria of adequacy of probability concepts, explain why they are important, and examine certain leading theories in the light of them. To clarify the significance of these criteria, it is necessary to begin with a brief discussion of the mathematical calculus or probability.

As I explained earlier, the mathematical theory of probability had its serious beginnings in the seventeenth century through the work of Pascal and Fermat. Under the guidance of various empirical and intuitive considerations, the mathematical theory developed into a powerful tool with important applications in virtually every branch of science as well as in pursuits like poker, business, and war. In the present century a number of axiomatic constructions of the calculus of probability have been given.[78] These axiomatic constructions can be regarded as abstract formal systems of pure mathematics.[79] A formal system or abstract calculus consists of a set of formulas. Some of these formulas are singled out and taken as primitive; they are known as *axioms*. The remaining formulas of the system—the *theorems*—can be deduced purely formally from the axioms. The axioms are unproved and unprovable within the system; in fact, they are strictly meaningless, as are all the theorems derived from them. The axioms are meaningless because they contain *primitive terms* to which, from the standpoint of the formal system, no meaning is assigned. The formal system, as such, is concerned only with the deductive relations among the formulas; truth and falsity have no relevance to the formulas. Such systems with undefined primitive terms are said to be *uninterpreted*.

The probability calculus can be set up as a formal system in which the only primitive undefined term is that which stands for probability. All other terms in the calculus have well-established meanings from other branches of mathematics or logic. They provide, so to speak, the logical apparatus for the deduction of theorems from the axioms.

Psychologically speaking, the formal system is constructed with one eye on possible meanings for the primitive terms, but logically speaking, these considerations are no part of the formal system. Formal systems are, however, subject to interpretation. An *interpretation* consists in an assignment of meanings to the primitive terms. Two kinds of interpretation are possible, abstract and physical. An abstract interpretation is one that renders the system meaningful by reference to some other branch of mathematics or logic, and it makes the formulas into statements about the abstract entities in that domain. For example, Euclidean plane geometry can be axiomatized. When the primitive term "point" is interpreted so as to refer to pairs of numbers, and the primitive term "straight line" is made to correspond to certain classes of pairs of numbers, the result is analytic geometry. This exemplifies the notion of an abstract interpretation. A physical interpretation, in contrast, renders the primitive terms, and consequently the whole system, meaningful through reference to some part of the physical world. When, for example, straight lines are interpreted in terms of light rays, and points in terms of tiny pieces of metal, physical geometry is the result. Whether the interpretation is physical or abstract, the specification of meanings makes the formulas of the formal system into statements that are either true or false with regard to the entities of some domain of interpretation. Because of the deductive nature of the formal system, any interpretation that makes the axioms into true statements will make the theorems as well into true statements. It is through physical interpretation that formal systems achieve applicability to physical reality and utility for empirical science.

1. The Probability Calculus. For the sake of definiteness in discussing the various candidates for interpretations of the probability calculus, as well as for use in later discussions, I shall present a set of axioms for the elementary calculus of probability and derive some simple results.[80] The axioms are not minimal, for they contain redundancies; they have been chosen for intuitive clarity and ease of derivation of theorems rather than for mathematical elegance. I urge the reader with little mathematical background to forebear and be patient and to try to follow the discussion. It presupposes nothing more difficult than elementary arithmetic, and all of the derivations are extremely easy. I shall, moreover, provide concrete illustrations for the axioms and theorems.

Since probability is a relational concept, we shall incorporate its relational character into the axioms. Probability will, therefore, be a two-place function. Since the easiest examples are from games of chance, we can think of probability as relating types of events such as tosses of dice, spins of roulette wheels, drawing the queen of diamonds, or having three cherries show in a Las Vegas slot machine. The probability symbol, "$P(,)$" thus has two blanks within the parentheses, one before the comma and one after. For purposes of illustration we may think of symbols representing classes as the appropriate kind of symbol to insert in these places. We shall use the capital letters toward the beginning of the alphabet, "A," "B," "C," . . . to stand for classes. Thus, "$P(A, B)$" is a typical probability expression, and it represents the probability *from A to B*—the probability, given A, of getting B. If A is the class of tosses of a certain die, and B the class of cases in which side six lands uppermost, then $P(A, B)$ is the probability of getting six when you toss that die. The value of a probability is some number between zero and one, inclusive. In fact, the probability symbol simply stands for a number, and these numbers can be added, multiplied, etc. in the usual arithmetical way. Hence, the operations used to combine probabilities are the familiar arithmetical ones. Within the probability expression, however, we have symbols standing for classes; these can be manipulated by simple logical techniques. Symbols for a few class operations are required.[81] "$A \cdot B$" stands for the *union* of A and B, that is, the class consisting of anything that belongs to A or B or both. "$A \cap B$" represents the *intersection* of A and B, that is, the class of things that belong to both A and B. "$\bar{A}$" designates the complement of A, the class containing everything not belonging to A. The capital Greek lambda "Λ" is the symbol for the *null class*, the class that has no members. We say that A is a *subclass* of B if every member of A is also a member of B. We say that two classes are *mutually exclusive* if they have no members in common—i.e., if their intersection is the null class.

The axioms may now be presented:

A1. $P(A,B)$ is a single-valued real function such that $0 \leq P(A,B) \leq 1$.

A2. If A is a subclass of B, $P(A, B) = 1$.

A3. If B and C are mutually exclusive $P(A, B, \cup C) = P(A, B) + P(A,C)$.

A4. $P(A, B \cap C) = P(A, B) \times P(A \cap B, C)$

Axiom 1 tells us that a probability is a *unique* real number in the interval zero to one (including these endpoints). Axiom 2 states that the probability of an A being a B is one if every A is a B. The remaining two axioms are best explained by concrete illustration. Axiom 3 tells us, for example, that the probability of drawing a black card from a standard deck equals the probability of drawing a club plus the probability of drawing a spade. It does not apply, however, to the probability of drawing a spade or a face card, for these two classes are not mutually exclusive. Axiom 4 applies when, for example, we want to compute the probability of drawing two white balls in succession from an urn containing three white and three black balls. We assume for illustration that the balls are all equally likely to be drawn and that the second draw is made without replacing the first ball drawn. The probability of getting a white ball on the first draw is one half; the probability of getting a white ball on the second draw *if the first draw resulted in white* is two fifths, for with one white ball removed, there remain two whites and three blacks. The probability of two whites in succession is the product of the two probabilities—i.e., one fifth. If the first ball drawn is replaced before the second draw, the probability of drawing two whites is one fourth.

I shall now derive four rather immediate theorems.

T1. $P(A, \bar{B}) = 1 - P(A, B)$.

Proof: By axiom 2,

$$P(A, B \cup \bar{B}) = 1,$$

for every member of A is either a member of B or not a member of B. Hence, A is a subclass of $B \cup \bar{B}$. Since nothing is both a member of B and not a member of B, B and $\bar{B}$ are mutually exclusive. By axiom 3,

$$P(A, B \cup \bar{B}) = P(A, B) + P(A, \bar{B}) = 1.$$

Theorem 1 follows by subtraction.

T2. $P(A, \Lambda) = 0$.

Proof: Since nothing is both B and $\bar{B}$, $B \cap \bar{B} = \Lambda$, the null class. But the complement, $\overline{B \cap \bar{B}}$, of the null class is the class $B \cup \bar{B}$ that contains everything that either is a B or is not a B. Substituting in theorem 1, we have

$$P(A, B \cap \bar{B}) = 1 - P(A, \overline{B \cap \bar{B}}) = 1 - P(A, B \cup \bar{B}).$$

Using the fact, established in the proof of theorem 1, that $P(A, B \cup \bar{B}) = 1$, theorem 2 follows.

T3. $P(A, C) = P(A, B) \times P(A \cap B, C) + P(A, \bar{B}) \times P(A \cap \bar{B}, C)$.

Proof: The class of things that belong to the class C is obviously the class of things that are both B and C or else both $\bar{B}$ and C; hence,

$$P(A, C) = P(A, [B \cap C] \cup [\bar{B} \cap C]).$$

Moreover, since nothing can be a member of both B and $\bar{B}$, $B \cap C$ and $\bar{B} \cap C$ are mutually exclusive. Axiom 3 therefore yields

$$P(A, [B \cap C] \cup [\bar{B} \cap C]) = P(A, B \cap C) + P(A, \bar{B} \cap C).$$

Axiom 4 gives

$$P(A, B \cap C) = P(A, B) \times P(A \cap B, C)$$

and

$$P(A, \bar{B} \cap C) = P(A, \bar{B}) \times P(A \cap \bar{B}, C).$$

Combining these results we get theorem 3.

T4. If $P(A, C) \neq 0$,

$$P(A \cap C, B) = \frac{P(A, B) \times P(A \cap B, C)}{P(A, C)}$$

$$= \frac{P(A, B) \times P(A \cap B, C)}{P(A, B) \times P(A \cap B, C) + P(A, \bar{B}) \times P(A \cap \bar{B}, C)}.$$

Proof: By axiom 4,

$$P(A, C \cap B) = P(A, C) \times P(A \cap C, B).$$

Therefore,

$$P(A \cap C, B) = \frac{P(A, C \cap B)}{P(A, C)} \tag{1}$$

if $P(A, C) \neq 0$. Since $B \cap C$ is obviously the same class as $C \cap B$, we have, using axiom 4,

$$P(A, C \cap B) = P(A, B \cap C) = P(A, B) \times P(A \cap B, C).$$

Using this result to replace the numerator in (1) establishes the first equality. Since theorem 3 equates the denominator of the middle member of the theorem with that of the third member, the entire theorem is established. Theorem 4 is a simple form of Bayes' theorem, and it will be used extensively in the discussion of subsequent problems.

I shall now present a concrete example of the application of each of the four theorems.

Theorem 1. The probability of throwing some number other than six with a standard die is equal to one minus the probability of getting six. This theorem, although extremely simple and obvious, is rather useful. Consider the probability of tossing at least one six in three trials—i.e., the probability of getting six on the first or second or third toss. Since these events are not mutually exclusive, axiom 3 does not apply. It is possible to calculate this probability directly, but it is much easier to do so by calculating the probability of its nonoccurrence and then using theorem 1. By two applications of axiom 4, we find that the probability of getting nonsix on the first *and* second *and* third tosses is $\frac{5}{6} \times \frac{5}{6} \times \frac{5}{6} = \frac{125}{216}$. Subtracting this value from one, we find that the probability of getting at least one six in three tosses is $\frac{91}{216}$ (which is considerably smaller than $\frac{1}{2}$). One of the problems posed by Chevelier de Méré that led to the beginning of the mathematical theory of probability is a more complicated instance of the same problem. The famous gentleman asked, "How many times must one toss a pair of fair dice in order to have at least a fifty-fifty chance of getting at least one double-six?" The naïvely tempting answer "18" is obviously wrong; it is by no means immediately evident what the right answer is.[82]

Theorem 2. This is obvious: The probability of getting a result that is both odd and even on a toss of a die is zero.

Theorem 3. Consider the following game of chance. Let there be two decks of cards, each containing twelve cards. The first deck contains two red cards and ten black; the second contains six red and six black. The player must first roll a die to determine from which deck to draw. If the side one shows, he draws from the deck containing six red cards; if any other side shows, he must draw from the deck with only two red cards. The draw of a red card constitutes a win. We can use theorem 3, which is known as the *theorem on total probability*, to compute the player's chance of winning. Let A be rolls of the die (which is tantamount to playing), let B be the side one showing (which is tantamount to drawing from the deck containing six red cards), and let C be drawing a red card. Substituting the appropriate values in the theorem yields

$$\frac{2}{9} = \frac{1}{6} \times \frac{1}{2} + \frac{5}{6} \times \frac{1}{6}.$$

The player's chance of winning is two ninths.

Theorem 4. Continuing with the game used to illustrate theorem 3, suppose a player has just made a winning draw, but we did not notice from which deck it came. What is the probability that he drew it from the half-red deck? Bayes' theorem supplies the answer. Using the result just established by theorem 3, we find that the probability that the win came from the half-red deck is

$$\frac{3}{8} = \frac{\dfrac{1}{6} \times \dfrac{1}{2}}{\dfrac{2}{9}}.$$

Notice that the probability of the winning card coming from that deck is less than one half, although the probability of getting a red card if you draw from that deck is considerably greater than the probability of getting a red card if you draw from the other deck. Given that a winning draw has occurred, the chances favor its having come from the predominantly black deck simply because the vast majority of draws are made from that deck.

Although a number of concrete examples have been presented to provide intuitive understanding of the axioms and theorems, these illustrations constitute no part of the formal calculus of probability itself. The proofs of theorems depend in no way upon the examples; they are carried out strictly formally and are entirely independent of any interpretation.

The foregoing discussion of the elementary calculus of probability provides a sufficient basis to proceed with the problem of interpreting the calculus. This is, I take it, *the* fundamental *philosophical problem of probability*. It is the problem of finding one or more interpretations of the probability calculus that yield a concept of probability, or several concepts of probability, which do justice to the important applications of probability in empirical science and in practical affairs. Such interpretations, whether one or several, would provide an explication of the familiar notion of probability. It is perhaps worth mentioning at this point that the problem is not one of empirical or quasi-empirical linguistics. We are not primarily concerned with the ways a language user, whether the man in the street or the scientist, uses the English word "probability" and its cognates. We are concerned with the logical structure of science, and we need to provide concepts to fulfill various functions within that structure. If the word "probability" and its synonyms had never occurred in any language, we would still need the concept for the purpose of logical analysis. As Carnap has remarked, if it did not already exist we would have to invent it. Moreover, the difficulties we shall discover—centering mainly on Hume's problem of induction— are ones that arise out of subtle philosophical analysis. Ordinary people are not aware of these problems, so ordinary usage cannot be expected to be sensitive to them.

2. *Criteria of Adequacy for Interpretations.* In order to facilitate our investigation of the philosophical problem of probability, I shall state three criteria which must be fulfilled, I believe, if we are to have a satisfactory interpretation of probability. Although the criteria seem simple and straightforward, we shall see that it is exceedingly difficult to find any interpretation that satisfies all three.

a) *Admissibility.* We say that an interpretation of a formal system is admissible if the meanings assigned to the primitive terms in this interpretation transform the formal axioms, and consequently all the theorems, into true statements. A fundamental requirement for probability concepts is to satisfy the mathematical relations specified by the calculus of probability. This criterion is not merely an expression of admiration of mathematics; important reasons can be given for insisting upon it. One reason is that the mathematical calculus has been developed with great care and precision over a long period of time and with due regard for a vast range of practical and theoretical problems. It would be rash indeed to conclude on the basis of casual reflection that the mathematical theory is likely to be wrong or irrelevant in relation to potential applications. Another reason for insisting upon admissibility is a consequence of the fact that violations of the formal properties of the calculus lead to *incoherent betting systems*. This consideration figures crucially in the personalistic interpretation of probability, which will be discussed below. For the moment, an example will suffice. Suppose, for instance, that someone were to violate theorem 1 and axiom 2 by assigning probability values that do not add up to one for all possible outcomes. He assigns, say, the value one third to the probability of heads and one third to the probability of tails on tosses of a coin whose outcome must be one or the other of these. If it lands on edge, we do not count that toss. Such a person would presumably give odds of two to one that the coin will not come up heads, and he will also give odds of two to one that it will not come up tails. If he makes both of these bets, however, he is bound to lose whatever happens. If it comes up heads he wins one dollar and loses two, and if it comes up tails the result is the same. Anyone who wants to use probabilities to determine betting odds must guard against such situations. It has been shown that satisfaction of the admissibility criterion is a necessary and sufficient condition for the avoidance of incoherent betting systems.[83]

b) Ascertainability. This criterion requires that there be some method by which, in principle at least, we can ascertain values of probabilities. It merely expresses the fact that a concept of probability will be useless if it is impossible in principle to find out what the probabilities are.[84]

c) Applicability. The force of this criterion is best expressed in Bishop Butler's famous aphorism, "Probability is the very guide of life." [85] It is an unescapable fact that we are seeking a concept of probability that will have practical predictive significance. For instance, knowledge of the probabilities associated with throws of dice should have an important bearing upon the kinds of bets we are willing to make. Knowledge of the probability of radioactive decay should have some bearing upon our prediction of the amount of a given substance that will remain undecayed after a certain time.

More generally, it appears that one or more probability concepts play fundamental roles in the logical structure of science. There are, for instance, statistical or probabilistic laws in science. The second law of thermodynamics, that in a closed system with a low entropy state the entropy will very probably increase, is a leading example. Any science that attempts precise measurement must deal with errors; the concept of error is basically probabilistic. Moreover, the results of scientific inference, in some important sense, are probable. Since scientific inference is ampliative, its conclusions do not follow with necessity or certainty from the data. The concept of scientific confirmation is another example of a fundamental scientific concept that is unavoidably probabilistic.

The foregoing remarks indicate, at least roughly, some of the functions our explication of probability must fulfill and some of the contexts into which it (or they) must fit. The force of the criterion of applicability is merely to call attention to these functions. An explication that fails to fulfill the criterion of applicability is simply not an explication of the concept we are trying to explicate.

It may now be obvious that the fundamental philosophical difficulty in the theory of probability lies in the attempt to satisfy simultaneously the criteria of ascertainability and applicability. Perhaps it is also obvious that this is Hume's problem of induction all over again in slightly different terminology. If these points are not obvious, I hope they will become so as we consider possible candidates for the interpretation of the probability concept.

Interpretations of Probability

This section will survey five leading interpretations of probability, confronting each of them with the three foregoing criteria.

1. The Classical Interpretation. This interpretation is one of the oldest and best known; it defines probability as the ratio of favorable to equally possible cases.[86] With a perfectly symmetrical die, for instance, the probability of tossing an even number is three sixths. Three sides have even numbers—the favorable cases—and there are six equally possible sides. The immediate difficulty with this interpretation is that "equally possible" seems to mean "equally probable," so the definition appears to be flagrantly circular. But the apparent circularity can be overcome if a definition of "equally probable" can be given which is independent of the definition of "probable" itself. The classical theorists attempted to offer such a definition by means of the *principle of indifference*. This principle states that two possibilities are equally probable if there is no reason to prefer one to the other.

The principle of indifference, lying as it does at the very heart of the classical interpretation, has been the subject of much controversy. Various objections have been brought against it.[87] First, it *defines* "probability" in terms of equally probable alternatives, so it presupposes a priori that every instance of probability can be analyzed in terms of equally probable cases. Suppose, for example, that we have a slightly biased coin—one for which the probability of heads is 0.51 and the probability of tails is 0.49. How are we to find the 100 equally probable occurrences, of which 51 are favorable to heads? Analogously, since the birth rate for boys slightly exceeds the birth rate for girls, how can we be assured a priori that we can find an appropriate number of equally probable alternatives in the genetic mechanism, of which a suitable number result in the birth of a boy? To suppose it is always possible to reduce unequal probabilities to sets of equiprobable cases is a rash and unwarranted assumption.

Another objection rejects any rule that pretends to transform ignorance automatically into knowledge. Knowledge of probabilities is concrete knowledge about occurrences; otherwise, it is useless for prediction and action. According to the principle of indifference, this kind of knowledge can result immediately from our ignorance of reasons to regard one occurrence as more probable than another. This is epistemological magic. Of course, there are ways of transforming ignorance into knowledge—by further investigation and the accumulation of more information. It is the same with all "magic"; to get the rabbit out of the hat you first have to put him in. The principle of indifference tries to perform *"real* magic."

The decisive objection against the principle shows that it gives rise to explicit logical contradiction.[88] Consider a simple example. Suppose we know that a car has taken between one and two minutes to traverse one mile, and we know nothing further about the amount of time taken. Applying the principle of indifference, we conclude that the probability that the time was between one and one-and-one-half minutes equals the probability that it was between one-and-one-half and two minutes. Our data can, however, be expressed in another way. We know that the *average* speed for the trip was between sixty and thirty miles per hour, but we know nothing further about the average speed. Applying the principle of indifference again, we conclude that the probability that the average speed was between sixty and forty-five miles per hour equals the probability that it was between forty-five and thirty miles per hour. Unfortunately, we have just contradicted the first result, because the time

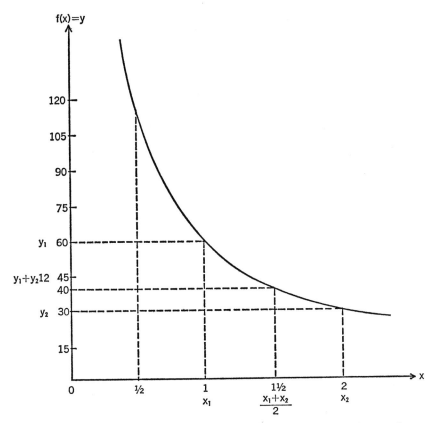

Figure 1. Graph of time and average speed for the fixed distance of one mile.

of one-and-one-half minutes corresponds to forty, not forty-five, miles per hour.

This example is not just an isolated case (although one contradiction ought to be enough), but it illustrates a general difficulty. A similar conflict can be manufactured out of any situation in which we have two magnitudes interdefined in such a way that there is a nonlinear relation between them. For a fixed distance, speed and time are reciprocal; for a square, area relates to the second power of the length of the side; etc. Figure 1 shows graphically the source of the paradox. For a nonlinear function, the value of the function for the *mid-point* $(x_1 + x_2)/2$ *between two values of the argument x* does not, in general, correspond to the *mid-point* $(y_1 + y_2)/2$ *between the values of the function* determined by those two values of the argument.

The whole set of paradoxes generated in the foregoing manner shows that the principle of indifference yields equivocal values for probabilities. The probability of averaging at least forty-five miles per hour over the mile is equal to one half and also to some number other than one half. Since axiom 1 of the probability calculus requires that probability values be unique, the classical interpretation violates the criterion of admissibility.

2. *The Subjective Interpretation.* Some authors have spoken as if probability is simply a measure of degree of belief.[89] If I believe with complete certitude that the sun will rise tomorrow, my degree of belief is one and so is my subjective probability. If I am just as strongly convinced that a penny will turn up heads as that it will not turn up heads, my degree of belief and subjective probability for each of these outcomes is one half. Leaving aside, for now, the very serious question of the adequacy of a purely subjective concept for application within empirical science, we can easily see that this interpretation fails to satisfy the criterion of admissibility. Certain seventeenth-century gamblers, for example, believed to a degree one thirty-sixth in each of the possible outcomes of a throw of two dice, and this degree was unaffected by the outcomes of the preceding throws. Moreover, these same men believed more than they disbelieved in getting at least one double six in twenty-four throws. It was the Chevelier de Méré's doubts that led him to approach Pascal with his famous problem. Computation showed, as it turned out, that the probability of getting double six, under the conditions specified, is less than one half. Since the degrees of belief do not coincide with the calculated values, the subjective interpretation does not constitute an admissible interpretation of the probability calculus.

3. *The Logical Interpretation.* Although we cannot interpret probability as degree of *actual* belief, it might still be possible to maintain that probability measures degree of *rational* belief. As a matter of fact, there is good reason to believe that many of the earlier authors who spoke as if they were adopting a purely subjective interpretation were actually much closer to an interpretation in terms of rational belief.[90] According to this interpretation, probability measures the degree of confidence that would be rationally justified by the available evidence. Although often formulated in terms of the psychological concept of belief, there is nothing at all subjective about this interpretation. Probability is regarded as an objective logical relation between statements that formulate evidence and other statements—*hypotheses*—whose truth or falsity is not fully determined by the evidence.[91]

According to the logical theory, there is a fundamental analogy

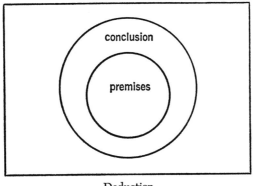

Deduction

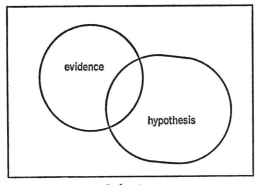

Induction

Figure 2

between inductive and deductive logic. Deductive logic embodies a concept of logical entailment between premises and conclusion. A conclusion that is logically entailed by true premises cannot be false. Inductive logic requires a logical concept of probability, also known as *degree of confirmation,* relating evidence to hypotheses. In this case, the evidence does not logically entail the hypothesis, for the hypothesis could be false even when the statements of evidence are true. But there is a relation of partial entailment, and this is what probability measures. The situation is shown diagrammatically in Figure 2. In each case, the rectangle represents all possible states of affairs. When premises entail a conclusion, every possible case in which the premises are true is a case in which the conclusion is also true; thus, the premise-circle is entirely contained within the conclusion-circle. When evidence partially entails a hypothesis, there is some degree of overlapping between those possible states of affairs in which the evidence holds and those in which the hypothesis is true. Degree of confirmation measures the amount of overlapping.

These considerations may be heuristically helpful, but the concept of logical probability must be made much more precise. In particular, we must specify what constitutes a possible state of affairs and how such things are to be counted or measured. We have a good understanding of how to measure areas; we must not be misled by geometrical diagrams into thinking we know how to measure degree of "overlapping" of possibilities or degree of partial entailment. This matter poses severe difficulties.

Rudolf Carnap, who has given the fullest account of degree of confirmation, proceeds by constructing a precise language and selecting the strongest descriptive statements that can be made in that language. Such languages are capable of describing various universes. A simple language can describe a simple universe; a more complex language is able to describe a more complex universe. Each of the strongest descriptive statements in a language gives a complete description of some possible state of the corresponding universe. Consider an extremely simple language. The illustrative language will have three terms, "*a*," "*b*," and "*c*," as names for individual entities, and one descriptive predicate "*F*" referring to a property these individuals may have or lack. In addition, it will have the usual logical apparatus. To have a concrete example, we may think of a universe that consists entirely of three balls, *a*, *b*, and *c*, such that the only property that can be meaningfully predicated of them is the property of being red. Although this universe, and the language used to describe it, are absurdly simple, they are sufficient to elicit many of the important properties of logical probability.

There are eight possible states of the universes describable by our language, depending upon which individuals have or lack the property red. Statements describing the possible states are *state descriptions*. Letting "*Fa*" mean "*a* is red," etc., "$\sim Fa$" mean "*a* is not red," etc., and the dot mean "and," the complete list of state descriptions is as follows:

1. $Fa \cdot Fb \cdot Fc$	5. $\sim Fa \cdot \sim Fb \cdot Fc$
2. $\sim Fa \cdot Fb \cdot Fc$	6. $\sim Fa \cdot Fb \cdot \sim Fc$
3. $Fa \cdot \sim Fb \cdot Fc$	7. $Fa \cdot \sim Fb \cdot \sim Fc$
4. $Fa \cdot Fb \cdot \sim Fc$	8. $\sim Fa \cdot \sim Fb \cdot \sim Fc$

Each state description is a conjunction of simple statements, each of which asserts or denies that a given individual has the property in question; moreover, each state description contains one such assertion or denial for each individual. Any statement that can be meaningfully formulated in this language can be expressed in terms of state descriptions. For instance, the statement, "There is at least one thing that has the property F," can be translated into the disjunction of state descriptions 1–7. The statement, "Individual a has property F," can be translated into the disjunction of state descriptions 1, 3, 4, and 7. The statement, "Everything has the property F," is equivalent to state description 1 by itself. In each of the foregoing examples, we say that the statement *holds* in the state descriptions mentioned, and the set of state descriptions in which a statement holds is called the *range* of the statement. The range of a statement consists of all the state descriptions that are logically compatible with it; those outside the range are incompatible with the statement in question.

At this point it is very tempting merely to count up the state descriptions in the two ranges and form their ratio. Letting "e" stand for evidence, "h" for hypothesis, and "$R(\ )$" for the number of state descriptions in the range of, we might hurriedly conclude that the degree of confirmation of h on e is given by

Any statement that can be formulated in the language can serve as a hypothesis, and any consistent statement can serve as evidence. To determine the degree to which a hypothesis is supported by evidence, we turn to the ranges of these statements. In particular, we compare the range of the evidence statement with the portion of its range that coincides with the range of the hypothesis. For instance, we might take as our hypothesis the statement that everything has the property F, and as our evidence that individual a has that property. The evidence holds in four state descriptions, as noted above, while evidence and hypothesis together hold in only one state description, namely, the first.

At this point it is very tempting merely to count up the state descriptions in the two ranges and form their ratio. Letting "e" stand for evidence, "h" for hypothesis, and "$R(\ )$" for the number of state descriptions in the range of, we might hurriedly conclude that the degree of confirmation of h on e is given by

$$\frac{R(e \cdot h)}{R(e)} = \frac{1}{4}$$

This amounts to an assignment of equal weights to all of the state descriptions. Since it is convenient to have the weights of the state descriptions add up to one, equal weighting will mean that each state description has the weight one eighth.

The assignment of equal weights to the state descriptions may be regarded as an application of the principle of indifference to the fundamental possibilities in our model universe. It evades the paradox associated with the classical unrestricted application. The classical theory of probability got into trouble, one might say, because of a failure to distinguish fundamental possibilities from derivative possibilities, and because of the consequent failure to stipulate exactly what properties the principle applies to and what ones it does not. Restriction of the principle of indifference to the state descriptions provides precisely the specification needed to avoid contradiction. The explication of probability in these terms has been thought to preserve the "valid core" of the traditional principle of indifference.

Carnap has shown, however, that the assignment of equal weights, although intuitively plausible, is radically unsatisfactory. Such an assignment would have the consequence that it is logically impossible to learn from experience! Consider as an hypothesis h the statement "Fc." Leaving factual evidence completely aside, h holds in four state descriptions and not in the other four. Its probability, a priori, is one half. Suppose now that we begin to accumulate factual evidence; for example, suppose we examine a and find it has property F. The evidence alone holds in state descriptions 1, 3, 4, and 7, while evidence and hypothesis together hold in 1 and 3. The probability of our hypothesis, even after we have found some evidence, is still one half. This hypothesis retains the same probability regardless of what observations we make of individuals a and b, and this probability is absolutely insensitive to whether the evidence is what we would usually regard as favorable or unfavorable to the hypothesis. It is evident that we must find a more satisfactory way of weighting the state descriptions, and this will, of course, involve assignments of unequal weights to different state descriptions.

To circumvent the difficulty about learning from experience, Carnap proposed a different system for assigning weights to state descriptions which he designated "m^*." [92] He argued for its plausibility along the following lines. The only thing that significantly distinguishes individuals from one another is some qualitative difference, not a mere difference of name or identity. Hence, the fundamental possibilities to which we assign equal weights should not discriminate on the basis of individuals. Consider, for instance, state descriptions 2, 3, and 4. They are all alike in affirming that two of the individuals possess the property F while denying it to the third. These state descriptions differ from one another only in identifying the individual that lacks property F. Similar remarks apply to state descriptions 5, 6, and 7; all of them deny the property F to two individuals while asserting that it holds of one. Carnap says that state descriptions that differ from each other only in the arrangement of the individual names are *isomorphic;* a collection of all the state descriptions isomorphic to each other is a *structure description.* In our simple language there are four structure descriptions: state description 1 by itself; state descriptions 2, 3, and 4; state descriptions 5, 6, and 7; and state description 8 by itself. A structure description can be construed as the disjunction of all the state descriptions that make it up; for example, the second structure description asserts that state description 2, 3, *or* 4 obtains. Thus, in effect, a structure description tells us *how many* individuals have the properties in question, but not *which ones*. A state description, of course, tells us both.

Carnap's system m^* takes the structure descriptions as fundamental and assigns equal weights to them. In our example, the weight of each would be one fourth. The principle of indifference is applied to structure descriptions in the first instance. Then it is applied once again to the state descriptions within any given structure description. In our example, this establishes the weight one twelfth for state descriptions 2, 3, and 4. They must have equal weights which add up to one fourth, the total weight for the structure description they compose. State descriptions 5, 6, and 7 are given the weight one twelfth for the same reason. State descriptions 1 and 8 each receive the weight one fourth, for each constitutes a structure description by itself. The system can be summarized as follows:

State Description	Weight	Structure Description	Weight
1. $Fa \cdot Fb \cdot Fc$	one-fourth }	I. All F	one-fourth
2. $\sim Fa \cdot Fb \cdot Fc$	one-twelfth ⎫		
3. $Fa \cdot \sim Fb \cdot Fc$	one-twelfth ⎬	II. $2\,F, 1 \sim F$	one-fourth
4. $Fa \cdot Fb \cdot \sim Fc$	one-twelfth ⎭		
5. $\sim Fa \cdot \sim Fb \cdot Fc$	one-twelfth ⎫		
6. $\sim Fa \cdot Fb \cdot \sim Fc$	one-twelfth ⎬	III. $1\,F, 2 \sim F$	one-fourth
7. $Fa \cdot \sim Fb \cdot \sim Fc$	one-twelfth ⎭		
8. $\sim Fa \cdot \sim Fb \cdot \sim Fc$	one-fourth }	IV. No F	one-fourth

Let us now consider, as before, the hypothesis "Fc" in the light of various evidence statements, this time using a concept of confirmation based upon m^*. In each case we simply calculate $m^*(e \cdot h)/m^*(e)$. First we note that the a priori probability of our hypothesis on the basis of no factual evidence at all is one half, for it holds in state descriptions 1, 2, 3, and 5, whose combined weight is one half. Now, suppose we know that a has the property F; let this be evidence e_1. "$Fa \cdot Fc$" holds in state descriptions 1 and 3, whose combined weights, one fourth and one twelfth, equal one third. "Fa" alone holds in state descriptions 1, 3, 4, and 7, whose weights total one half. The degree of confirmation of our hypothesis on this evidence is

$$c^* (h, e_1) = \frac{m^* (e_1 \cdot h)}{m^* (e_1)} = \frac{\frac{1}{3}}{\frac{1}{2}} = \frac{2}{3}$$

Happily, the observation that individual a has property F, which would be regarded intuitively as positive evidence for the hypothesis that c has the property F, does raise the probability of that hypothesis. You may verify by your own computation that

for e_2 ($Fa \cdot Fb$),	$c^*(h, e_2)$ = three-fourths
for e_3 ($\sim Fa$),	$c^*(h, e_3)$ = one-third
for e_4 ($\sim Fa \cdot \sim Fb$),	$c^*(h, e_4)$ = one-fourth
for e_5 ($Fa \cdot \sim Fb$),	$c^*(h, e_5)$ = one-half

Clearly, m^* yields a concept of degree of confirmation c^* that allows for the possibility of learning from experience.

Many objections have been raised against the explication of degree of confirmation as c^*, most of which were well known to Carnap and discussed explicitly by him. In the years since the publication of his major treatments of c^*, he has himself sought improved systems of inductive logic and has abandoned c^* except as a useful approximation in certain contexts. For example, one of the most serious shortcomings of the system based on m^* (and of many related systems as well) is the fact that the degree of confirmation of a hypothesis depends in an unfortunate way upon the language in which the confirmation function is defined. The addition of another predicate "G"—standing for "hard," let us say— would alter the probabilities of the statement that c has the property F in relation to the evidence statements given above—in relation to evidence that does not involve the new property at all! [93] To circumvent this difficulty, Carnap originally imposed the requirement of descriptive completeness of the language, but the requirement is not plausible, and Carnap never defended it enthusiastically. His more recent work dispenses with this completeness requirement without reintroducing the same difficulty.

Another shortcoming of the system based on m^* (as well as many other similar systems) is that in a language with infinitely many names for individuals, no universal generalization of the form "All F are G" can ever have a degree of confirmation other than zero on the kind of evidence that can be accumulated by observation. Carnap has recently been working with systems that do not have this drawback.

Carnap's earlier systems of inductive logic have been criticized— especially by those who are more interested in questions of practical statistical inference than in foundational questions—on the ground that the confirmation functions were defined only for extremely simple languages. These languages embody only qualitative predicates; since they do not contain quantitative concepts, they are patently inadequate as languages for science. In his more recent work, Carnap has been developing systems that are able to treat physical magnitudes quantitatively.

As the preceding remarks should indicate, Carnap has been acutely aware of various technical difficulties in his earlier treatments of the logical interpretation of probability, and he has made enormous strides in overcoming them.[94] There is, however, in my opinion, a fundamental problem at the heart of the logical interpretation. It is, I think, a difficulty of principle which cannot be avoided by technical developments. It seems to be intrinsic to the entire conception of probability as a logical relation between evidence and hypothesis.

The logical interpretation involves, in an essential way, the conception of probability as a measure of possible states of affairs. Whether the measure is attached to statements describing these possibilities (i.e., state descriptions or structure descriptions) or to the possibilities themselves (i.e., facts, propositions, models), the measure is indispensable. There are many alternative ways of assigning such a measure; for instance, there are infinitely many different ways of assigning nonnegative weights to the state descriptions of our simple illustrative language in such a way that together they total one. As a matter of fact, Carnap has described a continuum of weightings, and there are others beyond the scope of that collection.[95] Alternative methods of weighting have, of course, differing degrees of intuitive plausibility. The inescapable question is: How are we to select the appropriate weighting or measure from the superdenumerable infinity of candidates?

One feature of the choice has signal importance: *The choice must be a priori.* We may not wait to see how frequently a property occurs in order to assign it a weight; an a posteriori method of this sort would have to find its place within one of the interpretations still to be discussed. The problem is to show how we can make a choice that is not completely arbitrary. Assuming we have made a definite choice, this choice *defines* the notions of degree of confirmation and logical probability. It determines our inductive logic. As a consequence, degree of confirmation statements, or statements of logical probability, are *analytic* if they are true (self-contradictory if they are false). They are statements whose truth or falsity are results of definitions and pure logic alone; they have no synthetic or factual content. Given any hypothesis h and any consistent evidence statement e, the degree of confirmation $c(h, e)$ can be established by computation alone, as we saw in dealing with our examples above. The question is: *How can statements that say nothing about any matters of fact serve as "a guide of life?"* [96]

Carnap's immediate answer is that we do not use these degree-of-confirmation statements by themselves. In an attempt to answer this very question, he points out that the evidence statement e is synthetic, and it is the analytic degree of confirmation statement *in combinaiion with the synthetic evidence statement* that provides a guide to decisions and action. Very well, analytic statements alone do not serve as "a guide of life." A problem still remains. In the cases that interest us, we are trying to deal with unobserved matters of fact on the basis of evidence concerning observed matters of fact. We are trying to make a prediction or decision regarding a future occurrence. The evidence statement, although synthetic, is not a statement about any future event; it has factual content, but that content refers entirely to the past. How, we may ask, can a synthetic statement *about the past,* in conjunction with an analytic degree of confirmation statement, tell us anything about the future? How, in particular, can it serve as any kind of guide to prediction, decision, and action?

We must not allow a fundamental misconception to cloud this issue. The way in which the evidence statement and the degree of confirmation statement function is very different from the role of premises in an inference. Given that the degree of confirmation of hypothesis h on evidence e is p, and given also the truth of e, we are not allowed to infer h even if p is very near one. Rather, we must use our inductive logic according to certain definite rules of application. [97] First, there is the *requirement of total evidence.* If e is the evidence statement we are going to use, it must incorporate all relevant available evidence. This is an important respect in which inductive logic differs from deductive. If a conclusion B follows deductively from a premise (or set of premises) A, and if we know that the premise is true, we may assert the conclusion B, even if we know a great deal that is not stated in A. If B follows validly from A, it also follows validly from A conjoined with any additional premises whatever. By contrast, a hypothesis h may be highly confirmed with respect to evidence e, but its degree of confirmation on the basis of e and additional evidence e' may be very low indeed.

Given, then, that e is all the available relevant evidence, we are still not allowed to asset h. Instead, we may use our confirmation statement, "$c(h, e) = p$" to determine what would constitute a reasonable bet on h.

For example, suppose (since the arithmetic is already done) that we have a collection of three objects, and all we know is that two of them have been observed, and they are both red. What sort of bet should we be willing to make on the third one being red? Leaving certain niceties aside, if we accept c^* as an adequate explication of degree of confirmation, we should be willing to give odds of three to one that the next one is red, for the degree of confirmation is three quarters.[98]

Let us look at this situation in a slightly more dramatic way. Suppose I am thinking about making a wager on the outcome of the next race; in particular, I am thinking of betting on Kentucky Kid. Not being especially knowledgeable regarding horse racing or pari-mutuel betting, I bring along an advisor who is well versed in logical probability. I ask him whether KK will win. He tells me he does not know and neither does anyone else, since the race is not fixed. I tell him I had not expected a categorical and certain reply, but that I would like some information about it in order to decide how to bet. Going over the racing form together, we accumulate all of the relevant information about KK's past performance, as well as that of the other horses in the race. I tell him I find it all very interesting, but what about the next race? After a rapid calculation he tells me that the probability of KK's winning, with respect to all of the available relevant evidence, is one half. Under these circumstances, he tells me, a bet at even odds is reasonable. I am about to thank him for his information about the next race, when I reflect that the degree of confirmation statement is analytic, while the evidence statement refers only to past races and not to the future one I am concerned with, so I cannot see that he has supplied me with any information about the future race. I voice my discontent, saying I had hoped he would tell me *something* about the next race, but he has only given me information about past races. He replies that he *has* told me what constitutes a fair bet or a *rational degree of belief*. Surely, he says, you cannot ask for more. But, I object, how can a statement exclusively about the past also be a statement regarding rational belief with respect to future occurrences? What is the force of the term "rational" here? How is it defined? He takes me back to the beginning and explains the weighting of the state descriptions and the definition of "degree of confirmation." This is what we *mean* by "rational belief"; it is *defined* in terms of "degree of confirmation," which is a logical relation between evidence and hypothesis. My dissatisfaction remains. Will I be right in a high percentage of cases, I ask, if I expect occurrences that are highly probable? Will I be right less often if I expect occurrences that are quite improbable? If I bet in terms of rational degree of belief, will I win my fair share of bets? I cannot say for sure that you will, he replies, but that is a reasonable sort of thing to expect. But, I rejoin, in a sense of "reasonable" that has *no demonstrable connection whatever* with what actually happens in the future! As a matter of fact, you have chosen one from an infinitude of possible definitions of "degree of confirmation" that could have been used to define "rational belief." If you had chosen otherwise, what you now call "rational" might be considered highly irrational, and conversely. In the presence of such a wide variety of choice of possible definitions of "rational," it makes very good sense to ask, "Why be rational?" The answer, "Because it is rational," will not do, for as we have seen, that answer is equivocal.[99] The choice of a definition of "degree of confirmation" seems entirely arbitrary. Is there any way of justifying the choice? By this time the race is over, and neither of us noticed which horse won. So ends the dialogue.

Carnap's most recent view concerning the justification of the choice of a confirmation function rests the matter on our inductive intuition.[100] He has enunciated a number of axioms, and for each he offers an intuitive justification. These axioms determine the limits of the class of acceptable confirmation functions. It is no easy matter to articulate our inductive intuitions in a clear and consistent way. Intuitions are notoriously vague, and they tend to conflict with each other. By dint of careful reflection and comparison, as well as by consideration of a wide variety of examples of inductive reasoning, Carnap believes we can arrive at a fairly precise characterization of rational belief. This is the task of inductive logic, or the theory of logical probability.

Carnap's answer to the question of justification puts him, I think, rather close to those who adopt a postulational approach to the problem of induction, and to those who espouse an "ordinary language" dissolution of the problem. Perhaps the search for plausible postulates is nothing other than Carnap's search for intuitively justifiable axioms. At the same time, the search for axioms that characterize what we intuitively recognize as reasonable inductive inference would presumably come close to capturing the fundamental ordinary meaning of "rational belief." I have already indicated my reasons for dissatisfaction with both of these approaches. I think these reasons apply with the same force to Carnap's theory of degree of confirmation, as well as to any other version of the logical theory.

The logical theory of probability has no difficulty in meeting the criterion of *admissibility*.[101] Carnap has laid great stress upon the importance of avoiding incoherent betting systems, so he has been careful to insist upon an explication that conforms to the axioms of the mathematical calculus. Moreover, since degree-of-confirmation statements are analytic, they can, in principle, be established by mathematical computation. The logical interpretation has no difficulty in meeting the criterion of *ascertainability*. It is the criterion of *applicability* that poses the greatest difficulty for the logical interpretation. This theory provides no reason for supposing any connection whatever between what is probable and what happens often. It seems to provide no basis for expecting the probable in preference to the improbable. In my opinion, it lacks predictive content and thus fails to qualify as "a guide of life." This difficulty concerning the criterion of applicability is Hume's problem of induction once again: Can we offer any justification for the expectations we form, on the basis of observation and inductive inference, concerning unobserved matters of fact?

4. The Personalistic Interpretation. There is another outgrowth of the crude subjectivistic interpretation which, like the logical interpretation, satisfies the criterion of admissibility. It, too, substitutes the concept of rational belief for the concept of actual belief, but in a different way.[102] The purely subjective interpretation ran into trouble, we recall, not because of any individual assignment of probability values, but because of an inadmissible combination. This fact reveals a general feature of the probability calculus. Except for a few essentially vacuous cases, the probability calculus does not, by itself, establish any probability values. It does enable us to compute some values after some others have been supplied. We may thus distinguish fundamental probabilities from derived probabilities, although there is nothing absolute about this distinction. In one context a particular probability may be fundamental; in another, that same probability may be derived. The point of the distinction is to emphasize the fact that some fundamental probabilities are required as a basis for mathematical derivation of other probabilities. The probability calculus provides the relation of fundamental to derived probabilities, but it does not furnish the fundamental probabilities.

The personalistic theory allows, in effect, that the fundamental probabilities are purely subjective degrees of actual belief, but the probability calculus sets forth relations among degrees of belief which must be satisfied if these degrees are to constitute a rational system. Although the fundamental probabilities are subjective, their relation to derived probabilities is objective. There is a parallel with deductive logic. If I believe that all men are mortal, that Socrates is a man, and that

Socrates is immortal, I am guilty of irrationality, in the form of direct logical contradiction, in my system of beliefs. These three beliefs are not jointly tenable. Logic does not tell me which of them is incorrect, or which I ought to revise, but it does tell me that some revision is in order. Similarly, if my degree of belief in each possible outcome of a toss of two dice is equal to my degree of belief in every other outcome, if this degree of belief is unaffected by the outcomes of previous tosses, and if my degree of belief in getting double six at least once in twenty-four tosses exceeds my degree of belief in not getting it, then once again my system of beliefs is irrational. I have not become involved in a logical contradiction, unless I have already made some explicit commitment to the probability calculus for the ordering of beliefs, but there is another type of irrationality. The probability calculus tells me that. It does not determine which degree of belief is to be altered, but it does tell me that some alteration is required. I have already indicated the nature of the irrationality exhibited by degrees of belief that violate the relations stipulated by the probability calculus. Such systems of beliefs give rise to incoherent betting systems—i.e., to systems of bets such that the individual *must lose* no matter what the outcome of the occurrences upon which the wagers are made. An individual with degrees of belief of this sort will be willing to accept a series of bets in which book is made against him. A bookie who knew his beliefs could be certain of making him lose. The desire to avoid incoherent betting systems is an expression of a very practical type of rationality.

Since the personalistic theory of probability condemns as irrational any system of beliefs that violates the probability calculus, and admits as probabilities only systems of beliefs that conform to the calculus, it automatically satisfies the *admissibility* criterion. It also satisfies the *ascertainability* criterion, I believe. Any theory that pretends to treat degrees of belief in a scientific manner must have some way of measuring them. One can, of course, simply ask people how strongly they believe a given proposition and accept their verbal answer as to the degree of their belief. This method is not especially satisfactory. We seem to get more reliable information about subjective states by watching how people behave. Although the actual measurement of degrees of belief involves certain technical complications, the basic idea is rather straightforward.[103] Suppose, to use an example of L. J. Savage, that a subject S stands with an egg in each hand—a white egg in one hand and a brown egg in the other. We want to know whether he believes more strongly that the white egg is rotten or that the brown one is. We offer him a choice between two alternatives: either we will give him $1 if the white egg is rotten but nothing if it is not, or we will give him $1 if the brown egg is rotten but nothing if it is not. We promise, moreover, to replace both eggs with eggs of guaranteed freshness. By seeing which alternative S chooses we see which proposition he believes more strongly. In similar fashion, we can offer him alternatives with different sums of money, say a $1.50 if the brown egg proves rotten but still only $1 if the white egg does. We can, moreover, make comparisons with other kinds of situations. For example, we can offer him a choice between $2.50 if the white egg proves rotten and a $2 ticket on Kentucky Kid to win in the next race. By presenting a large number of choices of the foregoing kinds, a great deal can be learned about the subjective probabilities of S. Interesting techniques for measuring degrees of belief have been developed, and there is no reason to doubt that they can be further refined and perfected. It would be distinctly unwarranted to suppose that degrees of belief, because they are subjective, do not admit of objective empirical investigation. The measurement of degrees of belief comes down, fundamentally, to a determination of the kinds of bets a person is willing to accept. There is, consequently, an intimate connection between subjective probabilities and betting behavior, and this accounts for the fact that a strong emphasis upon the coherence of betting systems and the criterion of admissibility is entirely appropriate to the personalistic interpretation.

The personalistic theorists espouse a viewpoint that demands great tolerance concerning probabilities. They maintain, as would many theorists of other persuasions, that conformity of degrees of belief with the probability calculus is a necessary condition of rationality. Most other theorists would deny that it is a sufficient condition as well. If, however, the requirement of coherence is all that is necessary for a set of beliefs to be rational, it is possible to be rational and to hold beliefs that are incredibly irrational according to any of the usual standards. You are allowed any belief you can mention, as long as it is logically consistent, about unobserved events. You cannot be convicted of irrationality as long as you are willing to make the appropriate adjustments elsewhere in your system of beliefs. You can believe to degree 0.99 that the sun will *not* rise tomorrow. You can believe with equal conviction that hens will lay billiard balls. You can maintain with virtual certainty that a coin that has consistently come up heads three quarters of the time in a hundred million trials is heavily biased for *tails!* There is no end to the plain absurdities that qualify as rational. It is not that the theory demands the acceptance of such foolishness, but it does tolerate it.

It should be evident that the difficulties being mentioned fall under the criterion of *applicability*. There is, I think, very serious trouble here. Given any observations whatever of past occurrences, the probability calculus does not, by itself, determine what we must believe about the future, nor does it determine the strengths of any such beliefs.[104] For instance, a coin that has been observed to come up heads one hundred million times in a row may still be a fair coin that comes up tails about half the time in the long run. There is no logical contradiction in this supposition, and the probability calculus cannot fault it. The personalistic theory therefore leaves entirely unanswered our questions about inductive inference. It tolerates *any kind* of inference from the observed to the unobserved. This amounts to an abdication of probability from the role of "a guide of life."

Personalistic theorists have placed great emphasis upon an aspect of their theory I have purposely suppressed until now. I have wanted to stress the essential emptiness of their official concept of rationality. They have, however, explained at length how reasonable men can arrive at a high level of agreement on matters regarding which they originally disagreed, if they will only consider the evidence that is available to all. The mechanism by which this kind of consensus emerges is inference according to Bayes' theorem. All that is necessary is that we all make certain minimal concessions with respect to prior probabilities. I shall discuss Bayes' theorem, prior probabilities, and their roles in scientific inference at a later stage.[105] At present I simply want to remark that the concept of rationality involved in being a "reasonable man" is somewhat different from the notion of rationality defined solely in terms of a conformity of subjective probabilities to the mathematical calculus. A tiny degree, at least, of open-mindedness is now a requirement. This seems to me indicative of a general feature of the personalistic approach. It has correctly identified certain necessary conditions of rationality for subjective probabilities, but additional conditions must be found before we can pretend to have a viable conception of rationality and a concept of probability that satisfies the applicability criterion. It is essential that the additional conditions be stated explicitly and justified. This is precisely where Hume's problem of induction lies for the personalistic theory.

It is noteworthy that Carnap has found his logical interpretation of probability growing closer to the personalistic conception in the last few years.[106] He applauds the coherence requirement and the justification for it. He differs from the personalists, however, in his insistence upon many additional axioms beyond those of the mathematical calculus itself. In all of this I am in complete agreement with Carnap's evaluation of the situation, although I do regard his intuitive justification of his additional axioms as insufficient.

5. *The Frequency Interpretation.* According to a leading version of the frequency interpretation, probability is defined in terms of the limit of the relative frequency of the occurrence of an attribute in an infinite sequence of events.[107] To say, for instance, that the probability of getting heads with this coin is one half means that, in the potentially infinite sequence of tosses of the coin in question, the relative frequency with which heads occurs converges to the value one half. We may think of three coordinated sequences: the sequence of flips F of the coin, the sequence of results (heads H or tails T), and the sequence of fractions representing the relative frequency of heads up to and including that place in the sequence. Here are the results for the initial section of an actual sequence of tosses:

F	F	F	F	F	F	F	F	F	F	$\ldots$
H	T	H	H	H	T	H	T	H	H	$\ldots$
$\frac{1}{1}$	$\frac{1}{2}$	$\frac{2}{3}$	$\frac{3}{4}$	$\frac{4}{5}$	$\frac{4}{6}$	$\frac{5}{7}$	$\frac{5}{8}$	$\frac{6}{9}$	$\frac{7}{10}$	$\ldots$

In the third sequence, the denominator of each fraction represents the number of flips in the first sequence up to and including that place, while the numerator represents the number of heads in the second sequence up to and including that place. If the probability of heads is one half, according to the frequency interpretation, the fractions in the third unending sequence converge to the limit one half. The term "limit" is used in its standard mathematical sense:

> The sequence f_n ($n = 1, 2, 3, \ldots$) has the limit L as n goes to infinity if and only if, for every positive ϵ, no matter how small, there exists a number N such that, if $n > N$, $|f_n - L| < \epsilon$.

This definition means, as it is sometimes informally put, that the relative frequencies become and remain as close to L as you like for sufficiently large numbers of elements of the sequence.

In mathematics, the foregoing definition is usually applied to sequences that are generated according to some mathematical rule, for example, $1/n$ or $1/2^n$ where n runs through the positive integers. Each of these sequences has, of course, the limit zero. The sequence of coin tosses and the associated sequence of relative frequencies are not given by a mathematical rule; instead, they are generated by a set of empirically given physical events. I leave open the question of whether there is, in fact, a mathematical rule that would generate precisely the same sequence. If there is, we surely do not know what it is. Some authors have raised doubts about the meaningfulness of talking about limits in sequences of this sort, because there is no known or knowable rule from which to deduce whether or not the sequence has a limit. Nevertheless, the terms in which the definition is framed are entirely meaningful in application to physical events: "every," "there exists," "less than," "difference," "positive number," etc. They are combined, it is true, into an expression that cannot be verified deductively or mathematically, but this should be no source of concern. We are dealing with induction, not deduction. It remains to be seen whether we may properly speak of *inductive verification* of statements about limits of relative frequencies in empirically given sequences.[108]

Assuming that the concept of the limit can be tolerated, it is rather easy to show that the frequency interpretation satisfies the criterion of *admissibility*.[109] Furthermore, there is at least one fundamental and important sense in which the frequency interpretation satisfies the criterion of *applicability*. A statement about the probability of a particular type of event is an objective statement about the frequency with which events of that type will occur. Such statements are synthetic, and they have predictive content by virtue of applying to future events. I do not mean to say that the frequency interpretation faces no difficulties connected with applicability; there are, in fact, serious problems of this kind which I have no intention of minimizing. I shall discuss them later. First, however, we should turn our attention to the problem of ascertainability, for this is the crucial problem facing the frequency theory.

When a sequence is generated by a known mathematical rule, we can, as already noted, deduce statements about limits. We are not dealing with such cases. When a sequence is generated by a physical process that is well understood in terms of accepted physical theory, we may be able to make theoretical inferences concerning convergence properties. For instance, our present knowledge of mechanics enables us to infer the frequency behavior of many kinds of gambling mechanisms.[110] Our theory of probability must allow room for inferences of this kind. The basic probem, however, concerns sequences of events for which we are lacking such physical knowledge. We are dealing with the problem of induction, so we must not assume large parts of inductive science. Instead, we shall consider the question of what inferences, if any, concerning the limit of the relative frequency in a sequence can be made solely on the basis of observations of the initial portions of such sequences. Any such initial section contains, of course, a finite number of members. The first point to emphasize is, as already noted, that we can *deduce* no statement about the limit from a description of any initial section. *Any* value of the relative frequency in an observed initial section of *any* length is compatible with *any* value for the limit. This rather obvious fact has sometimes been taken to destroy the whole enterprise of attempting to make inferences concerning limits of relative frequencies. No such interpretation is warranted. All we can properly conclude is that the problem we are facing is an inductive problem, not a deductive problem, so it cannot have a deductive answer. We are dealing with ampliative inference; the inference from an observed relative frequency to the limit of the relative frequency is certainly of this type.

The situation is, actually, even worse. There is no guarantee that the relative frequencies converge to any limit at all. It is possible to define sequences of events for which the relative frequencies do not converge, and we cannot be sure that such sequences do not occur in nature. This fact should remind us once again of Hume's problem of induction. If a sequence of occurrences does manifest limiting frequencies, it exhibits a type of uniformity—a statistical uniformity. We cannot know a priori that nature is uniform, as Hume showed, and this result applies as much to statistical uniformities as to any other kind.

Hans Reichenbach, a leading proponent of the frequency interpretation, was well aware of all these difficulties, and he appreciated the force of Hume's arguments as applied to the problem of inferring limits of relative frequencies. He maintained, nevertheless, that there is an inductive rule for inferring limits of relative frequencies from observed frequencies in finite initial sections, and this rule is amenable to justification. The justification is a pragmatic one, and it constitutes a refinement of the pragmatic justification discussed above. Even in the refined form, the justification is not adequate, as I shall shortly explain, but I think it may constitute an indispensable part of an adequate justification.

Suppose we have an infinite sequence of events A, and we want to infer the limit of the relative frequency with which these events exhibit the characteristic B. Let $F^n(A, B)$ be the relative frequency of B among the first n members of A. We seek a rule for inferring from the value of $F^n(A, B)$ in an observed sample of n members to $\lim F^n(A, B)$ as $n \to \infty$. Reichenbach offers the rule of induction by enumeration for this type of inference:

Rule of Induction by Enumeration: Given that $F^n(A, B) = m/n$, to infer that $\lim_{n \to \infty} F^n(A, B) = m/n$.

It is to be understood that the initial section of n members whose relative frequency is given comprises all observed instances of A; when more instances of A are observed a new inference is made from the observed frequency in the larger sample, and the earlier inference from the smaller sample is superseded. The rule of induction by enumeration provides, in short, for the projection of observed statistical uniformities into the unobserved future. It lets us infer that the observed frequency is the same as the limit.[111]

Reichenbach's justification proceeds by acknowledging that there are two possibilities, namely, that the relative frequency with which we are concerned approaches a limit or that it does not, and we do not know which of these possibilities obtains. If the limit does exist, then so does the probability $P(A, B)$; if the limit does not exist, there is no such probability. We must consider each case. Suppose first that the sequence $F^n(A, B)$ ($n = 1, 2, 3, \ldots$) has no limit. In this case any attempt to infer the value of that (nonexistent) limit is bound to fail, whether it be by induction by enumeration or by any other method. In this case, all methods are on a par: they are useless. Suppose, now, that the sequence does have a limit. Let us apply the rule of induction by enumeration and infer that the observed frequency matches the limit of the relative frequency to whatever degree of approximation we desire. We persist in the use of this rule for larger and larger observed initial parts of our sequence as we observe larger numbers of members. It follows directly from the limit concept that, for any desired degree of accuracy whatever, there is some point in the sequence beyond which the inferred values will always match the actual limit within that degree of approximation. To be sure, we cannot say beforehand just how large our samples must be to realize this condition, nor can we be sure when we have reached such a point, but we can be sure that such exists. There is a sense, consequently, in which we have everything to gain and nothing to lose by following this inductive procedure for ascertaining probabilities—i.e., for inferring limits of relative frequencies. If the probability whose value we are trying to ascertain actually exists, our inductive procedure will ascertain it. If the probability does not exist, we have lost nothing by adopting that inductive procedure, for no other method could have been successful in ascertaining the value of a nonexistent probability.[112]

It is worth comparing the foregoing justification of induction by enumeration for the ascertainment of values of probabilities with the earlier and much looser pragmatic justification of induction. In the earlier argument, we considered the two possibilities that nature is uniform or that nature is not uniform. At the time, I remarked that these two alternatives are not necessarily exhaustive, and that we needed to be much clearer about the extent and degree of uniformity required. In the latter argument, we deal with the same set of alternatives, but now we can specify exactly what the uniformity consists in—namely, that the sequence of relative frequencies whose limit we are trying to infer is convergent. Moreover, the alternatives considered are exclusive and exhaustive: The sequence has a limit or it does not. In the earlier argument, it was not clear what constituted an inductive method; in the latter argument, it is specified precisely as the rule of induction by enumeration. In the earlier argument, we used notions like success and failure of inductive methods, again without any precise indication of their meanings. In the latter argument, their force is clear. To begin with, we choose some degree of approximation ϵ that will satisfy us for this particular probability. Then, success consists in inferring the value of the limit of the relative frequency on the basis of a sample large enough that this inference, as well as all subsequent inferences on the basis of larger samples, are accurate within $\pm \epsilon$. When Reichenbach claimed, in connection with the looser version of his argument, that the inductive method will work if any method will work, some people thought he was actually making an inductive generalization. In the tighter version of the argument we see that this claim is not inductive in character. It is a rather obvious—but nonetheless important—analytic consequence of the definitions of "limit of a sequence" and "induction by enumeration." It is not a surreptitious inductive justification of induction. The justification is deductive, but not in the way Hume's arguments ruled out. It does not prove deductively that all or most inductive inferences with true premises will have true conclusions. It does prove that induction by enumeration will enable us to make accurate inferences concerning limiting frequencies if any method can. This proof is, I submit, valid.

The chief defect in Reichenbach's justification is that it fails to justify a unique inductive rule, but rather, it justifies an infinite class of inductive rules equally well. Although induction by enumeration will work if any method will, it is *not* the only rule that has this characteristic. Reichenbach's argument shows that the same can be said for an infinite class of inductive rules. Reichenbach was aware of this fact, and he characterized the class as *asymptotic*.[113] A rule is asymptotic if it shares with the rule of induction by enumeration the property of yielding inferences that converge to the limit of the relative frequency whenever such a limit exists. The rule of induction by enumeration takes the observed frequency itself as the inferred value of the limit of the relative frequency. Any other rule that gives inferred values differing from the observed frequency, but in such a way that the difference converges to zero as the sample size increases, is asymptotic. Let $I_r^n(A, B)$ be the inferred value, on the basis of a sample of size n, of the limit of $F^n(A, B)$ according to rule R. (When it is clear what rule is involved, the subscript R may be omitted.) A rule is asymptotic if and only if

$$I^n(A, B) - F^n(A, B) \to 0 \text{ as } n \to \infty$$

Notice that this definition does not depend upon an assumption that the limit of the relative frequency exists, for the differences may converge whether or not the relative frequencies do. Notice also that induction by enumeration is asymptotic, for in its case the above difference is identically zero. It is evident that every asymptotic rule has the property used to justify induction by enumeration: If the relative frequency has a limit, the rule will produce inferred values that become and remain accurate within any desired degree of accuracy.

The fact that there are infinitely many asymptotic rules is not, by itself, cause for dissatisfaction with Reichenbach's argument. If this infinity contained only a narrow spectrum of rules that yield similar results and that quickly converge to one another, we could accept the small degree of residual arbitrariness with equanimity. The actual case is, however, quite the opposite. The class of asymptotic rules is so broad that it admits *complete* arbitrariness of inference. Although all of the rules of this type give results that converge to one another, the convergence is nonuniform. This means, in effect, that for any finite amount of evidence we might have, they are actually completely divergent. Given a sample of *any* finite size, and given *any* observed frequency in that sample, you may select *any* number from zero to one inclusive, and there is some asymptotic rule to sanction the inference that this arbitrarily chosen number is the probability. The class of asymptotic rules, taken as a whole, tolerates any inference whatever regarding the limit of the relative frequency.

For any particular probability sequence, certain asymptotic rules will give results that converge to the accurate value more rapidly than will others of the asymptotic rules. It might be tempting to suppose that induction by enumeration would give quicker convergence to the correct value than do the other asymptotic rules, or at least that it will usually do so, but no such thing can be proved. We have to find some other ground for choice if we hope to justify the selection of a unique rule. Reichenbach attempted to argue for induction by enumeration on the grounds of "descriptive simplicity," but this argument seems to me patently inapplicable.[114] Descriptive simplicity can be invoked only in the case of theories, statements, or rules that are empirically equivalent.[115] Although the asymptotic rules do all converge "in the limit," they cannot possibly be regarded as empirically equivalent because of the complete arbitrariness of inference they tolerate as a class.[116]

We must conclude that Reichenbach did not succeed in showing that the frequency interpretation can meet the criterion of *ascertainability*. Finding a way to satisfy this criterion is the form in which Hume's problem of induction arises for the frequency interpretation. In spite of Reichenbach's failure to give an adequate solution to this problem, he did accomplish two things. First, he showed us a direction in which to look for an answer to Hume's problem. The fact that his particular attempt at a pragmatic justification did not succeed does not prove that no pragmatic justification is possible. Second, he gave a convincing argument, I believe, for the rejection of nonasymptotic rules of inference. Although not many authors would accept Reichenbach's reason for insisting upon the asymptotic character of rules of inference, a large number and wide variety of theorists do insist upon the condition of asymptoticity, or *convergence* as I shall call it.[117] For instance, Carnap adopts just this condition as one of his axioms. The personalistic theorists achieve a similar result through the use of Bayes' theorem with certain requirements placed upon the prior probabilities. In spite of the fact that it is not often used for this purpose, Reichenbach's argument is a consideration in favor of each of these concepts of probability insofar as they deal with the problem of inferring "long-run" frequencies. It seems widely recognized, explicitly or implicitly, that it would be foolish indeed to apply a method for inferring limits of relative frequencies such that, if the limit exists, persistent use of the method is bound to produce ever-recurrent error. Reichenbach's argument is at least a beginning toward a solution of the problem of ascertainability for the frequency interpretation, but it is also a beginning toward a solution of the problem of applicability for the logical and personalistic interpretations. The crucial question is whether we can find additional grounds by which to narrow significantly the class of acceptable inductive rules.

Although I am convinced that the problem of ascertainability is the most fundamental difficulty the frequency interpretation faces, there are, as I said earlier, certain important problems of applicability. When I presented the criterion of applicability, I enumerated several different ways in which the concept of probability functions. It has often been maintained that the frequency interpretation, while adequate to fulfill some of these functions, is patently inadequate to others. Carnap, for example, does not advocate a logical interpretation to the complete exclusion of all other interpretations. Instead, he *insists* upon two concepts of probability, the logical concept and the frequency concept. The frequency concept may be entirely appropriate for the interpretation of statistical laws of physics, for example, but it is unsuitable as a basis for explicating the concept of probability as it enters into the confirmation of scientific hypotheses by observational evidence. For this purpose, he claims, logical probability is needed. I shall return to this topic below, for the problem of confirmation must be considered in detail. If Carnap is right, the frequency interpretation alone cannot satisfy the criterion of applicability, but it can in conjunction with other interpretations.

The frequency interpretation also encounters applicability problems in dealing with the use of probability as a guide to such practical action as betting. We bet on *single* occurrences: a horse race, a toss of the dice, a flip of the coin, a spin of the roulette wheel. The probability of a given outcome determines what constitutes a reasonable bet. According to the frequency interpretation's official definition, however, the probability concept is meaningful only in relation to infinite sequences of events, not in relation to single events. The frequency interpretation, it is often said, fails on this extremely important aspect of the criterion of applicability.

Frequentists from Venn to Reichenbach have attempted to show how the frequency concept can be made to apply to the single case. According to Reichenbach, the probability concept is extended by giving probability a "fictitious" meaning in reference to single events. We find the probability associated with an infinite sequence and transfer that value to a given single member of it.[118] For instance, we say that the probability of heads on any particular toss of our coin is one half. This procedure, which seems natural in the case of the coin toss, does involve basic difficulties. The whole trouble is that a given single event belongs to many sequences, and the probabilities associated with the different sequences may differ considerably. The problem is to decide from which sequence to take the probability that is to be attached "fictitiously" to the single event.

According to the frequency interpretation, probability is a relation between two classes. The notation, "$P(A, B)$," reflects this fact by incorporating expressions for two classes, one before the comma and one after it. The class mentioned first is the *reference class;* the other is the *attribute class.* In dealing with the problem of the single case, the attribute class gives us no particular trouble. The terms of the bet determine which attribute we seek: double six, heads, the ace of spades, etc. The problem of the single case *is* the problem of selecting the appropriate reference class. Consider, for example, how to determine what premium a given individual should be charged for his automobile insurance. The insurance company tries to assign him to a category of drivers who are similar to him in relevant respects. It matters, for instance, whether the driver is male or female, married or unmarried, an urban or a rural dweller, a teenager or not, etc. It does not matter what color the car is or whether it has an odd or even license number. Reichenbach said that one should choose the narrowest reference class for which reliable statistics are available. I would say, instead, that the single case should be referred to the *broadest homogeneous reference class* of which it is a member. In either formulation, the intent is fairly straightforward. A probability is something that has to be established inductively, and in order to ascertain the probability we must have enough instances to be able to make an inductive generalization. Thus, we do not want to try to refer single cases to classes that are too narrow, for if we do we will not have enough evidence upon which to base our inference. At the same time, we want our reference class to contain other relevant cases, not irrelevant ones. *Statistical relevance* is the key concept here. Suppose we ask for the probability that a given individual x has a characteristic B. We know that x belongs to a reference class A in which the limit of the relative frequency of B is p. If we can find a property C in terms of which the reference class A can be split into two parts $A \cap C$ and $A \cap \bar{C}$, such that

$$P(A \cap C, B) \neq P(A, B)$$

then C is *statistically relevant* to the occurrence of B within A. Of course, C must be the sort of property whose occurrence in an individual can be detected without knowing whether that particular entity also has the property B. If there is no such property C by means of which to effect a relevant subdivision of A with respect to the occurrence of B, A is *homogeneous* with respect to B. Consider the reference class A of tosses of our coin with respect to the attribute B of heads. Let us suppose we know that the probability $P(A, B) = \frac{1}{2}$. We do not have any way of making a relevant subdivision in this reference class. Let C be the property of being an even toss, so $A \cap C$ consists of the tosses numbered 2, 4, 6, ... Since the coin is fair, $P(A \cap C, B) = P(A, B) = \frac{1}{2}$. The same situation obtains if C is the class of tosses immediately following tosses on which heads occurred, if C is the class of tosses made before dark, or if C is the class of tosses made on Monday, Wednesday, or Friday. A homogeneous reference class is the essence of a fair gambling mechanism, as Richard von Mises has carefully explained.[119] By contrast, let A be the class of licensed drivers in the United States. Let B be the class of drivers who have accidents involving over $50 damage to the car they are driving. We all know that A is not homogeneous with respect to B in this case. A can be subdivided in terms of a number of relevant characteristics such as age, sex, habitat, amount of driving done, etc. These subdivisions must be made before trying to assign a probability to the occurrence of an accident for a particular driver x.

It would be most unrealistic to suppose that we can fulfill the requirement of selecting the broadest homogeneous reference class in all cases in which we have to make practical decisions about single events. We may suspect that a given reference class is inhomogeneous, but not know of any way to make a relevant partition of it. Under these circumstances let us say that the class is *epistemically homogeneous;* reference classes of this type are the best we have in many cases until knowledge is further advanced. Sometimes we know that a reference class is inhomogeneous, but it would simply be impractical to carry out a relevant subdivision. The coin example is a paradigm. With elaborate enough measurements of the initial conditions of the toss, and with a fancy enough set of calculations, we could, in principle, do a pretty good job of predicting which side will come up on a given toss. It is not worth the effort, and besides, the rules of the game do not allow it. Under these circumstances, let us say that the reference class is *practically homogeneous.* We often make do with reference classes of this kind. Moreover, a given reference class may admit of a relevant subdivision, but the alteration of probability achieved thereby may be too small to be worthwhile. The relevant subdivision might also effect a serious reduction in available statistics. The choice of a reference class is an extremely practical affair, in which we must balance a number of factors such as the size of the class, the amount of statistical evidence available, the cost involved in getting more data, the difficulty in effecting a relevant subdivision, and the amount at stake in the wager or decision.

Carnap has made an extremely important and useful distinction between inductive logic proper and the methodology of induction.[120] I alluded briefly to this distinction in explaining his view that inductive logic does not contain rules for the acceptance of hypotheses. Inductive logic contains the systematic explication of degree of confirmation, and analytic degree of confirmation statements that hold for a given confirmation function in a given language. The methodology of induction contains rules for the application of inductive logic—that is, rules that tell us how to make use of the statements of degree of confirmation in deciding courses of practical action. As I indicated, the requirement of total evidence is one of the important methodological rules, and the rule of maximizing estimated utility is another.[121] These rules tell us how to use the results of inductive logic, but they do *not* provide for inductive inferences in which the conclusion can be detached and asserted if the premises are true and the degree of confirmation is sufficiently high.

Reichenbach, unfortunately, did not make the same clear distinction between probability theory proper and the practical rules for the application thereof. Such a distinction would have been helpful, particularly for the problem of the single case. Reichenbach admits that the meaning of "probability" for the single case is fictitious. He does not offer rules which enable us to assign probability values univocally. It is apparent that very practical considerations determine the value actually assigned. It would have been better, I think, if he had refused to apply the term "probability" to single events at all, but had instead reserved some other term such as "weight" which he often used for this purpose.[122] We could then say that probability is literally and exclusively a concept that applies to infinite sequences, not to single cases. If we want to find out how to behave regarding a single case, we must use probability knowledge; the problem is one of deciding how to apply such knowledge to single events. Our rules of application would tell us to find an appropriate reference class to which our single case belongs and use the value of the *probability* in that infinite sequence as the *weight* attached to the single case. The rule of selecting the broadest homogeneous reference class becomes a rule of application, not a rule for establishing values of probabilities within the theory proper. This approach shows why very down-to-earth practical considerations play an important role in determining *weights* of single events. Weights can be used to determine betting odds, to compute mathematical expectations for various programs of action, and for other equally practical purposes. This treatment of the single case shows a deep analogy between the requirement of total evidence and the rule for selecting the appropriate reference class. Both rules are part of methodology, not of probability theory. Each rule requires us to make use of all relevant available information in arriving at practical decisions.

The present treatment of the single case should also remove any temptation to suppose that statements about single cases can be detached and asserted independent of evidence and without reference to the weight. The methodological rules for handling single events are not rules of inference. There is an important reason for this. Suppose, as most authors on induction have, that we can assert hypotheses about single events if we have sufficient inductive evidence. P. F. Strawson gives an apt example: "He's been travelling for twenty-four hours, so he'll be very tired." [123] Strawson remarks, "Plainly the statement made by the first clause . . . is regarded as a reason for accepting the statement made by the second clause. The second statement . . . is in some sense a *conclusion* from the first. . . ." [124] Accepting the conclusion that "he'll be very tired" may be well and good in ordinary circumstances, but it would be foolhardy if the question is whether to engage him in mortal combat as he steps from the train. Just how we regard the "conclusion" depends upon what is at stake. The situation is made quite clear by the famous lottery paradox. Imagine a fair lottery with as large a number n of tickets as you like. The probability of a given ticket winning is $1/n$, which is as small as you like. The probability that a given ticket will not win is $1 - 1/n$, which is as close to one as you like. If there is some probability value p, such that a hypothesis can be accepted if its probability exceeds p, then we can make the probability that the ticket will not win greater than p. Hence, we can accept the hypothesis. But, the same holds for each ticket in the lottery, so we can deduce that no ticket will win. This contradicts the assumption that it was a fair lottery in the first place. To avoid this sort of difficulty, Carnap does not allow the hypothesis to be detached and asserted. Instead, he permits the use of the value $1/n$ in determining a fair price to pay for a ticket. When probability is used in this way, no paradox arises. I am proposing the same approach as a modification of Reichenbach's treatment of the single case. The weight can be used to determine the price to pay for a ticket, but a large weight does not warrant an assertion about the occurrence or nonoccurrence of a single event.

Carnap's inductive logic, as I have already explained, does not give rise to the assertion of any synthetic statement. Evidence statements are, as noted, ordinarily synthetic, but they are presumably asserted on the basis of observation, not inductive inference. I have explained at length my reasons for objecting to the exclusively analytic character of probability statements. In the frequency interpretation, as I am treating it, synthetic probability statements are asserted on the basis of inductive evidence. This approach allows the use of induction by enumeration, or some other asymptotic method, to infer the limit of the relative frequency—i.e., the probability—from the observed frequency in a finite sample. These *synthetic* probability statements are then applied, according to the methodological rules, in order to obtain weights that can be used for practical decisions. Although the lottery paradox arises if we try to make assertions about the occurrence or nonoccurrence of single events, no such paradoxes can arise in connection with assertions concerning limits of relative frequencies. You can never settle a bet on such assertion. Notice that no probability is assigned to the statement of the limit of the relative frequency. It is simply asserted, on inductive evidence, until additional evidence requires its revision. When that happens, the former value is discarded and replaced by a new value based upon a larger body of inductive evidence.

The fundamental objection I raised against the logical conception of probability, with its analytic degree of confirmation statements, is that such probability statements cannot meet the applicability criterion and cannot function as "a guide of life." The frequency treatment of the single case, as just outlined, does seem to me to meet the applicability requirement.

In a penetrating analysis of the logical interpretation of probability, A. J. Ayer has raised a fundamental question about the requirement of total evidence, namely, what makes total evidence any better than any other kind of evidence? [125] The logical interpretation of probability gives us a whole array of degree of confirmation statements for any given hypothesis, with different degrees of confirmation for different bodies of evidence. All of these statements of degree of confirmation are on a par; they are true but they have no content. We are told to pick the number from the degree of confirmation statement that embodies total available evidence, and that is the number to be used in practical decision making. Why? Logically, this degree of confirmation statement is no better or worse than any of the others. Practically, can we show that we will be more successful if we follow this requirement than we would be if we threw out, say, all evidence collected on Sunday? Hume's argument shows that we can prove no such thing. It is perfectly consistent to suppose that the world is governed by a deity who disapproves of

Sunday data collecting, so he punishes those who use such data by making a great many of their predictions go wrong.

The frequency approach does *not* face the same difficulty. *If* we know the long-run probabilities, a certain type of success is assured by following the methodological rules for handling single events. A given individual deals with a great variety of single events. As an aggregate they may not have much in common. They may be drawn from widely different probability sequences. A man bets on the toss of some dice, he decides to carry his umbrella because it looks a bit like rain, he takes out an insurance policy, he plants a garden, he plays poker, he buys some stock, etc. This series of single cases can, however, be regarded as a new probability sequence made up of the single cases the individual deals with. It is demonstrable that he will be successful "in the long run" if he follows the methodological rules laid down. He will win a few and lose a few, but if he so acts that he has a positive expectation of gain in each case, he will come out ahead in the long run.[126] Of course, as Lord Keynes has reminded us, he will also be dead in the long run.[127]

The foregoing survey of five important attempts to provide an interpretation of the probability concept reveals that each one encounters severe difficulties in meeting at least one of the three criteria of adequacy. The classical and subjective interpretations fail on the criterion of admissibility, the frequency interpretation has difficulties with respect to the criterion of ascertainability, and the logical and personalistic interpretations run into troubles on the criterion of applicability. All of these interpretations have been considered separately. It would be natural to ask at this point whether some combination of interpretations, such as Carnap endorses, would mitigate the problem. The answer is, I think, emphatically negative. The amalgamation of two concepts, one of which is unsatisfactory from the standpoint of ascertainability while the other is unsatisfactory from the standpoint of applicability, yields a theory that has problems of both of these counts. It does not seem to produce a theory that overcomes both sorts of difficulties.

Inferring Relative Frequencies

Theorists of various different persuasions agree that relative frequencies are basically germane to probability theory, whether or not they are willing to *define* "probability" in terms of them. Carnap, who is the greatest proponent of the logical interpretation, insists that there are two concepts of probability—the logical concept and the frequency concept.

He argues, moreover, for an intimate relation between relative frequency and degree of confirmation. The use of probability as a fair betting quotient rests upon its relation to the frequency with which various kinds of events occur. In addition, degree of confirmation can be interpreted in appropriate circumstances as an estimate of a relative frequency— namely, when the hypothesis being confirmed is a statement about a single occurrence and the evidence is statistical evidence concerning the frequency of that type of occurrence in observed cases.[128] In these and other matters, Carnap seems not far from F. P. Ramsey, who is properly regarded as the originator of the personalistic interpretation. Ramsey, too, takes great care to point out fundamental relations between frequencies and partial beliefs.[129]

The reason for the fundamental connection is quite plain to see. Suppose a die is about to be tossed twelve times, and suppose that the relative frequency with which the side six will show in this set of tosses is one sixth. This means that six will occur twice. Suppose, moreover, that Smith agrees to bet on six at odds of five to one, and Jones agrees to accept these bets. The result is that Smith wins two bets and collects $5 on each, for a total of $10, while Jones wins ten bets and collects $1 on each, also for a total of $10. The two players come out even, neither winning anything from the other. This game would, of course, be utterly pointless if both players knew for sure what the outcome would be, but they cannot know any such thing in advance. However, each player would do his best to guess or infer the relative frequency of six, for the relative frequency determines what constitutes a fair bet or a bet that is advantageous to either party.

Let us approach the question of justifying a method for inferring relative frequencies as a problem of basic concern to any probability theory. Reichenbach attempts to justify induction by enumeration as the fundamental method for this purpose, but, as we have already noted, there are infinitely many alternative candidates, and his argument does not succeed in showing that induction by enumeration is superior to all the rest. Two alternatives, the a priori method and the counterinductive method, were mentioned above, but since neither is asymptotic they are both unacceptable. I shall assume that the reasons already given are a sufficient basis to insist upon asymptoticity in inductive rules.

The rule of induction by enumeration is the simplest of the asymptotic rules. This does not constitute any kind of justificatory argument, unless we can show that there are good reasons for preferring a simple rule to more complex ones, but it does make that rule a convenient point of departure. If a rule is asymptotic, the values we infer for the limit of the relative frequency must be determined, at least in part, by observed frequencies in observed samples, for the inferred values must converge to the observed frequencies as the sample size increases. For purposes of systematic exploration, it is convenient to represent any asymptotic rule R as follows:

$$\text{Given } F^n(A, B) = \frac{m}{n}, \text{ to infer } \lim_{n \to \infty} F^n(A, B) = \frac{m}{n} + c,$$

where $c \to 0$ as $n \to \infty$.

Induction by enumeration is the rule that results when c is identically zero. The other asymptotic rules impose some "corrective term" c which produces a difference between the observed frequency and the inferred value of the limit. The term c is obviously not a nonzero constant; what it is a function of will be a question of primary interest to us.

There is a basic fact about limits of relative frequencies that will help us to rule out a large class of asymptotic rules. Let A be any reference class, and let $B_1, B_2, \ldots, B_k$ be any mutually exclusive and exhaustive set of attributes in A. This means that every member of A has one and only one of these attributes B_i. For any initial section containing n members of A, let m_i be the number of members of the sample having attribute B_i; m_i/n is the observed frequency of B_i in that sample. For any positive n, all of the corresponding values of m_i must add up to n, and all of the values of the observed frequencies m_i/n must add up to one. Furthermore, no relative frequency can ever be negative. Therefore,

$$\frac{m_i}{n} \geq 0 \text{ and } \sum_{i=1}^{k} \frac{m_i}{n} = 1.$$

The same conditions hold for limits of relative frequencies:

$$\lim_{n \to \infty} F^n(A,B_i) \geq 0 \quad \text{and} \quad \sum_{i=1}^{k} \lim_{n \to \infty} F^n(A,B_i) = 1.$$

I have called these conditions for limits *normalizing conditions*. They are arithmetical truisms, and any statement about limits of relative frequencies that violates them is an outright contradiction. Any rule that produces inferred values of limits that fail to satisfy them is clearly unsatisfactory.[130]

The normalizing conditions would rule out the counterinductive method if it were not already knocked out by the convergence requirement. Suppose we have an urn from which we have drawn a number of balls, and among the observed cases one half are red (B_1), one fourth are yellow (B_2), and one fourth are blue (B_3). Suppose it is given that no other color is exemplified in that urn. The three-color attributes are mutually exclusive and exhaustive. The counterinductive rule requires us to infer that the limit of the relative frequency of B_i is $(n - m_i)/n$ whenever the observed frequency is m_i/n. Thus, we infer that the limit of the relative frequency of red is one half, the limit of the relative frequency of yellow is three fourths, and the limit of the relative frequency of blue is three fourths. These inferred values add up to two, which constitutes a violation of the normalizing conditions and a patent absurdity.

The normalizing conditions must hold for every value of n, so c cannot be a function (not identically zero) of n alone. If it were, we could choose some value of n for which c does not vanish and we would have

$$\sum_{i=1}^{k} \left[\frac{m_i}{n} + c(n) \right] = k \times c(n) + \sum_{i=1}^{k} \frac{m_i}{n} = 1 + k \times c(n)$$

which is a violation of the normalizing conditions.

The normalizing conditions tell us something rather important about the "corrective" term. Since observed frequencies must add up to the same total as the inferred values of the limits, whatever is added to one observed frequency by the "corrective" term must be taken away from other observed frequencies. This feature of the "corrective" term must be built into the rule. When the "corrective" term is seen in this way, it leads us to suspect immediately that the decision as to what observed frequencies should be increased and what ones decreased may be entirely arbitrary.

It is important to note that the "corrective" term cannot be a function of observed frequencies alone. It cannot be a Robin Hood principle that takes from the rich and gives to the poor, nor can it be a biblical principle that gives more to those who already have much and takes away from those who have little. This fact can be proved as follows: Since the normalizing conditions must be satisfied for every value of n, fix n. Consider first a case in which k, the number of attributes, is equal to n, the number of elements in the sample, and in which each attribute occurs just once. In this case,

$$\frac{m_i}{n} = \frac{1}{k} = \frac{1}{n}.$$

According to the normalizing conditions, the inferred values must sum to one, so we have

$$\sum_{i=1}^{k}\left[\frac{m_i}{n} + c\left(\frac{1}{k}\right)\right] = k \times c\left(\frac{1}{k}\right) + \sum_{i=1}^{k}\frac{m_i}{n} = k \times c\left(\frac{1}{k}\right) + 1 = 1.$$

Hence,

$$k \times c\left(\frac{1}{k}\right) = 0,$$

and since $k \neq 0$,

$$c\left(\frac{1}{k}\right) = c\left(\frac{1}{n}\right) = 0.$$

Now let m_1 be any number such that $0 \leq m_1 \leq n$. Let $m_i = 1$ for $i = 2$, $3, \ldots, k$. This time the normalizing condition yields

$$\sum_{i=1}^{k}\left[\frac{m_i}{n} + c\left(\frac{m_i}{n}\right)\right] = \frac{m_1}{n} + c\left(\frac{m_1}{n}\right) + \sum_{i=2}^{k}\left[\frac{m_i}{n} + c\left(\frac{1}{n}\right)\right] = 1.$$

Since, as we have just shown, $c(1/n) = 0$,

$$\frac{m_1}{n} + c\left(\frac{m_1}{n}\right) + \sum_{i=2}^{k}\frac{m_i}{n} = 1 = \sum_{i=1}^{k}\frac{m_i}{n} + c\left(\frac{m_1}{n}\right).$$

Since

$$\sum_{i=1}^{k}\frac{m_i}{n} = 1,$$

it follows that

$$c\left(\frac{m_1}{n}\right) = 0.$$

Since the argument is perfectly symmetrical with respect to i,

$$c\left(\frac{m_i}{n}\right) = 0$$

for any possible value of m_i. If c is a function of the relative frequency alone, it is identically zero.

Another possible basis for the "corrective" term is the language in which we are attempting to carry out our inference. For example, the a priori rule mentioned above makes its inferred value depend upon the number of predicates used to describe the balls drawn from the urn.

Since there are three color *terms* involved, it sanctions the conclusion that the limit of the relative frequency is one third for each. Unlike the counterinductive method, it does not violate the normalizing conditions, but like that rule, it does violate the convergence requirement. This rule, of course, does not really make any use of the observed frequency, but we can still speak of it in terms of the observed frequency plus a "corrective" term. In this case, $c = -m_i/n + 1/k$.

I have argued elsewhere that rules which make the "corrective" term depend upon the features of language are not to be considered acceptable.[131] For example, the inferred value of the limit of the relative frequency of *red* draws from the urn can be changed from one third to one fourth by the simple device of defining two new terms, "dark blue" and "light blue," which are together equivalent to "blue," thereby transforming k from three to four. It seems evident that such an arbitrary alteration of an irrelevant aspect of the language ought not to have any bearing upon the inference we make concerning the limiting frequency of red balls being drawn from the urn.

In order to exclude rules that share this type of defect, I have suggested the *criterion of linguistic invariance* as a requirement to be met by any inductive rule. The general idea behind this criterion is that inductive relations between objective evidence and factual hypotheses depend upon the *content* of the evidence statements and the hypotheses, but not upon the linguistic form in which they are stated. We would all agree, for instance, that it makes no difference whether evidence and hypothesis are stated in terms of the metric system or the English system. They can be stated in either way, and translated back and forth. If an experimental finding strongly confirms a physical hypothesis, it does so regardless of which formulation is chosen. Similarly, given that the evidence and hypothesis can be equivalently formulated in English, French, German, or Russian, the inductive relation is independent of the choice of language. More precisely, the criterion can be stated as follows:

> *The criterion of linguistic invariance:* If S and S′ are statements in the same or different languages such that (1) S asserts that a certain relative frequency $F^n(A, B)$ obtains in a sample of size n, (2) S′ is equivalent to S by virtue of the semantical and syntactical rules of the languages in which they occur, and (3) rule R sanctions the inference from S that
>
> $$\lim_{n \to \infty} F^n(A, B) = q$$

then R must not sanction the inference from S' that

$$\lim_{n \to \infty} F^n(A, B) = q$$

where $p \neq q$.

The foregoing formulation is framed with particular reference to rules for inferring limits of relative frequencies from observed frequencies. More generally, the criterion could be stated:

> If (1) e and e' are any two evidence statements in the same or different languages, (2) h and h' are two hypotheses in the same languages as e and e', respectively, and (3) e is equivalent to e' and h is equivalent to h' by virtue of the semantical and syntactical rules of the languages in which they occur, then the inductive relation between e and h must be the same as the inductive relation between e' and h'.

This general requirement can, it seems to me, be transformed into the following consistency requirement for inductive logic:

> No inductive rule shall permit mutually incompatible conclusions to be drawn from any single consistent body of evidence.

This principle can be illustrated by application to the a priori rule. Given that seven tenths of the observed draws from the urn have yielded red, infer that the limit of the relative frequency of red is one third. This inference (in which the observed frequency enters only vacuously) is formulated in the language containing the predicates "red," "yellow," and "blue." Formulating the parallel inference in the language containing the predicates "red," "yellow," "light blue," and "dark blue," we find we are permitted to infer, from the fact that seven tenths of the observed draws from the urn have yielded red, that the limit of the relative frequency of red is one fourth. These two conclusions from the same consistent body of observational evidence are incompatible. For this reason, as well as failure to satisfy the convergence requirement, the a priori rule is unsatisfactory.[132]

Carnap's earlier systems of inductive logic were subject to precisely the same criticism unless it was blocked by the rather unappetizing requirement of descriptive completeness.[133] Without this requirement, it was possible to show that the addition or removal of irrelevant predicates (not occurring in either the evidence or the hypothesis) could alter the degree of confirmation and consequently the estimate of the relative frequency.

I shall illustrate with a concrete example, but in order to do so I must introduce Carnap's concept of a *Q-predicate*.[134] A Q-predicate is, in certain ways, strongly analogous to a state description. A state description is the strongest type of *statement* that can be formulated in a language for inductive logic; a Q-predicate is the strongest kind of *predicate* that can be formulated in such a language. In our simple illustrative language we had only one predicate "F," so there were only two things we could say about a given individual, namely, that it has the property F, or that it does not have the property F. "F" and "~F" are the two Q-predicates in that language. Suppose, now, that we expand that language by adding another primitive predicate "G" that is logically independent of "F." In this larger language we can say much more about our individuals, namely, for each individual x there are the following four possibilities:

$$1.\ Fx \cdot Gx \qquad 3.\ {\sim}Fx \cdot Gx$$
$$2.\ Fx \cdot {\sim}Gx \qquad 4.\ {\sim}Fx \cdot {\sim}Gx$$

These are the Q-predicates. Notice that these are not state descriptions, for each one refers to only one individual, while state descriptions must describe each individual. In general, for a language containing k primitive predicates that are logically independent of each other, there are 2^k Q-predicates obtained by either affirming or denying each primitive predicate of any individual. A Q-predicate provides a complete description of any individual. Any predicate in the language is equivalent to one or more of the Q-predicates. For instance, "F" is equivalent to the disjunction of the first two Q-predicates above.

A general formula can be given for the so-called "singular predictive inference" on the basis of the Q-predicates.[135] Let "M" be some predicate —not necessarily a primitive predicate or a Q-predicate—that can be expressed in the language. Let h be the hypothesis that a given unobserved individual has the property M. Let e be the statement that n individuals (not including the one mentioned in h) have been examined, and m of them have been found to exhibit the property M. The probability that an unobserved individual has the property M, on the basis of this evidence, is given by

$$c^*(h, e) = \frac{m + w}{n + 2^k}$$

where w is the number of Q-predicates to which M is reducible, i.e., w is the *logical width* of M. In our miniature language with three individual names and one primitive predicate (two Q-predicates), we calculated the probability that the third individual c had the property F, given that *a* and *b* both had that property. The degree of confirmation was found to be three fourths, in obvious agreement with the above formula, for in that case $n = 2$, $m = 2$, $w = 1$, and $2^k = 2$.

Let us compute the same probability in a new language which is identical to the former language except for the addition of the new primitive predicate "*G*." The evidence *e* and hypothesis *h* remain unchanged. Now, however, as already noted, "*F*" is no longer a *Q*-predicate, but is expressible in terms of the first two *Q*-predicates. Therefore, *w* now equals two and 2^k now equals four. In the new language, as the above formula reveals, the degree of confirmation of precisely the same hypothesis on precisely the same evidence has changed from three fourths to two thirds! This is an obvious violation of the criterion of linguistic invariance.[136]

The criterion of linguistic invariance has, itself, been challenged in various ways. Its strongest defense is, in my opinion, on the grounds that it is a consistency requirement whose violation allows for the possibility of explicit logical contradiction. Suppose, for example, that we can infer from one set of premises S that

$$\lim_{n \to \infty} F^n(A,B) = p$$

and from a logically equivalent set of premises S' we can infer that

$$\lim_{n \to \infty} F^n(A,B) = q$$

where $p \neq q$. Under the normal rules of logical procedure, we could substitute S for S' in the second inference, with the result that we would have two distinct values *p* and *q* for the same limit on the basis of one consistent set of premises S. Since it is a fundamental fact that limits of sequences are unique wherever they exist, the foregoing inference has resulted in a self-contradiction.

Moreover, if limits of relative frequencies are to be taken as probabilities, such inferences will lead to a violation of the criterion of admissibility, for the probability calculus requires the uniqueness of probabilities.

The foregoing justification of the criterion of linguistic invariance seems to me to be decisive for any inductive theory that admits rules of acceptance. Carnap's inductive logic admits no such rules, so the criterion of linguistic invariance cannot be defended for its ability to exclude rules of acceptance that lead to contradiction. An inductive logic that has no rules of acceptance has no worries on this score. There is, however, another argument that can be brought to bear. If degrees of confirmation are linguistically variant in the manner illustrated above, they can lead to incoherent betting systems. Consider the odds to be given or taken in a bet on whether the third ball to be drawn from the urn will be red. Since the degree of confirmation of red is (by the second calculation) two thirds, a bettor Smith should be willing to give odds of two to one that the next draw will yield red. At the same time, the degree of confirmation of red is (by the first calculation) three fourths, so Smith should be willing to take odds of three to one that the next draw will be nonred. If he does both of these things, a book can be made against him. A sly bookie could get him to bet \$3 on red at odds of one to three, and \$1.25 on nonred at odds of two to one. With these bets he must lose whatever happens. If red occurs, he wins \$1 on the first bet and loses \$1.25 on the second; if nonred occurs, he wins \$2.50 on the second bet and loses \$3 on the first. This is not a happy situation for Smith.

At one time I thought that the convergence requirement, the normalizing conditions, and the criterion of linguistic invariance were sufficient to justify induction by enumeration as the basic inductive rule for inferring limits of relative frequencies. I no longer hold this view. Alternative inductive rules that are not eliminated by these considerations can be formulated. Ian Hacking has shown, for instance, that rules deviating from induction by enumeration, in a way that depends upon the internal structure of the observed sample, can satisfy all of these requirements.[137] He has not, however, produced a rule that he or anyone else would be anxious to defend. Carnap, however, has been working on serious proposals that deviate from induction by enumeration and cannot be eliminated by the above criteria.[138]

Using the three criteria, I have shown that the "corrective" term c cannot be a function of n alone or of m_i/n alone. The criterion of linguistic invariance rules out any c that is a function of i or k (alone or in combination with other variables) if k is the number of *predicates* and i is an index of *predicates*. Predicates are linguistic entities—names of attributes or properties—so their number and arrangement can be altered by arbitrary linguistic manipulations. If, however, c is taken to be a function of the *attributes* themselves, rather than names of them, the criterion of linguistic invariance is inapplicable. Attributes, in contrast to predicates, are not linguistic entities, so their nature is not affected by linguistic manipulations.

Although the problem of the "corrective" term is not entirely resolved, I find it difficult to conceive of an inductive method, embodying a nonvanishing "corrective" term that is a function of the attributes themselves, that is not perniciously arbitrary in some fashion. In his excellent survey of a continuum of inductive methods, Carnap showed how it is possible to isolate an *empirical factor* and a *logical factor*.[139] The empirical factor is the observed frequency; the logical factor is the "corrective" term. If the logical factor depends upon the language, the criterion of linguistic invariance will eliminate the rule. The logical factor might, however, depend upon the attributes themselves. Suppose, for example, that the logical factor depends upon the number of attributes that are exemplified anywhere in the universe. We could hardly be expected to know that number prior to all applications of inductive logic. Suppose instead that the logical factor depends upon the number of attributes in a "family"; in our examples, the colors constitute a family of attributes. Again, it would seem that any partition of the color spectrum into separate color attributes would involve some sort of arbitrariness. Moreover, even if we know somehow the precise number of color properties, the color spectrum could be partitioned in infinitely many ways to yield the correct number of divisions. If it is not the number of properties we need, but rather some characteristics of these properties, things become no easier. We may think of green as a cool color and red as a hot color, but what possible bearing could these characteristics of the colors have upon the frequency with which they occur? These characteristics of the colors are nonfrequency characteristics—in sharp contrast to the fact that green is a color you run into a lot in nature, while red is comparatively rare. It would seem to follow, from Hume's arguments concerning our inability to know a priori about the connections between distinct properties, that we cannot know anything about the relations between frequency and nonfrequency characteristics of colors prior to the use of induction. What kind of knowledge could it be? The nonfrequency characteristics of properties are to be built into the very inductive rules for inferring frequencies, and these rules are designed to produce useful knowledge of frequencies. Is the "corrective" term an expression of a new kind of synthetic a priori proposition concerning the relation between the phenomenological characteristics of color attributes and the frequencies with which these attributes occur? I am deeply troubled by the logical interpretation of probability, for it seems to escape the pernicious arbitrariness of linguistic variance only by embracing what may turn out to be an even more pernicious apriority.

The personalistic theorist has a much easier answer to the question about the "corrective" term. We need not, he would say, imagine ourselves facing a question about frequencies with a blank mind which is only capable of recording observations and making inductive inferences. We have some sort of prior opinion about the frequencies we are trying to infer. We use observational data to modify that prior opinion. If the observed frequency does not coincide with the prior opinion, the prior opinion is able to supply the "corrective" term. The details of the inference are given by Bayes' theorem, which will be discussed more fully below.

The frequency theorist is by no means stuck with the observed frequency as the inferred value of the limit of the relative frequency in all cases. Induction by enumeration is a method to be applied only where we have no information beyond the observed frequency in the sample upon which to base our inference. Even in that case, it is perfectly consistent to maintain that probability is, by definition, the limit of the relative frequency, but probabilities are to be ascertained by some rule besides induction by enumeration. If, however, induction by enumeration is adopted as the basic inductive rule, it is still subject to correction. Suppose, for instance, that a die has been tossed thirty times and the side one has come up six times for a relative frequency of one fifth. We examine the die and see that it appears to be symmetrical, and the tossing mechanism appears to be unbiased. We do *not* conclude that the limit of the relative frequency of side one is one fifth, for we have a great deal of other experience with the tossing of symmetrical objects, and this experience confirms by and large the view that the alternatives are equiprobable. This is not a regression to the classical interpretation. It is an inductive inference from a large body of frequency information. In such cases the inference from the large body of frequency data supersedes the inference by induction by enumeration from the more restricted data regarding only the class of tosses of that particular die.

Before leaving the discussion of rules for inferring limits of relative frequencies, I must explain one serious argument against induction by enumeration. This point has been made by Carnap. We have already seen that an incoherent betting system is one in which the bettor must lose no matter what happens. The requirement of coherence guards against this situation. Another undesirable type of betting system is one in which the bettor may lose, but he cannot win. This is not quite as bad as incoherence, for it does leave open the possibility that he will come out even. As long, however, as winning is an impossibility, a system of bets is irrational. Carnap therefore sets up a stronger requirement than coherence; it is known as *strict coherence*.[140] Induction by enumeration, it turns out, seems to violate this condition. Suppose that all observed *A* have been *B*, so the observed frequency is one. That is the value we infer for the limit. If this value is translated into betting odds, it means that the bettor will risk *any stake whatever* against an opponent's stake of zero value that the next *A* will be a *B*. This is surely an irrational kind of bet. If the bettor "wins" he wins nothing, whereas if he loses, he loses a stake that has a value.

In view of this undesirable feature of induction by enumeration, we might be tempted to introduce the "corrective" term simply as a safety factor. Its function would be to keep inferred values away from the extremes of zero and one. It is hard to know exactly what form the safety factor should take. If it is too cautious it will make us pass up favorable bets because of the risk; if it is too liberal it will lead us to make rash bets. The fact of the matter is, of course, that a statement about the limit of the relative frequency is synthetic, and we can never be sure of the truth of a synthetic assertion. Hence, we must not take any such inferred value and use it uncritically to determine betting odds. Other factors enter in, especially the amount of inductive evidence we have to support the inference in question.

The Confirmation of Scientific Hypotheses

Quite early in this essay, I acknowledged the fact that induction by enumeration is a far cry from what we usually regard as scientific inference. When we think of scientific reasoning, we are likely to bring to mind the grand theories like those of Galileo, Newton, Darwin, or Einstein, and to contemplate the manner in which they were established. This is in obvious contrast to the attempt to infer the limit of a relative frequency from the observed frequency in an initial section of a sequence of events. Scientific inference is usually thought to be hypothetico-deductive in structure. Induction by enumeration is puerile, as Francis Bacon remarked, and the hypothetico-deductive method is regarded as a great improvement over it. As we saw earlier, however, the hypothetico-deductive method is a mode of *ampliative* inference, and this warrants our treating it as a species of induction. It differs in fundamental respects from deduction.

During the nineteenth century, two ways of contrasting induction and deduction gained some currency, and they are still with us. Both arose from a consideration of the hypothetico-deductive method, and both are fundamentally mistaken. First, induction was held to be the inverse of deduction. In the hypothetico-deductive schema, a *deduction* from premises to conclusion establishes a prediction to be confronted with empirical fact. If the prediction happens to be true, an *induction* from the conclusion to the premises confirms the hypothesis.[141] Second, it was also held that deductive inference is a method of justification, while inductive inference is a process of discovery. The deduction of a prediction from a hypothesis and initial conditions is the heart of the inference by which we test hypotheses. The inductive inference is taken to be the process of trying to think up an appropriate hypothesis to serve as a premise in the foregoing deduction. William Whewell called it "guessing." [142]

The distinction between discovery and justification is extremely important, but it is not coextensive with the distinction between induction and deduction. Our earlier discussion of the hypothetico-deductive method gives ample reason for refusing to merge these two distinctions. The justification of hypotheses is not purely deductive. Even after a hypothesis has been thought up, there is still a nondemonstrative inference involved in confirming it. To maintain that the truth of a deduced prediction supports a hypothesis is straightforwardly inductive. Leaving the problem of discovery entirely aside, we must still separate deductive and inductive elements of scientific inference.

The view that induction is the inverse of deduction appears to be based upon an extremely widespread misconception concerning the relations between induction and deduction. This notion may not often be explicitly stated and defended, but it seems to arise easily if one reflects a little upon the nature of logic. It may rank as the leading unconscious misconception regarding induction. This view takes inductions to be defective deductions—deductions that do not quite make the grade. An induction, according to this notion, is some sort of approximation that does not fully achieve the status of valid deduction. Inductive inferences are seen as fallacies we are not quite willing to reject outright; they are more to be pitied than condemned.

Pervasive misconceptions usually have an element of truth, and this one is no exception. Deductions *are* limiting cases of inductions in certain respects. The logical necessity relating premises and conclusion in valid deduction can be regarded as the limiting case of the high probabilities we attempt to achieve for our inductions.[143] At the same time, the emptiness of valid deduction is also a limiting case of decreasing the ampliative character of inductions, but this side of the coin seems not to be as frequently noticed. The main trouble with the "almost-deduction" theory of induction is that it does not furnish a concept of approximation to deduction that enables us to distinguish good inductions from plain logical errors. If anything, it tends to direct attention away from finding one. Instead of motivating a careful logical analysis of induction, it tends to make us think we should behave like social workers, providing underprivileged inductive inferences with the necessities enjoyed by valid deductions.

Let me take a moment to mention some of the defects from which these inferences that do not quite make the grade may suffer. For one thing, an inference may be an *enthymeme*—i.e., a valid deduction with a suppressed premise. Inductions have this characteristic; they can be transformed into valid deductions by supplying a suitable premise. The most monstrous *non sequitur* ever to find its way into a freshman theme can also be transformed into a valid deduction in this way! Enthymematic character certainly cannot serve as a criterion of inductive correctness.

Another defect consists in having premises that differ only slightly from those required to satisfy a valid deductive schema. For instance, an almost universal premise may be all we have when a strictly universal premise is needed. Thus, we may think that contraposition, although not strictly valid, is inductively sound. We may think it a good induction to infer "Almost all philosophers are unkind" from "Almost all kind people are nonphilosophers." Unfortunately, the moment we depart from strict universality in our premises we forego any semblance of logical correctness, deductive or inductive. In this case it is an all-or-none affair; approximation does not help.[144]

Most deductive fallacies that have been named and catalogued bear some resemblance to valid deductive forms. Furthermore, they are arguments people are tempted upon occasion to accept. When one becomes aware that his pet argument commits a common fallacy—say, the fallacy of the undistributed middle—the obvious move is to claim that it was never meant as a valid deduction, but only as an induction. In this way, deductive fallacies become, *ipso facto,* correct inductions. "All logicians are mongolian idiots" thus qualifies as a sound inductive conclusion from the premises "All logicians are living organisms" and "All mongolian idiots are living organisms."

The hypothetico-deductive method is another type of argument that seems to approximate deductive validity. From a hypothesis, in conjunction with statements of initial conditions whose truth is not presently being questioned, a prediction is deduced. Observation reveals that the prediction is true. We conclude that the hypothesis is confirmed by this outcome. The inference is, as certain nineteenth-century theorists insisted, an inverse of deduction. By interchanging the conclusion with one of the premises it can be transformed into a valid deduction. Without the interchange, however, the inference goes from conclusion to premise, for we seek to establish the hypothesis on the ground of the true prediction. It is a deductive fallacy closely akin to affirming the consequent. These are not adequate credentials for admission into the class of correct inductions.

Questions of deductive validity are generally referred to systems of formal logic, and they usually admit definite and precise answers. Questions of inductive correctness are far more frequently answered on an intuitive or common-sense basis. Although there have been various efforts, of which Carnap's is the leading example, to formalize inductive logic, such systems have not gained wide acceptance. In spite of their existence, few important questions are decided on a formal basis. Actually, however, the mathematical calculus of probability itself is an invaluable formal tool which is too often ignored in the treatment of problems in inductive logic.[145] It provides, as I shall try to show, important insight into the structure of scientific inference. In order to prepare the ground for the application of the mathematical calculus of probability to the problem of the confirmation of scientific hypotheses, I shall first discuss two important contemporary attacks upon the hypothet-ico-deductive method.

1. Hanson's Logic of Discovery. Even when we recognize that inductive inference is not properly characterized as a process of discovery, and even if we admit the existence of an inductive logic of justification, there still remains the important question of whether any kind of logic of discovery can exist. The received answer among contemporary philosophers of science is negative. The process by which we think up scientific hypotheses is, they say, strictly a psychological affair. It is not and cannot be reduced to a set of rules of procedure. The discovery of hypotheses requires insight, ingenuity, and originality. The process of finding answers to scientific questions cannot be transformed into a mechanical routine. Science, they say, is not a sausage machine into which you feed the data and by turning a crank produce finished hypotheses.

The standard answer is, nevertheless, a very disappointing one. It is frustrating for someone who is seriously grappling with a difficult scientific problem to be told that logic has no help whatever to offer him in thinking it through. Only after the interesting, original, creative work is done can logic be brought to bear. According to the received opinion, logical analysis can be used for the dissection of scientific corpses, but it cannot have a role in living, growing science. This view relegates philosophy of science to an intolerable position in the eyes of some philosophers. In protest, N. R. Hanson has tried to show that logic has bearing upon the unfinished business of science by arguing that, in addition to the admittedly psychological aspects of scientific innovation, certain logical considerations properly enter into the discovery of hypotheses.[146]

The issue can be thrown into relief by considering the situation in deductive logic, where important answers have been rigorously established.[147] The problem is familiar from elementary mathematics. Some kinds of problems can be solved by following a routine procedure; others cannot. If such a procedure does exist, we say that there is an *algorithm.* The most obvious example is that differentiation is routine; integration is not. In deductive logic we can distinguish several situations. First, given a set of premises, we may be asked to find a valid conclusion of some particular sort. For example, given two categorical propositions, there is a mechanical method for finding all valid syllogistic conclusions. Such methods exist only for very restricted realms of logic. Second, given a set of premises and a conclusion, we may be asked to determine whether that conclusion follows validly from those premises. In this case, we are not asked to discover the conclusion, but we are, in effect, being asked to discover a proof. If there is a mechanical method for answering this kind of question, we say that a *decision method* exists. For the propositional calculus we have a decision method in the truth tables, but there is no decision method for the whole of the lower functional calculus. It is not merely that we have failed to devise a decision method; the impossibility of a decision method has been proved.[148] Third, given a set of premises, a conclusion, and an alleged demonstration of the conclusion, we may be asked to determine whether the demonstration is valid. This is the kind of question deductive logic is designed to answer. Such a logic is a logic of justification, not a logic of discovery. The question of the existence of a deductive logic of discovery can be stated precisely and answered unambiguously.

Turning to the problem of a logic of discovery for empirical science, we must be careful not to pose the question in an unreasonable way. To suggest that there might be a mechanical method that will necessarily generate true explanatory hypotheses is a fantastic rationalistic dream. Problems of discovery completely aside, there is no way of determining for certain that we have a true hypothesis. To make such a demand upon a logic of discovery is obviously excessive. Not since Francis Bacon has any empiricist regarded the logic of science as an algorithm that would yield all scientific truth.

What might we reasonably demand of our logic of discovery if there is to be such a thing? Hanson, and Peirce before him, answer not that it must generate true hypotheses, but that it should generate *plausible conjectures*. Hanson believes this demand can be fulfilled. He begins by distinguishing "reasons for accepting a hypothesis *H*" from "reasons for suggesting *H* in the first place." He elaborates as follows:

> What would be our reasons for accepting *H*? These will be those we might have for thinking *H* true. But the reasons for suggesting *H* originally, or for formulating *H* in one way rather than another, may not be those one requires before thinking *H* true. They are, rather, those reasons which make *H* a *plausible type of conjecture*.[149]

Philosophers who have argued against the existence of a logic of discovery have maintained that the process of discovery is governed entirely by psychological factors. Hanson readily admits the existence of nonlogical aspects of the discovery of hypotheses, but he claims that there are, in addition, perfectly good logical reasons for regarding hypotheses of a particular type as those most likely to succeed. These reasons are logically distinct from the kinds of reasons that later, in the case of successful hypotheses, make us elevate the hypothesis from the status of plausible conjecture to the status of acceptable, true, or highly confirmed hypothesis. Hanson continues:

> The issue is whether, *before* having hit a hypothesis which succeeds in its predictions, one can have good reasons for anticipating that the hypothesis will be one of some particular *kind*. Could Kepler, for example, have had good reasons, before his elliptical-orbit hypothesis was established, for supposing that the successful hypothesis concerning Mars' orbit would be of the noncircular kind?[150]

There is a crucial switch in these two sentences. In the first, Hanson refers to what happens before we have "hit" a hypothesis; this means, I take it, before it came to mind. In the second sentence, he discusses what happens before a hypothesis is "established," but not necessarily before anyone thought of it. There is, presumably, a time between first thinking of a hypothesis and finally accepting it during which we may consider whether it is even plausible. At this stage we are trying to determine whether the hypothesis deserves to be seriously entertained and tested or whether it should be cast aside without further ceremony.

I do not want to be misunderstood as attempting a historical or psychological account of the actual course of scientific thought. The point is strictly logical. There are, it seems to me, three logically distinct aspects of the treatment of scientific hypotheses. It is easy to talk in terms of a temporal sequence of steps, but this is merely a manner of speaking. It does not matter which comes first or whether they are, in fact, mixed together. There are still three distinct matters: (1) thinking of the hypothesis, (2) plausibility considerations, and (3) testing or confirmation.

Hanson has argued (correctly I think) that there is an important logical distinction between plausibility arguments and the testing of hypotheses, but he has (mistakenly I think) conflated plausibility arguments with discovery. Continuing with Kepler as an example, Hanson discusses hypotheses that would have been rejected by Kepler as implausible.

Other *kinds* of hypotheses were available to Kepler: for example, that Mars' *color* is responsible for its high velocities, or that the dispositions of Jupiter's moons are responsible. But these would not have struck Kepler as capable of explaining such surprising phenomena. Indeed, he would have thought it *un*reasonable to develop such hypotheses at all, and would have argued thus.[151]

Kepler would, quite plainly, have rejected such hypotheses *if they had occurred to him*. There is no reason to suppose, however, that these considerations were psychologically efficacious in preventing Kepler from thinking of such hypotheses (although they might have been efficacious in preventing him from mentioning them) and in causing him to think of others instead. Furthermore, it does not matter in the slightest. What does matter is that, had such unreasonable hypotheses crossed Kepler's mind, plausibility arguments would have sufficed to prevent them from coming to serious empirical testing.

One basic question remains. Plausibility arguments have been distinguished from hypothesis testing and confirmation on the one hand and from the psychology of discovery on the other. What, precisely, is their status? Are plausibility considerations psychological or subjective in character? Do they play a legitimate role in science, or do they merely express the prejudices of the scientist or the scientific community? Are they different in kind from the considerations involved in the confirmation of hypotheses? An answer to this question will be forthcoming when we look more closely at what the probability calculus tells us about confirmation.

2. *Popper's Method of Corroboration.* In my earlier discussion of Karl Popper's attempt to avoid the problem of induction, I explained his

rejection of induction by enumeration and his denial that the hypothet-ico-deductive method is a suitable way of confirming scientific hypotheses. Popper maintains it is *not* the function of science to produce highly probable hypotheses or hypotheses that are highly confirmed by the evidence. If it were, the way would be left open for relatively vacuous hypotheses that are better classed as metaphysics than as science. The aim of science is rather to find hypotheses that have great content and make important assertions about the world. Such hypotheses are bold conjectures, and their very boldness makes them highly falsifiable. Moreover, every effort must be made to find evidence that does falsify such hypotheses. A highly falsifiable hypothesis that has withstood serious efforts at falsification is highly corroborated.

The process of corroboration bears some resemblance to confirmation. An unsuccessful attempt to falsify a hypothesis is precisely what the hypothetico-deductive theorist would identify as a positive confirming instance. There is, however, a crucial difference. The hypothetico-deductive theorist attempts to start with probable hypotheses and find further support for them through positive confirmations. If more than one hypothesis is available to explain all the available data, the hypothetico-deductivist would choose the most probable one. Popper's method of corroboration, by contrast, tries to begin with the least probable hypothesis, for probability is related inversely to content.[152] It seeks to falsify this hypothesis. Failure to do so tends to increase the degree of corroboration. If more than one hypothesis remains unfalsified, we select the least probable one. Thus, one might say, Hanson attacks the hypothetico-deductive method for failure to take account of *plausibility* arguments, while Popper attacks the same method for failure to incorporate *implausibility* considerations. While it appears that Hanson's attack and Popper's attack are mutually incompatible, I shall try to show that each one has a valid foundation, and each points to a fundamental shortcoming of the hypothetico-deductive approach. I shall argue that the logical gaps in the hypothetico-deductive method can be filled by means of the ideas suggested by Hanson and Popper and that these ideas lead us to indispensable, but often neglected, aspects of the logic of scientific inference.

3. *Bayesian Inference.* The basic trouble with the hypothetico-deductive inference is that it always leaves us with an embarrassing superabundance of hypotheses. All of these hypotheses are equally adequate to the available data from the standpoint of the pure hypothetico-deductive framework. Each is confirmed in precisely the same manner by the same

evidence.[153] An hypothesis is confirmed when, in conjunction with true statements of initial conditions, it entails a true prediction. Any other hypothesis that, in conjunction with (the same or different) true statements of initial conditions, entails the same prediction is confirmed in the same way by the same evidence. It is always possible to construct an unlimited supply of hypotheses to fill the bill. It is essentially a matter of completing an enthymeme by supplying a missing premise, and this can always be done in a variety of ways. The hypothetico-deductive method is, therefore, hopelessly inconclusive for determining the acceptability of scientific hypotheses on the basis of empirical data. Something must be done to improve upon it.

It is at this point that the probability calculus can come to our aid. In a preceding section I showed how a simple form of Bayes' theorem follows from axioms for the probability calculus: [154] If $P(A, C) \neq 0$,

$$P(A \cap C, B) = \frac{P(A, B) \times P(A \cap B, C)}{P(A, C)}$$

$$= \frac{P(A, B) \times P(A \cap B, C)}{P(A, B) \times P(A \cap B, C) + P(A, \bar{B}) \times P(A \cap \bar{B}, C)}.$$

As a theorem in the uninterpreted calculus of probability, it is entirely noncontroversial. It was concretely illustrated by means of a simple example. Its application to examples of that type is also straightforward. Now, let me stretch and bend the meanings of words a bit in order to begin an explanation of the application of Bayes' theorem to the problem of the confirmation of scientific hypotheses. In the previous example, we might say, Bayes' theorem was used to calculate the probability of a "cause" and to assign a probability to a "causal hypothesis." A red card was drawn, and we asked how this "effect" came about. There are two "possible causes"—throwing a one and drawing from the half red deck or throwing some other number and drawing from the largely black deck. While we are still abusing causal language, let us describe the probabilities required to calculate the probability of the "causal hypothesis." We need two other probabilities in addition to $P(A \cap B, C)$, the probability of the "effect" given the "causal hypothesis." We need $P(A, B)$, the *prior probability* of the "cause," and we need $P(A, C)$ or $P(A \cap \bar{B}, C)$, depending on the version of Bayes' theorem we pick. $P(A, C)$ is the probability of the "effect" regardless of the "cause" from which it issues; $P(A \cap \bar{B}, C)$ is the probability of the "effect" if our "causal hypothesis" is false.

There is no difficulty in understanding all these probabilities in our simple game of chance, but things get much more complex when we try to apply Bayes' theorem to genuine scientific hypotheses. Serious problems of interpretation arise. I shall claim, nevertheless, that Bayes' theorem provides the appropriate logical schema to characterize inferences designed to establish scientific hypotheses. The hypothetico-deductive method is, I think, an oversimplification of Bayes' theorem. It is fallacious as it stands, but it can be rectified by supplementing it with the remaining elements required for application of Bayes' theorem.

Let us, therefore, compare the hypothetico-deductive method with Bayes' theorem. From an hypothesis H and statements of initial conditions I, an observational prediction O is deducible. For purposes of this discussion we assume I to be true and unproblematic. Under this assumption H implies O. We can provide a loose and preliminary interpretation of Bayes' theorem, even though many difficult problems of interpretation remain to be discussed. Let "A" refer to hypotheses like H; let "B" refer to the property of truth; and let "C" refer to the observed result with respect to the prediction O. If positive confirmation occurs "C" means that O obtains; in the negative case "C" designates the falsity of O. This interpretation makes the expression on the left-hand side of Bayes' theorem refer to precisely the sort of probability that interests us; "$P(A \cap C, B)$" designates the probability that a hypothesis of the sort in question, for which we have found the given observational result, is true. This is the probability we are looking for when we deal with the confirmation of scientific hypotheses.

In order to compute the value of $P(A \cap C, B)$, the *posterior probability* of our hypothesis, we need, as we have seen, three probabilities. The hypothetico-deductive method provides only one of them. Given that H implies O and that O obtains, $P(A \cap B, C) = 1$. Inspection of Bayes' theorem reveals, however, that this value is entirely compatible with a small posterior probability for the hypothesis. A small value for $P(A, B)$ and a large value for $P(A \cap \bar{B}, C)$ nullify any tendency of the confirmation to enhance the value of $P(A \cap C, B)$. Successful confirmation requires attention to all three required probabilities, only one of which is provided by the hypothetico-deductive argument. Notice, however, that Bayes' theorem embodies the asymmetry between confirmation and falsification. If H implies O and O does not obtain, then $P(A \cap B, C) = 0$, and it follows immediately that the posterior probability of the hypothesis, $P(A \cap C, B)$, likewise equals zero. Falsification holds a special place in the logic of scientific inference, as Popper has emphasized.[155]

We are left with the task of interpreting the remaining probability expressions so that they will have meaning for the logic of scientific inference. Consider the prior probability $P(A, B)$. It is the probability that our hypothesis is true regardless of the outcome of our prediction. This probability is logically prior to the empirical test provided by the hypothetico-deductive method. How are we to make sense of such a probability? Regardless of our detailed answer, one preliminary point is apparent. Prior probabilities fit the description of Hanson's plausibility arguments. Plausibility arguments embody considerations relevant to the evaluation of prior probabilities. They are logically prior to the confirmatory data emerging from the hypothetico-deductive schema, and they involve direct consideration of whether the hypothesis is of a type likely to be successful. These plausibility arguments do not, of course, constitute a logic of discovery. *They are not only admissible into the logic of justification; they are an indispensable part of it.* Bayes' theorem requires the prior probabilities as well as the confirmatory data, so plausibility arguments as well as hypothetico-deductive arguments are essential elements of a logic of scientific inference. We shall have to discuss these plausibility arguments with more precision, but we have at least succeeded in locating them in the general schema.

The denominator of Bayes' theorem can be written in either of two ways because of the theorem on total probability.[156] The simpler form involves $P(A, C)$, the probability of obtaining the observational result regardless of the truth of our hypothesis H. The more complex form requires $P(A, \bar{B})$ and $P(A \cap \bar{B}, C)$. $P(A, \bar{B})$ is logically linked with $P(A, B)$, so it involves nothing new. $P(A \cap \bar{B}, C)$ is logically independent of $P(A \cap B, C)$; it is the probability of getting our observational result if the hypothesis H is false. Either form of the theorem makes it obvious that we must consider the probability that our prediction would come true even if our hypothesis were false. Other things being equal, the less probable our observational result if the hypothesis is false, the more this observational result confirms the hypothesis.

I have already discussed Popper's eloquent plea for the view that scientific hypotheses, to be worthwhile, must run the risk of falsification. The more falsifiable they are, and the more strenuously we have tried to falsify them, the better they are, as long as they survive the tests without being falsified. Popper maintains that the more falsifiable they are the less probable they are (and this is a *prior* probability). To the extent that hypothetico-deductive theorists have been aware of prior probabilities, they have claimed that hypotheses are better confirmed if they have higher prior probabilities—i.e., if they are more plausible. Popper claims better corroboration for hypotheses that are more audacious and less plausible.

I cannot accept Popper's view that we ought not to be concerned with confirming hypotheses and enhancing their posterior probabilities. It seems to me that Bayes' theorem gives us an unequivocal answer to the question of whether we ought to regard high prior probability as an asset or a liability. Plausibility contributes positively to the acceptability of hypotheses. Nevertheless, Popper has, it seems to me, a fundamental insight. There is another way for a hypothesis to run a risk of falsification, and this is revealed by Bayes' theorem. A hypothesis risks falsification by yielding a prediction that is very improbable unless that hypothesis is true. It makes a daring prediction, for it is not likely to come out right unless we have hit upon the correct hypothesis. Confirming instances are not likely to be forthcoming by sheer chance. This state of affairs is reflected in a small value for $P(A \cap \bar{B}, C)$. The hypothesis that runs this kind of risk of falsification without being falsified gains more in posterior probability than one that runs less of such risk. This does not mean, however, that the hypothesis itself must be implausible. A small value for $P(A \cap \bar{B}, C)$ is perfectly compatible with a large value for $P(A, B)$. This question of falsifiability is nicely illustrated by an example from the history of optics. Early in the nineteenth century, when the wave theory of light was coming into its own, Poisson deduced as a consequence of that theory that the shadow of a disc should have a bright spot in its center. Poisson regarded this derivation as a *reductio ad absurdum* of the wave theory, but Arago was later able to announce triumphantly that a positive result was obtained when the experiment had been performed. The wave theory had been confirmed! [157] This was indeed an impressive confirmation, for the predicted consequence surely seemed utterly unlikely on any other hypothesis. It is not that the wave theory itself was so improbable; the thing that was really improbable was the occurrence of the bright spot in the middle of the shadow *if the wave theory were not true*.

Compare the foregoing example with one of the opposite sort. About fifteen years ago a pseudo-psychological theory known as *dianetics* gained considerable popularity.[158] This theory embodied an explanation of psychological disorders and recommended a course of treatment. Dianetic therapy was widely practiced, and it seems undeniable that a number of "cures" were effected. People with neurotic symptoms who underwent the prescribed treatment exhibited definite improvement.

These results must be considered confirming evidence for dianetic theory, but they lend very little support to it. The trouble is that the same results are very probable even if the dianetic hypothesis is false, so $P(A \cap \bar{B}, C)$ is high. It is well known that many psychological disorders are amenable to faith healing. They can be cured by *any* method the patient sincerely believes to be effective. There is no doubt that many people had great faith in dianetics, so faith healing constitutes a better explanation of the cures than does the dianetic "hypothesis" itself.

In most of Popper's statements about probability and content he makes it fairly clear that he regards a low *prior* probability as a desirable feature in a scientific hypothesis.[159] There is one passage, however, in which he seems strongly to suggest that he is referring, not to prior probability, but to the probability $P(A \cap \bar{B}, C)$ of the experimental result in case the hypothesis is false. This is the probability for which, in contrast to the prior probability of the hypothesis, a *low* value tends to enhance the posterior probability of the hypothesis.

A theory is tested not merely by applying it, or by trying it out, but by applying it to very special cases—cases for which it yields results different from those we should have expected without that theory, or in the light of other theories. In other words we try to select for our tests those crucial cases in which we should expect the theory to fail if it is not true. Such cases are "crucial" in Bacon's sense; they indicate the crossroads between *two* (or more) theories. For to say that without the theory in question we should have expected a different result implies that our expectation was the result of some other (perhaps an older) theory, however dimly we may have been aware of this fact. But while Bacon believed that a crucial experiment may establish or verify a theory, we shall have to say that it can at most refute or falsify a theory. It is an attempt to refute it; and if it does not succeed in refuting the theory in question—if, rather, the theory is successful with its unexpected prediction—then we say that it is corroborated by the experiment. (It is the better corroborated the less expected, or the less probable, the result of the experiment has been.)[160]

I have quoted this passage, not to try to reveal any inconsistency in Popper's writings, but rather to show how admirably his conception, as expressed in the foregoing remarks, fits the Bayesian schema. The quoted statement does a splendid job of describing the concrete example from optics.

Bayes' theorem casts considerable light upon the logic of scientific inference. It provides a coherent schema in terms of which we can understand the roles of confirmation, falsification, corroboration, and plausibility. It yields a theory of scientific inference that unifies such apparently irreconcilable views as the standard hypothetico-deductive theory, Popper's deductivism, and Hanson's logic of discovery. However, it still poses enormous difficulties of interpretation. We have been concerned so far mainly with the formal characteristics of Bayes' theorem, and the hints at interpretation have been purposely vague. The formal schema requires prior probabilities, but what precisely are they? To link them with Hanson's plausibility arguments does not get us far. The notion of prior probability cries out for further clarification, and it must be sought in the light of the interpretation of the probability concept in general. I shall discuss this issue from the standpoint of each of the three leading interpretations presented above.

1. According to the logical interpretation, as we have seen, probability is fundamentally an a priori measure of possible states of affairs. The state descriptions provide a list of all possible states of the universe, and weights are assigned to them. A scientific hypothesis will be true if certain of these state descriptions hold, but false if others do. The set of all state descriptions compatible with the hypothesis is its range, and the prior probability of the hypothesis is the sum of the values attached to the state descriptions in its range. The accumulation of observational evidence enables us to calculate posterior probabilities of hypotheses in accordance with Bayes' theorem, and the prior probabilities are available as required. For the reasons already stated, I reject this interpretation precisely because it embodies a priori prior probabilities. They play an indispensable role in determining the probabilities of factual hypotheses, and their status is extremely dubious.

2. According to the personalistic interpretation, probabilities are simply degrees of belief in the truth of statements. The probability calculus imposes conditions upon the relationships among these various degrees of conviction, but if they do not violate these conditions they are rational. That is all the personalistic interpretation requires. Prior probabilities are totally unproblematic for the personalist. When a hypothesis is entertained we have a certain degree of conviction in its truth. It does not matter whether this is based upon solid evidence, sheer prejudice, or unfettered emotion. This *is* the prior probability of the hypothesis. Further experience may affect this degree of belief, thus issuing in posterior probabilities. Bayes' theorem expresses the relations that must hold among these various degrees of belief if the probability calculus is not to be violated. Theorists who cannot swallow a priori prior probabilities may find it difficult to see where prior probabilities of any other kind are to be found. The personalistic theorists answer this question for them. Prior opinion is always available, so the prior probabilities required by

Bayes' theorem are never lacking. So completely are the personalists wed to Bayes' theorem that they have even taken its name and are now known as "Bayesians." [161]

An examination of Bayes' theorem reveals the fact that a prior probability of zero or one determines by itself the same value for the posterior probability. In the remaining cases, the prior probability has only a part in determining the posterior probability. Under some rather mild assumptions, the role played by the prior probabilities becomes smaller and smaller as observational evidence increases. This fact has been rightly accorded a central place in the arguments of the Bayesians. We come to any problem, according to the personalistic theorist, with opinions and preconceptions. The prior convictions of reasonable people can differ considerably. As these individuals accumulate a shared body of observational evidence, the differences of opinion will tend to disappear and a consensus will emerge. The influence of the prior opinion will fade in the face of increasing evidence if the prior opinions do not have the extreme values zero and one. It is not necessary that these individuals be genuinely open-minded about the various hypotheses; it is enough if their minds are slightly ajar.[162] Before the advent of the personalistic theory, there was great reluctance to admit that Bayes' theorem could be applied at all in dealing with the confirmation of scientific hypotheses. The trouble seemed to lie with the prior probabilities. Any way of handling them seemed to make them unacceptably a priori or subjectively slippery. Methods of confirmation which would not require these unrespectable entities were sought. The Bayesian attitude toward this program is nicely captured in a paraphrase of a statement by de Finetti, the foremost contemporary personalistic theorist: "People noticing difficulties in applying Bayes' theorem remarked, 'We see that it is not secure to build on sand. Take away the sand, we shall build on the void.' " [163] The personalist, however, rejects the methods that ignore prior probabilities, and he willingly embraces them with their full subjectivity. As an excellent recent account of the Bayesian approach puts it: "Reflection shows that any policy that pretends to ignore prior opinion will be acceptable only insofar as it is actually justified by prior opinion." [164] By showing how the use of Bayes' theorem leads to substantial intersubjective agreement, the personalists argue that the subjectivity of prior probabilities is not pernicious.

I enthusiastically applaud the emphasis the personalistic theorists have placed upon the use of Bayes' theorem, but I cannot accept their far-reaching subjectivism. Although satisfaction of the relations established by the probability calculus is a necessary condition for the rationality, it is not a sufficient condition. Other requirements for rational belief need to be found. The Bayesians themselves seem to acknowledge this need when they impose further conditions upon the prior probabilities in order to insure convergence of opinion in the light of evidence. Prior probabilities are not, of course, alone in being subjective. All of the other probabilities that enter into Bayes' theorem are likewise subjective. This includes the probability $P(A \cap B, C)$ that the observational evidence would occur if the hypothesis in question were true, and the probability $P(A \cap \bar{B}, C)$ that it would occur if the hypothesis were false. All these subjective probabilities may actually be based upon extensive observation and inductive generalization therefrom, but they may also be lacking any foundation whatever in objective fact. As nearly as I have been able to tell, there is no reason within the personalistic framework to reject as irrational a set of opinions which conflicts with the bulk of experience and dismisses this fact on the ground that most observation is hallucinatory. Moreover, I cannot see any ground for characterizing as irrational opinions that have arisen out of observation by application of some perverse inductive method. Although the personalist can reject a series of opinions based upon the counterinductive rule because it violates the normalizing conditions, it is easy to formulate a normalized counterinductive rule that satisfies these conditions but still makes past experience a negative guide to the future:

$$\text{From } F^n(A, B) = \frac{m}{n}, \text{ to infer } \lim_{n \to \infty} F^n(A, B) = \frac{1}{k-1} \times \frac{n-m}{n}$$

The fact that this rule is not asymptotic would not invalidate its use on strictly personalistic grounds. Personalistic theorists do not actually condone misuses of experience in either of the foregoing ways, but the principles by which they avoid them need to be spelled out, examined, and justified.

3. As we have seen, the frequency interpretation defines probability as the limit of the relative frequency with which an attribute occurs in an infinite sequence of events. This definition gives rise immediately to the problem of application of probability to the single case. In my earlier discussion of the frequency theory I outlined a way of dealing with this problem. At the same time, I mentioned another problem of application that presents difficulties for the frequentist. This is the problem of explicating the logic of the confirmation of scientific hypotheses in terms of frequencies. It has been persuasively argued that the relation between

evidence and scientific hypothesis cannot be understood exclusively in terms of frequency concepts—in particular, it has seemed outrageous to maintain that prior probabilities of scientific hypotheses could be construed as relative frequencies.[165] The two problems are not unrelated, for the probability of hypotheses is an instance of the problem of the single case. Any given scientific hypothesis, as a single entity, is either true or false—just as a single toss of a coin results in a head or does not.

The specification of the attribute class is of no particular difficulty for the frequentist attempting to apply probability to the single case; the whole difficulty rests with the selection of the reference class. The rule is to select the broadest homogeneous reference class available. In the effort to show how the frequency concept of probability can be made relevant to the probability of hypotheses through the use of Bayes' theorem, we must find the appropriate prior probability $P(A, B)$.[166] This is the probability that hypotheses of a certain type are true. The attribute of truth is given directly by the fact that we are looking for true hypotheses. In attempting to choose an appropriate reference class, we are trying to find out what type of hypothesis is likely to be true. This is how Hanson describes the plausibility considerations whose importance he so staunchly defends. A hypothesis that belongs to the class of plausible conjectures is one that has a high prior probability. One that belongs to the class of preposterous conjectures is one that has a vanishingly small prior probability. The interesting question is how we are to determine what considerations are relevant to plausibility or prior probability. Characteristics that are statistically relevant to the truth or falsity of scientific hypotheses are properties that determine a homogeneous reference class. To evaluate a given hypothesis H, we try to find a (practically or epistemically) homogeneous reference class A to which H belongs. A must be a class of hypotheses within which we can say something about the relative frequency of truth. The probability $P(A, B)$ is the probability of truth for hypotheses of this class, and this probability is assigned as a weight to the hypothesis H. This weight, which might be distinguished as a *prior weight*, expresses the plausibility of H.

The characteristics by means of which the reference class A is determined are properties that are logically independent of the confirmatory evidence for the hypothesis H. A prior probability is logically, although not necessarily temporally, prior to the observational verification of the prediction made on the basis of the hypothetico-deductive schema. In many of the interesting cases, the prior probability is not used to determine prior weight; instead, the probability itself is fed into Bayes' theorem along with other probabilities, in order to calculate the posterior probability $P(A \cap C, B)$. This probability yields a *posterior weight* which is based upon plausibility considerations *and* confirmatory evidence.

As examples of the kinds of considerations that serve as a basis for plausibility judgments, Hanson mentions analogy and symmetry. I should like to attempt a larger and more systematic classification. There are, it seems to me, three important types of characteristics that may be used as a basis for plausibility judgments. These characteristics determine the relevant reference class, but they may also be regarded as criteria of plausibility that hypotheses must confront. Success in meeting a given criterion will classify a hypothesis with other plausible hypotheses; failure will group it with implausible ones.

1. Formal criteria. Scientific hypotheses are proposed, not in an epistemic vacuum, but against the background of many previously accepted hypotheses and many that have already been rejected. The newly proposed hypothesis may bear to accepted hypotheses deductive relations that are germane to the plausibility of the new one. If an old hypothesis H_1 entails a new hypothesis H_2, then the *prior probability* of H_2 is at least as great as the *posterior probability* of H_1. If a new hypothesis H_3 is incompatible with an old hypothesis H_4, then the prior probability of H_3 is no greater than the probability that H_4 is false—i.e., one minus the posterior probability of H_4. This point is well illustrated by Velikovski's notorious book, *Worlds in Collision*. This so-called theory, designed to explain certain alleged events as related in the *Old Testament*, entails the falsity of virtually all of modern physics. When the editors of *Harpers Magazine* complained that the scientific world was falling down on its objectivity by refusing to subject Velikovski's "theory" to extensive physical tests, they were overlooking the power and legitimacy of plausibility arguments and prior probabilities.[167]

2. Pragmatic criteria. Although we have all been warned repeatedly about the dangers of confusing the source of a theory with its truth, or the origin with the justification, there are cases in which it is possible to establish a probability relation between the truth of a hypothesis and the circumstances of its discovery. If a religious fanatic without any training in physics or mathematics shows up on our doorstep with a new hypothesis to replace Einsteinian relativity, complaining that most scientists refuse him a fair hearing, we justly place a low estimate on the chances that his hypothesis is true. Considerations of this kind are legitimate only if there is a known probability relation between the character of the individual presenting the hypothesis and the truth of the

hypothesis he advances. If, however, the rejection of the hypothesis is based only upon an emotional reaction to its origin—e.g., the fellow has a beard, which makes a very unfavorable impression—it is flagrantly fallacious.

Pragmatic criteria are, perhaps, less reliable than others, but they are used by scientists, and there is no need to be embarrassed by the fact. They are as objective as any other kinds of considerations. Martin Gardner provides many fascinating examples of the application of pragmatic criteria.[168]

3. Material criteria. Just as relations of entailment or incompatibility can exist between different hypotheses, so too, I think, can there be significant inductive relations among them. This, I suspect, is what Hanson regards as analogy. Certain types of hypotheses have been successful; we may legitimately expect new hypotheses that are similar in relevant respects to be successful as well. Hypotheses are considered plausible, then, on the basis of their analogy with other successful hypotheses. The material criteria encompass those respects in which hypotheses may be relevantly similar to one another.

It is beyond the scope of this essay to attempt any exhaustive list of considerations relevant to the prior probabilities of scientific hypotheses. Relevance is an empirical matter, so the determination of relevant characteristics of hypotheses is a task for empirical science rather than philosophy. It is possible, nevertheless, to indicate what is involved in the material criteria by citing a few familiar examples.

Although no one can say just what simplicity is, everyone seems to agree that it is a very desirable characteristic of scientific hypotheses. A certain type of simplicity lends beauty and elegance to the hypothesis and ease to its application, but such economic and aesthetic considerations are secondary when an issue of truth or falsity is at stake. At this point a different type of simplicity is invoked. We place more confidence in simple than in complex hypotheses for purposes of explaining a given body of fact.[169] We judge the simpler hypothesis more likely to be true. We have learned by experience that this works, and at the same time we have learned by experience to avoid oversimplification.

Hypotheses can sometimes be distinguished through the kinds of causal processes they countenance. For instance, the fight to purge science of its teleological elements has been long and arduous. The explanation of natural phenomena in terms of conscious purposes must have seemed extremely plausible to primitive man. One notable way in which the physics of Galileo and Newton improved upon the physics of

Aristotle was by eliminating the teleological elements in the latter. The admirable success of nonpurposeful explanation in physics provided an important precedent for nonteleological evolutionary theories in biology. The success of these theories in biology has provided a strong basis for assigning low prior probabilities to teleological hypotheses in psychology and sociology. A teleological biological theory like Lecomte du Noüy's *Human Destiny* suffers from a high degree of implausibility.

As a final example, let me sketch some plausibility arguments relating to the nature of physical space. Nothing could seem less plausible to primitive man than the idea that space is homogeneous and isotropic. Everyday experience incessantly confirmed the notion that there is a physically preferred direction. This theory was charmingly elaborated by Lucretius, who held that the primordial state of the universe consisted of all the atoms falling downward. Moreover, this theory implied that space is inhomogeneous. A distinction among different locations was required to support the theory of uniform downward motion as opposed to rest. The doctrine of inhomogeneity and anisotropy persisted in the geocentric cosmologies, and in the early heliocentric ones as well. By Newton's time it had waned considerably. On the supposition that space is Euclidean and lacking in privileged locations or directions, a rather strong plausibility argument can be made for the inverse square law of gravitational attraction. Since the surface of a sphere is proportional to the square of its radius, the supposition that the gravitational force "spreads out" uniformly through space leads to the conclusion that it is inversely proportional to the square of the distance.

These considerations of homogeneity and isotropy extend to the twentieth century and underlie the plausibility arguments for special relativity. As Adolf Grünbaum has convincingly argued, Einstein saw in his famous principle of relativity a notion so plausible that it demanded formulation and incorporation into physical theory.[170] The principle of relativity is not proved by these plausibility arguments, but it does achieve the status of a hypothesis that deserves elaboration and testing. The plausibility arguments that support the principle of relativity are so compelling that some theorists have elevated the principle to the status of a priori truth.[171] I think my brief sketch shows that its plausibility was won by long, hard experience, and that its contradictory, although extremely implausible, is not *logically impossible*.

I hope these few examples of material criteria provide some idea of the kind of plausibility argument falling under that head. The material criteria are the most important and the most interesting. Formal criteria, based upon deductive relations among hypotheses, are less frequently applicable. When they are applicable they tend to provide only maximum or minimum values. Pragmatic criteria tend to be less reliable, but not so unreliable as to be illegitimate. Material criteria supplement both other kinds and fill out the plausibility argument.

The foregoing three types of plausibility considerations—the formal criteria, the pragmatic criteria, and the material criteria—have been offered in an attempt to show how the frequency interpretation of probability can be used to approach the prior probabilities of scientific hypotheses. We have now seen how each of the major probability theories views the prior probabilities. We have seen, accordingly, that there are three distinct answers to the question of the grounds on which we can legitimately decide what kinds of hypotheses are likely to succeed. Some people would say that there are a priori principles to determine prior probabilities; they belong in the camp of the logical theorists. Others would say it is a matter of subjective predilection; they belong in the camp of the personalistic theorists. I think that both of these answers are fundamentally mistaken. There is, in my opinion, only one acceptable answer: *experience.* Those who agree in regarding experience as the only foundation for prior probabilities belong in the camp of the frequentists. This is why I remain an unregenerate frequentist against what seem to many theorists to be overwhelming difficulties. Any other answer regarding the status of prior probabilities is, to me, epistemologically unthinkable.

It may appear that my whole discussion has done very little to show how the frequentist can assign anything like precise values of prior probabilities. In fact, it may seem quite doubtful that it even makes sense to suppose exact numerical values can be established. Such an evaluation would not be too far from the truth, but fortunately it is not especially damaging to the frequency position. Numerical precision is not required, for Bayes' theorem will be applicable if we can merely judge whether or not our hypothesis is totally implausible, preposterous, and absurd. The important issue is whether the prior probability can be taken as zero for all practical purposes. If so, the hypothesis can be disqualified from further consideration—at least for the time being. Inspection of the formula reveals that a value of zero for $P(A, B)$ settles the question—in that case $P(A \cap C, B)$ is likewise zero. If however, the prior probability of the hypothesis is nonzero, the question of its posterior probability remains open. Even a very small prior probability is compatible with a very high posterior probability. Suppose we have a hypothesis with a low, but nonvanishing, prior probability. Suppose, however, that $P(A \cap \bar{B}, C)$ is also very small—i.e., the hypothesis has been confirmed by an observation whose likelihood is very small on the assumption that the hypothesis is false. Under these conditions, the posterior probability of the hypothesis can be quite large. As the personalistic theorists have emphasized, in nonextreme cases the prior probability tends to be swamped by increasing observational evidence.[172] This is a mathematical characteristic of Bayes' theorem as a formula in the uninterpreted probability calculus, so it depends in no way upon the interpretation one chooses. Thus, it is true for the frequentist as well, so that a large inaccuracy in the assessment of the prior probability may have a negligible effect upon the resulting posterior probability if a reasonable amount of confirmatory evidence is accumulated.

The Bayesian theory of scientific inference finds a very natural place for what has been known traditionally as *induction by elimination*. When Bacon sought a method to supersede induction by enumeration, he developed a system that proceeded by eliminating false hypotheses. John Stuart Mill followed him in this move. Popper's deductivism is certainly a method of elimination—of falsification—although it is controversial whether to regard it as inductive as well. The traditional objection against induction by elimination is that it is impotent in the face of an unlimited supply of possible hypotheses, for we never arrive at a unique hypothesis as a result. While this objection is valid against any form of induction by elimination that proceeds by trying to eliminate from the class of all possible hypotheses, it is not pertinent to the eliminative inference based upon Bayes' theorem. There are, as I have emphasized repeatedly, infinitely many possible hypotheses to handle any finite body of data, but it does not follow that there is any superabundance of *plausible* ones. Indeed, in practice it is often extremely difficult to think up even a couple of sensible hypotheses to explain a given problematic datum. If we put plausibility arguments—perhaps I should say "implausibility arguments"—to the purely negative task of disqualifying hypotheses with negligible prior probabilities, falsification or elimination becomes a practical approach. This is, it seems to me, the valid core of the time-honored method of induction by elimination. Like the hypothetico-deductive method, induction by elimination becomes intelligible and defensible when it is explicated in the light of Bayes' theorem, and when the indispensable role of prior probabilities is recognized.

Two basic objections have often been raised against the notion that the confirmation of scientific hypotheses could be explicated by means of the frequency interpretation. One is the objection just discussed concerning the difficulty of interpreting prior probabilities as frequencies. The second objection seems to have little to do with prior probabilities, but it becomes tractable in the Bayesian framework. It is universally recognized that the degree to which a hypothesis is confirmed depends not only upon the number of confirming instances, but also upon their variety. For instance, observations of the position of Mars confirm Newton's theory, but after a certain number of these observations each new one contributes very little to the confirmation of the theory. We want some observations of falling bodies, some observations of the tides, and a good torsion balance experiment. Any confirming instance of one of the subsequent sorts would contribute far more to the confirmation of the theory than would another observation of Mars. All of this is intuitively obvious, but—so the objection goes—the frequency interpretation cannot incorporate this basic fact about confirmation into its theory. The most it can do is *count* confirming instances; it cannot distinguish among them qualitatively.[173]

A consideration of prior probabilities seems to me to show how the problem of variety of instances can be overcome. We must note, first of all, that there is a fundamental difficulty in the very concept of variety. Any observation is different from any other in an unlimited number of ways, and any observation is similar to any other in an unlimited number of ways. It is therefore necessary to characterize similarities and differences that are relevant to confirmation. I suggest the following approach. A general hypothesis has a certain domain of applicability, and the basic idea behind the variety of instances is to test the hypothesis in different parts of its domain. It is always possible to make arbitrary partitions of the domain, but a splitting of the domain is significant only if it is not too implausible to suppose that the hypothesis holds in one part of the domain but not in another. Now we could strongly insist upon having observations of Mars on Tuesdays and Sundays as well as the other days of the week, in months whose names contain the letter "r," in years that leave a remainder of three when divided by seven, etc. However, we do not find it plausible to suppose that Newton's law holds for Mars in some of these subdomains but not in others. By contrast, it is not completely absurd to suppose that Newton's law would be suitable for bodies of astronomic dimensions located at astronomic distances from one another, but that it does not hold for smaller masses and shorter distances. Consequently, the observation of falling bodies is relevantly different, for one of the bodies involved is small even though the other (earth) is large. After observation has verified the law for falling bodies, the torsion balance experiment is very important, for it measures gravitational attraction between two bodies both of subastronomic size. The variety of instances helps us to eliminate other hypotheses, but such elimination has a point only if the alternative hypotheses being tested have nonnegligible prior probabilities.

Conclusion

The analysis of the inference by which scientific hypotheses are confirmed by observational evidence shows, I believe, that its structure is given by Bayes' theorem. This schema provides a place for the hypothetico-deductive method, showing that it is fallacious in its crude form, but that it can be made into a valid method when appropriately supplemented. Two kinds of probabilities are needed to supplement the hypothetico-deductive schema. We must assess the probability that our observational results would obtain even if the hypothesis under consideration were false. For strongest confirmation, this probability should be small. This seems a natural interpretation of Popper's methodological requirement that scientific hypotheses must be audacious and take risks. We must, in addition, assess the prior probabilities of the hypotheses we are considering. This is a reasonable interpretation of Hanson's demand for plausibility arguments.

I have argued not only that the inference schema is Bayesian, but that the probabilities that enter into the schema are to be interpreted as frequencies. It is through this interpretation, I believe, that we can keep our natural sciences empirical and objective. It enables us to show the relevance of probabilities to prediction, theory, and practical decision. Under this interpretation, induction by enumeration or a similar rule constitutes the basic inductive method for ascertainment of probabilities, but the Bayesian schema exhibits unmistakably the presence of enumerative and eliminative aspects of scientific inference, and it shows the relations between them.

If the frequency interpretation is adopted, Bayes' theorem cannot be applied until we have some experience with the success or failure of general hypotheses. On pain of infinite regress, we cannot claim that all such experience involves previous application of the Bayesian method. Instead, we must claim, logically prior to the use of Bayes' theorem some generalizations must have been established through induction by enumeration. These are hypotheses based upon crude inductive generalization, but they constitute the logical starting point. Each of them is rather shaky, owing to the childish quality of the induction by enumeration which supports it, but the more sophisticated inferences that follow can be very well founded. As evidence accumulates and further inductions are made, the results become more and more securely established.

The extensive examination of the foundations of scientific inference reveals, however, that neither induction by enumeration nor any comparable method has yet been satisfactorily justified. We cannot claim to have a well-established method for ascertaining fundamental probabilities. Hume's problem of the justification of induction remains at the foundations of scientific inference to plague those who are interested in such foundational studies.

NOTES

This essay is based upon five lectures in the Philosophy of Science Series at the University of Pittsburgh. The first two lectures, *Foundations of Scientific Inference: I. The Problem of Induction, II. Probability and Induction,* were presented in March 1963. The next two lectures, *Inductive Inference in Science: I. Hypothetico-Deductive Arguments, II. Plausibility Arguments,* were delivered in October 1964. The final lecture, *A Priori Knowledge,* was given in October 1965. The author wishes to express his gratitude to the National Science Foundation and the Minnesota Center for Philosophy of Science for support of research on inductive logic and probability.

1. Aristotle, *Posterior Analytics,* 100^b.
2. See, for example, Descartes, *Discourse on Method,* Pt. II, *Meditations,* or *Principles of Philosophy,* Pt. I.
3. Quoted from *Descartes Selections,* ed. R. M. Eaton (New York: Charles Scribner's Sons, 1927).
4. Francis Bacon, *Novum Organum,* aphorism xix.
5. For an excellent account of the development of calculus and the foundational problems it encountered see Carl B. Boyer, *The History of the Calculus and its Conceptual Development* (New York: Dover Publications, 1959); previously published under the title *The Concepts of the Calculus.*
6. For a simple exposition of this paradox see Bertrand Russell, *Introduction to Mathematical Philosophy* (London: Allen & Unwin, 1919), Chap. 13.
7. See Roderick M. Chisholm, "Sextus Empiricus and Modern Empiricism," *Philosophy of Science,* 8 (July 1941), 371–84.
8. I. Todhunter, *A History of the Mathematical Theory of Probability* (London, 1865).
9. John Venn, *The Logic of Chance,* 4th ed. (New York: Chelsea, 1962); 1st ed. 1866 (London).
10. *Collected Papers of Charles Sanders Peirce,* eds. C. Hartshorne and P. Weiss (Cambridge: Harvard U. Press, 1931), 6 vols.
11. John Maynard Keynes, *A Treatise on Probability* (London: Macmillan, 1952), 1st ed. 1921.

12. David Hume, *Enquiry Concerning Human Understanding*, sec. IV.

13. Sec. VII, 1.

14. For a more detailed account of the relation between deductive validity and factual content, see pp. 164–67.

15. The problem of the synthetic a priori is discussed in sec. II, 4.

16. Hume, *Human Understanding*.

17. Ibid.

18. Max Black, *Problems of Analysis* (Ithaca: Cornell U. Press, 1954), Chap. 11.

19. Ibid., pp. 196–97.

20. Lewis Carroll, "What the Tortoise Said to Achilles," in *The Complete Works of Lewis Carroll* (New York: Random House, n.d.).

21. I presented the following self-supporting argument for the counterinductive method in "Should We Attempt to Justify Induction?" *Philosophical Studies*, 8 (April 1957), 45–47. Max Black in "Self-supporting Inductive Arguments," *Models and Metaphors* (Ithaca: Cornell U. Press, 1962), Chap. 12, replies to my criticism, but he does not succeed in shaking the basic point: The counter-inductive rule is related to its self-supporting argument in precisely the same way as the standard inductive rule is related to its self-supporting argument. This is the "cash value" of claiming that the self-supporting argument is circular. Peter Achinstein, "The Circularity of a Self-supporting Inductive Argument," *Analysis*, 22 (June 1962), considers neither my formulation nor Black's answer sufficient, so he makes a further attempt to show circularity. Black's reply is found in "Self-Support and Circularity: A Reply to Mr. Achinstein," *Analysis*, 23 (December 1962). Achinstein's rejoinder is "Circularity and Induction," *Analysis*, 23 (June 1963).

22. Max Black, "The Justification of Induction," *Language and Philosophy* (Ithaca: Cornell U. Press, 1949), Chap. 3. The view he expresses in this essay, I believe, is closely related to the "probabilistic approach" I discuss below in Sec. II, 7.

23. Max Black, *Problems of Analysis*, p. 191.

24. Ibid., p. 206.

25. Compare Richard Bevan Braithwaite, *Scientific Explanation* (New York: Harper & Row, 1960), Chap. 8. I think the same general view is to be found in A. J. Ayer, *The Problem of Knowledge* (Penguin Books, 1956), p. 75. I have discussed Ayer's view in "The Concept of Inductive Evidence," *American Philosophical Quarterly*, 2 (October 1965).

26. See Braithwaite for a systematic exposition of this conception.

27. Sec. VII, "The Confirmation of Scientific Hypotheses," is devoted to a detailed analysis of this type of inference.

28. See John Patrick Day, *Inductive Probability* (New York: Humanities Press, 1961), p. 6. The nineteenth-century notion that induction is a process of discovery and the problem of whether there can be a logic of discovery are discussed in sec. VII below.

29. See e.g., Karl R. Popper, *The Logic of Scientific Discovery* (New York: Basic Books, 1959), sec. 30, and Thomas S. Kuhn, *The Structure of Scientific Revolutions* (Chicago: U. of Chicago Press, 1962). A fuller discussion of the relations among such concepts as deductive validity and content is given in sec. II, 5 below.

30. The most comprehensive statement of Popper's position is to be found in *The Logic of Scientific Discovery*. This is the English translation, with additions, of Karl R. Popper, *Logik der Forschung* (Wien, 1934).

31. "I think that we shall have to get accustomed to the idea that we must not look

upon science as a 'body of knowledge,' but rather as a system of hypotheses; that is to say, a system of guesses or anticipations which in principle cannot be justified, but with which we work as long as they stand up to tests, and of which we are never justified in saying that we know that they are 'true' or 'more or less certain' or even 'probable.'" *The Logic of Scientific Discovery*, p. 317.

32. I believe Popper openly acknowledges the nonampliative character of deduction. See "Why are the Calculi of Logic and Arithmetic Applicable to Reality," in Karl R. Popper, *Conjectures and Refutations* (New York: Basic Books, 1962), Chap. 9.

33. See *The Logic of Scientific Discovery*, Chap. 10.

34. Ibid., p. 270.

35. I shall return to Popper's methodological views in the discussion of confirmation in sec. VII. In that context I shall exhibit what I take to be the considerable valid content of Popper's account of the logic of science.

36. For a full account of the nature of logical systems, see Alonzo Church, *Introduction to Mathematical Logic* (Princeton: Princeton U. Press, 1956), I, especially secs. 7–10 and 30.

37. Church provides a full account of interpretations of logical systems. See especially sec. 43.

38. The possibility of drawing a useful distinction between analytic and synthetic statements has been vigorously challenged by Willard Van Orman Quine in "Two Dogmas of Empiricism," *From a Logical Point of View* (Cambridge: Harvard U. Press, 1953). I am evading the problems Quine raises by supposing that we can identify logical constants, definitions, and semantic rules.

39. For an excellent discussion of this conception see Willard Van Orman Quine, "Truth by Convention," in *Readings in Philosophical Analysis*, eds. H. Feigl and W. Sellars (New York: Appleton-Century-Crofts, 1949).

40. Arthur Pap, *Introduction to the Philosophy of Science* (New York: The Free Press of Glencoe, 1962), Chap. 6, becomes confused on this point. This confusion constitutes his basis for rejection of the doctrine of conventionalism regarding the status of logical truth.

41. Lucretius, *The Nature of the Universe*, trans. Ronald Latham (Baltimore: Penguin Books, 1951), p. 31.

42. Milton K. Munitz, *Space, Time and Creation* (New York: Collier Books, 1957), Chap. 9.

43. Lucretius, pp. 66 ff.

44. René Descartes, "Of God: That He Exists," *Meditations*, III.

45. Pap, p. 97.

46. For a detailed discussion of this type of time structure, see Adolf Grünbaum, *Philosophical Problems of Space and Time* (New York: Knopf, 1963), Chap. 7.

47. See Arthur Pap, *Semantics and Necessary Truth* (New Haven: Yale U. Press, 1958), p. 103 and passim, for discussion of this and other examples.

48. Immanuel Kant, *Critique of Pure Reason* and *Prolegomena to Any Future Metaphysic*.

49. For a history of these geometrical developments, see Roberto Bonola, *Non-Euclidean Geometry* (New York: Dover Publications, 1955).

50. See Hans Reichenbach, *Philosophy of Space and Time* (New York: Dover Publications, 1958), Chap. 1, and Adolf Grünbaum, op. cit., Pt. I.

51. For an extremely readable account of the Russell-Whitehead approach, see Bertrand Russell, *Introduction to Mathematical Philosophy* (London: Allen & Unwin, 1919). For an exposition and discussion of current views on the status of

arithmetic, see Stephan Körner, *The Philosophy of Mathematics* (London: Hutchinson U. Library, 1960).

52. Norman Kemp Smith, *Immanuel Kant's Critique of Pure Reason* (London: Macmillan, 1933), p. 218.
53. David Hume, *Human Understanding,* sec. IV.
54. Ibid.
55. Ibid.
56. Ibid.
57. Ibid.
58. Ibid.
59. Ibid.
60. Wesley C. Salmon, "The Uniformity of Nature," *Philosophy and Phenomenological Research,* 14 (September 1953).
61. Bertrand Russell, *Human Knowledge: Its Scope and Limits* (New York: Simon & Schuster, 1948).
62. John Maynard Keynes, *A Treatise on Probability* (1952), Chap. 22.
63. Russell, *Human Knowledge,* p. 496.
64. Ibid.
65. Ibid.
66. Ibid., Pt. VI, Chap. 9.
67. Ibid., p. 494.
68. Arthur Burks, "The Presupposition Theory of Induction," *Philosophy of Science* 20 (July 1953) and "On The Presuppositions of Induction," *Review of Metaphysics,* 8 (June 1955).
69. Sec. III.
70. Max Black, "The Justification of Induction," in *Language and Philosophy.*
71. Among the authors who subscribe to approaches similar to this are A. J. Ayer, *Language, Truth and Logic* (New York: Dover Publications, 1952); Paul Edwards, "Russell's Doubts about Induction," *Mind,* 58 (1949), 141–63; Asher Moore, "The Principle of Induction," *J. of Philosophy,* 49 (1952), 741–58; Arthur Pap, *Elements of Analytic Philosophy* (New York: Macmillan, 1949), and *An Introduction to the Philosophy of Science;* and P. F. Strawson, *Introduction to Logical Theory* (London: Methuen, 1952).
72. I have criticized this type of argument at some length in "Should We Attempt to Justify Induction?" *Philosophical Studies,* 8 (April 1957), and in "The Concept of Inductive Evidence," *American Philosophical Quarterly,* 2 (October 1965). This latter article is part of a "Symposium on Inductive Evidence" in which Stephen Barker and Henry E. Kyburg, Jr. defend against the attack. See their comments and my rejoinder.
73. This point has enormous import for any attempt to construct an inductive justification of induction. To decide whether the fact that induction has been successful in the past is positive evidence, negative evidence, or no evidence at all begs the very question at issue.
74. As I attempted to show in "Should We Attempt to Justify Induction?" this equivocation seems to arise out of a failure to distinguish *validation* and *vindication.* This crucial distinction is explicated by Herbert Feigl, "De Principiis non Disputandum . . . ?" in *Philosophical Analysis,* ed. Max Black (Ithaca: Cornell U. Press, 1950).
75. Hans Reichenbach, *Experience and Prediction* (Chicago: U. of Chicago Press, 1938), Chap. 5, and *The Theory of Probability* (Berkeley: U. of California Press, 1949), Chap. 11.
76. Sec. V, 5.

77. Leonard J. Savage, *The Foundations of Statistics* (New York: Wiley, 1954), p. 1.

78. The most famous axiomatization is that of A. N. Kolmogorov, *Foundations of the Theory of Probability* (New York: Chelsea, 1956). This work was first published in 1933.

79. An excellent introductory account of axiomatic systems can be found in Raymond L. Wilder, *Introduction to the Foundations of Mathematics* (New York: Wiley, 1956), especially Chaps. 1 and 2. Logical systems of the kind discussed in sec. II, 4, above can be presented axiomatically.

80. The axioms to be presented here are adapted from those given by Reichenbach in *The Theory of Probability*, secs. 12–14.

81. There are many excellent texts in which the basic logic of sets is presented— e.g., Wilder, Chap. 3, and Patrick Suppes, *Introduction to Logic* (Princeton: Van Nostrand, 1957), Chap. 9.

82. The Chevelier de Méré was aware that the probability of getting at least one six in three tosses of one die is less than one half while the probability of getting at least one six in four throws is over one half. He reasoned that, since the probability of a six on one throw of a die is one sixth while the probability of double six on one throw with a pair of dice is one thirty-sixth, the probability of double six in twenty-four tosses of a pair of dice should exceed one half. This is not correct. The probability is given by $1 - (35/36)^{24} = 0.4914$. In twenty-five tosses the probability exceeds one half.

83. For a simple and lucid account, see John G. Kemeny, "Carnap's Theory of Probability and Induction," in *The Philosophy of Rudolf Carnap*, ed. P. A. Schilpp (LaSalle, Illinois: Open Court, 1963), pp. 719 ff.

84. Carnap has appropriately distinguished classificatory, comparative, and quantitative concepts of probability. See *Logical Foundations of Probability* (Chicago: U. of Chicago Press, 1950; 2d ed., 1962), secs. 4, 5, and 8. The requirement of ascertainability should be taken as requiring the possibility in principle of classifying, comparative ordering, and quantitative evaluation respectively for the foregoing types of concepts. I have proceeded as if a quantitative concept is possible and desirable. For those who have serious doubts regarding quantitative probability concepts, see *Logical Foundations of Probability*, secs. 46–48.

85. Bishop Joseph Butler, *The Analogy of Religion* (1736), Preface (quoted by Carnap who quoted from Keynes; *Logical Foundations of Probability*, p. 247.)

86. Laplace is the most famous proponent of this view; see Pierre Simon, Marquis de Laplace, *A Philosophical Essay on Probabilities* (New York: Dover, 1951).

87. Excellent critical discussions are given by Richard von Mises, *Probability, Statistics and Truth*, 2d rev. English ed. (New York: Macmillan, 1957), pp. 66–81, and Hans Reichenbach, *The Theory of Probability*, secs. 68–69.

88. This contradiction is known as the "Bertrand Paradox." See von Mises, p. 77.

89. One can find formulations that sound subjective in many authors—e.g., Bernoulli, De Morgan, Keynes, Laplace, and Ramsey. On the question of whether these formulations are to be taken literally, see Carnap's illuminating discussion in *Logical Foundations of Probability*, sec. 12.

90. Ibid.

91. The classic elaboration of the logical interpretation is given in John Maynard Keynes, *A Treatise on Probability*. The most thorough and precise elaboration is to be found in Rudolf Carnap, *Logical Foundations of Probability*. For a brief and intuitively appealing presentation, see John G. Kemeny, "Carnap's Theory of Probability and Induction."

92. *Logical Foundations of Probability*, Appendix.

93. The details are given below, pp. 232–37.
94. See especially Rudolf Carnap, "Replies and Systematic Expositions," sec. V, "Probability and Induction" in *The Philosophy of Rudolf Carnap,* and the "Preface to the Second Edition" of *Logical Foundations of Probability.*
95. Rudolf Carnap, *The Continuum of Inductive Methods* (Chicago: U. of Chicago Press, 1952).
96. Carnap's early answer to this question was given in "Probability as a Guide of Life," *J. of Philosophy,* 44 (1947), 141–48, and was incorporated into *Logical Foundations of Probability,* sec. 49. The adequacy of the answer was challenged by Ernest Nagel in "Carnap's Theory of Induction," in *The Philosophy of Rudolf Carnap,* and Carnap responded in "Replies and Systematic Expositions," sec. 30 in the same book.
97. See *Logical Foundations of Probability,* secs. 44, 45, and 49–51.
98. Ibid., secs. 50–51.
99. See sec. II, 7 above.
100. Carnap's views on the problem of justification have undergone considerable development. In "On Inductive Logic," *Philosophy of Science,* 12 (1945), 72–97, sec. 16, he endorses Reichenbach's program of attempting a pragmatic justification of induction and regards Reichenbach's argument as a positive step in the right direction, although it does not constitute a complete justification. In *Logical Foundations of Probability* (1950), sec. 41F, Carnap argues that we can establish as an analytic degree of confirmation statement that on available evidence it is probable that the degree of uniformity of nature is high. Thus, "it is reasonable for X to take the general decision of determining all his specific decisions with the help of inductive methods, because the uniformity of the world is probable and therefore his success in the long run is probable on the basis of his evidence . . ." (p. 181). In his "Replies and Systematic Expositions," in *The Philosophy of Rudolf Carnap,* he says, "I understand the problem of the justification of induction as the question as to what kinds of reasons can be given for accepting the axioms of inductive logic. . . . It seems to me that the reasons to be given for accepting any axiom for inductive logic have the following characteristic features . . . :
     (a) The reasons are based upon our intuitive judgements concerning in-
         ductive validity, i.e., concerning inductive rationality of practical de-
         cisions (e.g., about bets).
   Therefore:
     (b) It is impossible to give a purely deductive justification of induction.
     (c) The reasons are a priori" (p. 978).
101. Because of an isomorphism between class logic and sentential logic, Carnap's logical interpretation can be seen to satisfy the axioms presented in sec. IV above, if the arguments of the probability function are taken as sentences instead of classes. Notice that the order of the arguments must be reversed.
102. Frank Plumpton Ramsey, "Truth and Probability," *The Foundations of Mathematics and Other Logical Essays,* ed. R. B. Braithwaite (New York: Humanities Press, 1950), provides the point of departure for this theory. Its leading current exponent is Bruno de Finetti. See *Studies in Subjective Probability,* eds. H. E. Kyburg, Jr., and H. E. Smokler (New York: Wiley, 1964), for a selection of the most important papers on the personalistic interpretation.
103. See Leonard J. Savage, *The Foundations of Statistics,* Chap. 3, sec. 1, for a discussion of measurement of personal probability.

104. It is for this reason that the probability calculus cannot, by itself, provide a justification of induction.
105. Sec. VII, 3.
106. See Rudolf Carnap, "The Aim of Inductive Logic" in *Logic, Methodology and Philosophy of Science,* eds. E. Nagel, P. Suppes, and A. Tarski (Stanford U. Press, 1962).
107. The classic presentation of the frequency interpretation is John Venn, *The Logic of Chance* (see Note 9). Two of the most important twentieth-century expositions are Richard von Mises, *Probability, Statistics and Truth,* and Hans Reichenbach, *The Theory of Probability.* Not all versions of the frequency interpretation require that probability sequences be infinite. For finite frequency theories, see R. B. Braithwaite, *Scientific Explanation,* Chap. 5, and Bertrand Russell, *Human Knowledge,* Pt. V, Chap. 3.
108. This type of objection was raised against my paper, "On Vindicating Induction," in *Induction: Some Current Issues,* eds. H. E. Kyburg, Jr., and E. Nagel (Middletown, Conn.: Wesleyan U. Press, 1963) by Max Black and others. See Black's comments, the discussion, and my reply in that volume.
109. For the proof, see Reichenbach, *The Theory of Probability,* sec. 18.
110. Ibid., sec. 69.
111. The foregoing formulation differs from Reichenbach's in that his formulation mentions a degree of approximation δ, but since no method of specifying δ is given, it seems to me the rule becomes vacuous. Ibid., p. 446. It seems better to state the rule so that it equates the observed frequency and the inferred value, making it a pragmatic matter to determine, in any given case, what degree of approximation of inferred value to the true value is acceptable.

    It is also advisable, I think, to regard inductive rules as rules of inference and to avoid referring to them as rules of estimation. The main reason for this decision is that Carnap has preempted the term "estimate" in such a way that rules of estimation are not acceptance rules. Statements about estimates are analytic in just the same way as confirmation statements. Values of estimates can never be detached and asserted. It is my view that inferences concerning limits of relative frequencies yield synthetic statements that can be detached and asserted. For this reason, I always speak of *inferred values* but never of *estimates.*
112. Ibid., sec. 91.
113. Ibid., p. 447.
114. Ibid.
115. For a discussion of Reichenbach's concepts of descriptive and inductive simplicity, see *Experience and Prediction,* sec. 42.
116. See Wesley C. Salmon, "The Predictive Inference," *Philosophy of Science,* 24 (April 1957), 180–82.
117. This is the condition grossly misnamed "consistency" by Sir Ronald A. Fisher, *Statistical Methods for Research Workers* (London: Oliver & Boyd, 1954), pp. 11–12.
118. Reichenbach, *The Theory of Probability,* secs. 71–72.
119. von Mises, *Probability, Statistics and Truth,* pp. 23 ff.
120. Carnap, *Logical Foundations of Probability,* secs. 44–45.
121. Ibid., secs. 49–51.
122. Reichenbach, *Experience and Prediction,* sec. 34. "We may say: *A weight is what a degree of probability becomes if it is applied to a single case*" (p. 314, italics in original).
123. Strawson, *Introduction to Logical Theory,* p. 235.

124. Ibid.
125. A. J. Ayer, "The Conception of Probability as a Logical Relation," in *Observation and Interpretation*, ed. S. Körner (London: Butterworth's, 1957).
126. Reichenbach, *The Theory of Probability*, sec. 72, especially p. 374, and sec. 56.
127. I have no desire to minimize the problem of the short run, which is quite distinct from the problem of the single case. See my papers "The Short Run," *Philosophy of Science*, 22 (July 1955); "The Predictive Inference," *Philosophy of Science*, 24 (April 1957); and "Vindication of Induction," in *Current Issues in the Philosophy of Science*, eds. H. Feigl and G. Maxwell (New York: Holt, Rinehart & Winston, 1961).
128. Carnap, *Logical Foundations of Probability*, secs. 9, 10, 41, and 42. Hugues Leblanc, *Statistical and Inductive Probabilities* (Englewood Cliffs, N.J.: Prentice-Hall, 1962), is devoted to demonstrating the close relations between the logical concept and statistical frequencies. Henry E. Kyburg, Jr., *Probability and the Logic of Rational Belief* (Middletown, Conn.: Wesleyan U. Press, 1961), argues for a logical interpretation in which probability statements are metalinguistic statements that mention finite frequency statements.
129. Ramsey, "Truth and Probability."
130. Wesley C. Salmon, "Regular Rules of Induction," *The Philosophical Review*, 65 (July 1956); "Vindication of Induction"; and "On Vindicating Induction."
131. Wesley C. Salmon, "Vindication of Induction"; "On Vindicating Induction"; "Inductive Inference," in *Philosophy of Science: The Delaware Seminar*, II, ed. B. H. Baumrin (New York: Wiley, 1963).
132. The criterion of linguistic invariance is discussed in the articles mentioned in the preceding note. In additon, it is further discussed and elaborated in two others of my articles: "Consistency, Transitivity, and Inductive Support," *Ratio* (forthcoming), and "Use, Mention, and Linguistic Invariance," *Philosophical Studies*, 7 (December 1965). It has been argued by Stephen Barker in "Comments on Salmon's 'Vindication of Induction,'" in *Current Issues in the Philosophy of Science*, and by Richard Rudner in his comments on my article and on Barker's discussion thereof, ibid., that no inductive rule can satisfy the criterion of linguistic invariance, and this includes induction by enumeration. Nelson Goodman's "grue-bleen" paradox is cited as the reason for this failure. I agree that this paradox poses a serious problem, and I have attempted to offer a solution in "On Vindicating Induction." This resolution requires that certain restrictions be placed upon the rule of induction by enumeration.
133. Carnap, *Logical Foundations of Probability*, sec. 18B and "Preface to the Second Edition."
134. Ibid., secs. 31–34.
135. Ibid., sec. 110C.
136. Kyburg, *Probability and the Logic of Rational Belief*, p. 49, discusses this difficulty, presenting a more realistic example.
137. Ian Hacking, "Salmon's Vindication of Induction," *J. of Philosophy*, 62 (May 1965).
138. John G. Kemeny, "Carnap's Theory of Probability and Induction," p. 722 f, proposes as a general *condition of adequacy* for any explication of degree of confirmation, "$c(h,e)$ is to depend only on the proposition expressed by h and e." Kemeny's discussion makes it clear that this condition, although far stronger than the criterion of linguistic invariance, does entail it. Carnap explicitly endorses this condition of adequacy; see "Replies and Systematic Expositions," p. 980.
139. Carnap, *The Continuum of Inductive Methods*, sec. 7.

140. See Kemeny, "Carnap's Theory of Probability and Induction," pp. 719–20; and Carnap, *The Continuum of Inductive Methods*, p. 43.
141. This view was espoused by W. Stanley Jevons, *The Principles of Science* (London: 1874).
142. William Whewell, *On the Philosophy of Discovery* (London: John W. Parker, 1860).
143. A word of caution is essential here. While axiom 2 of the probability calculus (p. 193 above) assures us that the probability of *h* on *e* is one if *e* entails *h*, the converse does not hold. See Carnap, *Logical Foundations of Probability*, sec. 58. For the analogous situation in the frequency interpretation, see Reichenbach, *The Theory of Probability*, pp. 54–55.
144. See Salmon, "Consistency, Transitivity, and Inductive Support," for further elaboration.
145. Ibid.
146. Norwood Russell Hanson, "Is There a Logic of Discovery?" *Current Issues in the Philosophy of Science*. I have tried to draw the distinction between a logic of discovery and a logic of justification in Hanson's spirit, but the contrast is drawn too dramatically. To suppose that the logic of justification is a "logic of the Finished Research Report" (p. 21) is tantamount to assuming that creative thought proceeds entirely unfettered by any critical standards until the creative work is finished. This supposition seems entirely implausible to me. I should think it is psychologically more realistic to regard discovery as a process involving frequent interplay between unfettered imaginative creativity and critical evaluation.
147. For an extremely lucid discussion of discovery and justification in deductive and inductive logic, see Carnap, *Logical Foundations of Probability*, sec. 43.
148. Church, *Introduction to Mathematical Logic*, sec. 46.
149. Hanson, "Is There a Logic of Discovery?" p. 22.
150. Ibid., p. 23.
151. Ibid.
152. Popper, *The Logic of Scientific Discovery*, p. 270.
153. I have tried to explain this elementary point in detail in *Logic* (Englewood Cliffs, N.J.: Prentice-Hall, 1963), sec. 23.
154. Pp. 194–5 above.
155. "Only if *the asymmetry between verification and falsification* is taken into account—that asymmetry which results from the logical relation between theories and basic statements—is it possible to avoid the pitfalls of the problem of induction." *The Logic of Scientific Discovery*, p. 265, italics in original.
156. Theorem 3, p. 194 above.
157. Max Born and Emil Wolf, *Principles of Optics* (New York: Pergamon Press, 1964), p. 375.
158. L. Ron Hubbard, *Dianetics: The Modern Science of Mental Healing* (Hermitage House, 1950). For an interesting account, see Martin Gardner, *Fads and Fallacies in the Name of Science* (New York: Dover, 1957), Chap. 22.
159. Popper, *The Logic of Scientific Discovery*, p. 270.
160. Popper, *Conjectures and Refutations*, p. 112.
161. "Bayesian statistics is so named for the rather inadequate reason that it has many more occasions to apply Bayes' theorem than classical statistics has." Ward Edwards, Harold Lindman, and Leonard J. Savage, "Bayesian Statistical Inference for Psychological Research," *Psychological Review*, 70 (May 1963). Under this "definition" of the Bayesian approach, Reichenbach would have to be included. "The range of application of Bayes' rule is extremely wide,

because nearly all inquiries into causes of observed facts are performed in terms of this rule. The *method of indirect evidence,* as this form of inquiry is called, consists of inferences that on closer analysis can be shown to follow the structure of the rule of Bayes." *The Theory of Probability,* p. 94. See also pp. 363, 432.

162. See Edwards, Lindman, and Savage, pp. 197–98 and 201–02.

163. Ibid., p. 208.

164. Ibid.

165. See, e.g., Ernest Nagel, *Principles of the Theory of Probability, International Encyclopedia of Unified Science,* I, no. 6 (Chicago: U. of Chicago Press, 1955), sec. 8.

166. The main ideas in the following discussion of the frequency interpretation's approach to the probability of hypotheses were presented in my paper, "The Empirical Determination of Antecedent Probabilities," read at the 1952 meeting of the American Philosophical Association, Western Division. Some of the formal details were contained in my paper, "The Frequency Interpretation and Antecedent Probabilities," *Philosophical Studies,* 4 (April 1953).

The use of Bayes' theorem as a schema that enables the frequency interpretation to deal with the probability of hypotheses was pointed out by Reichenbach (see Note 161 above). His discussion proved quite confusing (see Nagel, *Principles of the Theory of Probability,* sec. 8). The present discussion, it is hoped, will help to clarify the position. I am deeply indebted to Reichenbach for specific suggestions concerning the interpretation of Bayes' theorem which he conveyed to me in private conversation a short time prior to his death.

167. See Gardner, *Fads and Fallacies,* pp. 28–33; and *Harpers Magazine,* 202 (June 1951), 9–11.

168. *Fads and Fallacies.*

169. For a discussion of the important distinction between two types of simplicity, descriptive simplicity and inductive simplicity, see Reichenbach, *Experience and Prediction,* sec. 42.

170. Adolf Grünbaum, *Philosophical Problems of Space and Time,* Chap. 12.

171. See, e.g., Derek F. Lawden, *An Introduction to Tensor Calculus and Relativity* (London: Methuen, 1962), p. 7.

172. See Note 162 above.

173. Nagel, *Principles of the Theory of Probability,* pp. 410 ff.

JOSEPH T. CLARK, S.J.

The Canisius College of Buffalo

The Physiognomy of Physics

> I have learned something else from the theory of gravitation: No ever so inclusive collection of empirical facts can ever lead to the setting up of such complicated equations. A theory can be tested by experience, but there is no way from experience to the setting up of a theory. Equations of such complexity as are the equations of the gravitational field can be found only through the discovery of a logically simple mathematical conditions which determines the equations completely or (at least) almost completely. Once one has those sufficiently strong formal conditions, one requires only little knowledge of facts for the setting up of a theory; in the case of the equations of gravitation it is the four-dimensionality and the symmetric tensor as expression for the structure of space which, together with the invariance concerning the continuous transformation-group, determine the equations almost completely.
>
> —Albert Einstein
> "Autobiographical Notes," in *Albert Einstein, Philosopher-Scientist,* I

IN A TENDENTIOUSLY TECHNOLOGICAL SOCIETY, such as our own, it is inevitable that a select corps of expertly competent and singularly conscientious scholars, long familiarly at ease with the thought patterns and logical styles successfully operative within their own specialized career disciplines—economics, government, history, philosophy, political science, sociology—should at some time or other become incurably curious about the mystique, the motivations, and the methodology of the physical scientists who first spawned and currently continue to sustain and advance the extraordinary endeavors of their contemporary enterprise.

276

Such compulsive curiosity is not idle nor peripheral nor dilettante. It is, rather, vital and central and even indispensable for the health and preservation of an integrated intellectual culture. To ignore, to suppress, to inhibit the itch of such imperious inquisitiveness, either out of fear of the effort or distaste for the discipline required to comprehend the pseudo-secrets of professional science, is to elect to make tragically permanent a temporary state of happenstance ignorance, and to settle voluntarily without extenuating excuse for a lifetime of superstitious awe before the incomprehensible prestidigitations of a counterfeit scientific priestcraft. To be acutely conscious of such curiosity, on the other hand, to take serious cognizance of it, and to try manfully to satisfy its demands for understanding, is to enlist one's own personal energies in the ongoing crucially important crusade to stop the spread of the mass schizophrenia that is a current curse on our contemporary intellectual culture.

It is therefore the high purpose of these present pages to attempt to exhibit in briefest compass for the benefit of intelligent and interested outlander layfolk the authentic face and genuine form of physical science. It would indeed be preposterous to suppose that one could learn from so small an essay *all* about physics. But it remains to be seen from the subsequent performance whether or not it is still possible to learn, even in adult life, from so small an essay just what physics is all *about*.

To succeed at all in this challenging endeavor, one must first make a stupendous and heroically sustained effort to erase from malformed memory every last vestige of that massive and monumental misconception of nineteenth-century methodologists: the bogus bifurcation of all human thought processes into the pretended dichotomy of (1) *deduction*, and (2) *induction*.

But to achieve successfully such wholesale obliteration of this mischievous myth from the warehouse of one's mind, it is essential first to see by penetrating personal insight the precise point of the crucial distinction, but recently restored to the public domain of contemporary intelligence by the researches of modern mathematical logicians, between (1) a law of logic and (2) a rule of inference.

This distinction between both is crucial despite the superficial resemblances between each to be found in the fact that both a law of logic and a rule of inference each equally entail the grammatical structure of a conditional compound sentence: an antecedent sentence often introduced by the identifying particle, "if," and a consequent sentence regularly identified by the paired introductory particle, "then."

An elementary sample of such a conditional compound sentence is

If it is raining, then the streets are wet.   (1)

Therein the antecedent sentence states a sufficient condition for wet streets, namely, rain; and the consequent sentence announces a necessary condition for the occurrence of rain, namely, wet streets.

Such a conditional compound sentence is unequivocally false when it is the case that it is indeed raining, but it is not the case that the streets are wet. And such a conditional compound sentence is certainly true when it is the case both that it is raining and the streets are in point of fact wet.

But such a conditional compound sentence is also to be construed, reasonably enough, as true when it is not the case that it is raining, yet it is nevertheless the case, as a matter of observed fact, that the streets are quite unambiguously wet. For the conditional compound sentence in question does not purport to claim that rain is both a sufficient and a necessary condition for wet streets. That sentence does not state that the streets are wet if and only if it is raining, but merely that never the former, if at all, without the latter.

Such a conditional compound sentence, finally, is also to be reckoned, reasonably enough, as true when it is both not the case that it is raining and not the case that the streets are wet. For neither circumstance—not the former, actual rain, nor the latter, wet streets—was asserted categorically and apodictically to be the case, but only that the former only if the latter.

In briefest recapitulation of the foregoing remarks, let us agree to say that a conditional compound sentence is truth-functionally false if and only if its antecedent sentence is true and its consequent sentence is conjointly false.

But it turns out, significantly enough, that certain such conditional compound sentences are always true and never false. Such conditional compound sentences are therefore indefeasibly valid and, consequently, constitute a certain set of laws of logic.

For example, let the lowercase alphabet literal "p" stand as dummy surrogate for any declarative sentence that you please, say "It is raining." Likewise, let the lowercase alphabet literal "q" stand as a companion dummy surrogate for any other declarative sentence that you care to select, say, "The streets are wet." Then the conditional compound sentence which runs in conventional Whitehead-Russellian symbolic notation as

$$p \supset q . p . \supset q \qquad (2)$$

and may conveniently be read in idiomatic vernacular as "If it is the case both that if p, then q, and it is the case that p, then it is the case that q," can never be false within the confines of a universe of discourse characterized by two and only two truth values, but is always true or invariably and indefeasibly valid. For it turns out upon inspection that whenever the consequent sentence "q" is false, so too in each and every case is the antecedent sentence, "$p \supset q \cdot p$." And under such circumstances, as has already heretofore been remarked, the entire unit conditional compound sentence is construed, reasonably enough, as itself true.

At this point in the proceedings it is of paramount importance for the success of our diagnostic endeavors to note that such laws of logic—for all their absolute and monolithic splendor—are not rules of inference. For such laws of logic are in effect nothing else but certain conditional compound sentences, and merely exhibit *via* dummy surrogates the brute fact of an imposing, indeed, but inert validity. But a rule of inference authorizes and empowers and enfranchises a thinker in a given context of culture to do something about it, namely, to come on this precise account into the logically lawful possession of a new and true sentence "q."

The law of logic, for example, previously instanced

$$p \supset q \cdot p \supset q \qquad (2)$$

is the ultimate ground for the infallible rule of inference, known in the jargon of the ancient craft of logicians as *modus ponendo ponens,* or the method of the independent affirmation of the antecedent sentence of a conditional compound sentence. Hence, if there is in fact adequate warrant for the veracity in our world of the assertion that wet streets necessarily accompany rain, and it is also the case that one is further in a position to certify that it is in fact now raining, then his reserve stock of known true sentences, say n by prior inventory account, may now legitimately be expanded and increased to a new $n + 1$ total by detaching according to the established rule of inference the consequent sentence from the original conditional compound sentence, and knowing thereafter for certain sure—without the cumbersome necessity of personal empirical inspection with umbrella in hand and rubbers afoot out of doors—that the streets are infallibly wet. The particular event recounted in this illustrative instance is indeed trivial, for rain is routine. But the methodology is not, for this deductive procedure is one important way in which the substance of human knowledge grows, efficiently, effectively, economically, since thereby reason escapes the annoying limitations of perpetual skin surface contact with objects in the world.

This crucial distinction between a law of logic and a rule of inference is not only of profound theoretical interest to the professional logician. This same distinction is also the source of that single invaluable insight which now—for the very first time—makes a sound methodological analysis of the logic of science a feasible enterprise of serious scholarship. For this distinction makes mandatory the authentic bifurcation of all types of human reasoning into two and only two classes—not *de*duction and *in*duction—but rather *de*duction and *re*duction.

It turns out after thorough inspection that each and every instance of reasoning or inference or explanation or proof, wherever it may chance to occur, in mathematics, in physics, in history, in philosophy, in each and every department of intellectual culture, is ultimately reducible to a single pair of paradigm premises, so arranged with respect to each other that the first is a conditional compound sentence, such as

$$p \supset q, \tag{3}$$

and the second is either the assertion of

$$p, \tag{4}$$

or the assertion of

$$q. \tag{5}$$

The twin cases may effectively be schematized, as follows:

(1)	(2)
If p, then q.	If p, then q.
But p.	But q.
Therefore q.	Therefore p.

Any inference that reproduces the basic structure of schema 1 is *de*duction. Any inference that reproduces the basic structure of schema 2 is *re*duction.

The rule of inference, as already hinted, which guides the thought processes depicted by schema 1, is the celebrated *modus ponendo ponens*, or the method of the independent affirmation of the antecedent sentence in the original parent conditional compound sentence. This rule of inference is solidly established on a firm law of logic and is therefore indubitably infallible in each instance of its appropriate application. And here, incidentally, is precisely the systematic source whence a magisterial mathematics derives its majestic mantle of imperturbable certainty.

The rule of inference which guides the thought processes depicted in outline by schema 2 may at first sight appear highly suspect to discerning intelligence, and with eminently good reason, for it is notorious in professional logical circles that the conditional compound sentence which runs in conventional symbolic notation as

$$p \supset q \cdot q \supset p \tag{6}$$

and may be conveniently read in idiomatic vernacular as "If it is the case both that if p, then q, and it is the case that q, then it is the case that p" does not turn out to be true in each and every case and is therefore not a law of logic.

But to assert, and quite correctly, that some given form of conditional compound sentence is not true in all cases, is not the same as to declare that the sentence formula in question is unfailingly false in each and every case, for a sentence that is not true in all cases may still generate nevertheless a rule of inference that works in some cases. And here, incidentally, is precisely the systematic source of the tantalizingly tentative, provocatively provisional, and therefore repeatedly reformable formulas of the physical sciences. It is, however, an unquestionable and reassuring fact of intellectual history that this scientific rule of inference, when employed with expert finesse in specifically delimited areas of investigation, enjoys a frequency index of spectacular successes that is astronomically high, else there would not now be, as there is in our twentieth-century culture, the imposing presence of a progressively cumulative and continually contemporary science of physics. Physics feeds and waxes fat on repetitive chains of reductive reasoning, and principally in two significant and vitally correlated ways: (1) predominantly *re*gressive reduction and (2) predominantly *pro*gressive reduction.

In predominantly regressive reduction one takes as a preferable point of departure the experientially known and established truth in contemporary context of the content of the consequent sentence and then moves creatively in thought toward the sophisticated construction of an as yet tentative and provisional antecedent sentence with which the former can be connected as a logically necessary consequence. Here precisely is the logical locus of the celebrated raw data or impartially observed matters of fact with which the science of physics inaugurates each new phase in its historical and helical sequence of suitable solutions to authenticated problems. Such predominantly regressive reduction is also the rational anatomy of the procedures of thought heretofore known to classical philosophers of science as theory construction, the logic of discovery, or explanation of a given set of phenomena.

In predominantly progressive reduction one takes as a preferable point of departure the as yet tentative and provisionally constructed antecedent sentence and then moves in thought toward a decisive confrontation in experience with the contextual content of the consequent sentence, connected with the former as a logically necessary consequence. Here precisely is the logical locus for consciously contrived experimentation in the physical sciences. And such progressive reduction is also exactly the rational anatomy of the thought processes heretofore known to classical philosophers of science as verification, or confirmation, and their opposites: falsification or disconfirmation.

A final further distinction, pertinent to the processes of reductive reasoning, but in the newer perspectives of these present pages only of minimal importance, arises out of the quantificational index attached to the antecedent sentence.

If the antecedent sentence is in effect a generalization of the pertinent contents of the consequent sentence, then the reduction for all practical purposes becomes fused with a process of *induction*. If such, however, is not the case, then it is important to specify the thought process as reductive, indeed, but *non*inductive.

This latter distinction, incidentally, precisely discloses the only logically fundamental difference that conscientious contemporary analysis can discern between the standard thought patterns and processes of the physical scientist and those of the general historian.

There is, of course, at least one other and strikingly spectacular difference between the representative inference patterns of the typical physicist and those of the conventional historian. It is the fertile presence of a mathematical syntax in the one and its conspicuous absence in the other.

This difference, although not logically fundamental, is methodologically of profound technical importance to the reductive processes of physical science. It therefore must be the second major task of a physiognomist of physics to divulge just exactly what is the function of mathematics in the reductive reasonings of physics.

To succeed at all in this second challenging endeavor, one must first make another stupendous and heroically sustained effort to erase from malformed memory every last vestige of that massive and monumental misconception of ancient and medieval and eighteenth-century British methodologists: the bogus identification of the logical structure of mathematics as the science of quantity.

But to achieve successfully, once again, such wholesale obliteration of this second mischievous myth from the warehouse of one's mind, it is first necessary to comprehend with authentic insight the rational anatomy of the mathematical enterprise itself. But such authentic insight into the logical structure of mathematics is neither easily nor often obtained by persons outside the fraternity of professional mathematicians.

The main cause for such widespread failure to comprehend the genuine character of mathematical science is not far to seek, for mathematics remains, at least until yesterday morning, in a comatose condition all through the elementary grades. All too often, in fact, mathematics barely comes to live its own life in secondary school or in routine freshman or sophomore college courses. It therefore happens all too frequently that even in college the student does not come into contact with living, but only with fossilized, mathematics. There he studies in large part mere techniques of formal manipulation, useful indeed in solving technical problems in physical engineering, but more disastrously harmful than educationally helpful in the development of an authentic conception of contemporary mathematics, which is so conspicuously nonmanipulational, but rather ideational.

School mathematics of traditional type is thus not a safe basis for a sound and accurate analysis of the logical structure of mathematical science. It is therefore a mistake of colossal proportions to construe the science of professional mathematicians as merely conventional school mathematics writ large.

Projective geometry, for example, does not start in a college course where elementary, secondary-school plane geometry stopped. In fact it does not presuppose among its logical resources any of the prior results of that elementary geometry. Projective geometry stands on its own constructive foundations and is developed logically from its own initial and relatively primitive propositions. Not only is there a complete absence of developmental continuity from elementary geometry on to a more complicated version of the same in projective geometry, there is also a surprising and instructive reversal of logical role. One discovers that the projective geometry which usually comes after elementary geometry in curricular sequence is logically prior to it. The fact is that only at the tail end of a comprehensive projective geometry does there emerge the logically less significant, less interesting, and strangely singular case of Euclidean metrical geometry.

Similarly, modern abstract algebra is in no way a rectilinear extension of conventional secondary-school algebra, for this latter subject turns out in effect to be nothing more than a heavy-handed version of an inadequately formulated universal arithmetic. Modern algebra, on the contrary, is a fascinating study of set-theoretical structures, established immediately upon the logic of relations and immeasurably removed from a mere computation with letters from the alphabet instead of with digits from the multiplication table. And modern abstract algebra in a manner more impressive still than projective geometry succeeds in embracing under one comprehensive logical point of view not only the entire relational content of elementary algebra but also the theory of invariances in geometrical transformations. It is undeniable therefore that the total result of the conventional curriculum is systematically to distort correct perspective on the logical structure of mathematics as a whole.

Such institutionalized distortion is an intellectual tragedy of deplorable dimensions, for it is perfectly possible for the educable layman of the twentieth century to know precisely what mathematics is all about and what it means to be a mathematician. It is, for example, now conspicuously clear that mathematics may initiate its constructions from any alternative choice of relational situation whatsoever. There is no one and uniquely privileged point of logical departure. The elements of any set have all, but only, those properties with which the relatively primitive propositions of a given axiomatic system purport to endow them. There is thereafter only one technical objective: to elaborate the logical consequences of such an initial pattern of correlatedness. To succeed in accomplishing this objective without committing incidental fallacies of contradiction in the process is by that very fact to create a branch of mathematics. To begin at the given point of departure and to follow the subsequent deductions without misconstruing elements and links in the sequence, this is precisely what it is to learn a branch of mathematics. It is clear to the contemporary mathematical conscience that the primary definitions and postulates relative to any given axiomatic system are neither rigidly uniform deliverances from a homogeneous human experience nor inescapable necessities of all rational thought. The mathematician is entirely free within the widely variable limits of his own creative intelligence to devise whatever logically consistent patterns and universes he desires and has the technical competence to construct. In the conscientious performance of this professional task the mathematician is in no sense under the illusion that he is discovering by the wizardry of abstract and meta-empirical methods the fundamental structures of our extended world. Nor does the mathematician at work presume that he is dealing with a set of absolute and eternal truths. All mathematical truths are innocently timeless, not mystically eternal.

In short, the career mathematician is both a fertile creator and an incisive critic of the consistency and rigor and elegance of patterns of ideas. The elements with which he deals are of a purely constructive nature. As such, they have no significant reference or relevance to perceptible objects of sense experience. If the mathematician speaks a language that is embroidered on occasion with picturesque expressions that carry empirical overtones, such as transformations in space, it is only because he has to name his creations for purposes of intrascientific communication with his colleagues. And the only names available to man must inevitably bear historically inveterate and telltale traces of the only world that is directly accessible to him. It would, however, be a tragic mistake to misconstrue these metaphorical reminders of phenomenal experience. As employed in mathematics of the professional type, the fundamental terms, such as relation, transformation, and function, mean essentially the same thing. In other words, relation theory, transformation theory, and function theory are but three linguistically different expressions for one and the same central content of ideas. The truth of the matter is that the mathematician remains uniquely dedicated to one clearly defined objective: the exploration of the relational morphology and comparative anatomy of abstract mathematical patterns, structures, orders, designs, rhythms, harmonies. Mathematics is not, then, the science of quantity. *It is the master science of order in general.*

If such is the case, then it is not too difficult to discern precisely the logical function of mathematics in the elaboration of physical science. Wherever and whenever a branch of mathematics is engrafted upon a scientific theory, it puts at the disposal of the scientist all the dialectical resources, all the implicational architecture, all the deductive fertility, all the relational structure, and all the established theorems of its developed axiomatic system. When employed in the predominantly regressive phase of the reductive reasoning process, mathematics helps immeasurably to determine whether the ingeniously contrived antecedent sentence is really adequate to pass muster as a logically sufficient condition for the known contextual content of the consequent sentence. When used in the predominantly progressive phase of the reductive reasoning process, mathematics is all but indispensable in the design of suitable experimental tests to determine whether nature also recognizes the specifically determined content of the consequent sentence as a logically necessary condition for the antecedent sentence, as tentatively contrived in theory construction. In short, in physics it is mainly mathematics that links antecedent sentence and consequent sentence in the paradigmatic schema 2 form of the conditional compound sentence model of reductive reasoning.

But the logical structure of the grafting process whereby an independently prefabricated mathematical system of abstract relations and relata becomes vitally fused with the conceptual scheme of a scientific theory for observable phenomena, and results, when successful, in a spectacularly effective correlation between precise theoretical predictions and micrometrically measured experimental fact has sometimes been a puzzling problem for contemporary philosophers of science. The fundamental question is this: How and why does a science that is pure and abstract apply to the concrete world of sense perceptions? The question is a sound one and merits a decisive answer.

The core of the answer that these present pages in the newer perspective purport to supply lies in the fruitful concept of isomorphism. And by isomorphism in this context is meant a one-to-one correspondence C between the elements and relations of a prefabricated mathematical structure M and the objects and relations of a physical structure P, where relations of order n, such as dyadic, triadic, and so forth, correspond to relations of order n, and such that whenever a relation R holds between the elements of M, the corresponding relation R^* holds under C between the corresponding objects of P, and conversely.

In arithmetic, for example, which is the science of number and not the art of computation, the study of relational characters and not the rote identification of related terms, there exists by right of constructive definition and mathematically inductive proof the additive relation whereby, let us say,

$$c = a + b. \qquad (7)$$

Two observations at this point are of central logical importance. The first is this: The additive relation is uniquely and unalterably and by right of intellectual copyright an inviolably and unreproducibly mathematical relation which can therefore admit only and exclusively mathematical entities as its related terms or arguments, and in particular only and exclusively numbers of a consciously constructed and rigorously defined set. The further relation above between "c" and "$a + b$" is not just any sort of a vague relation of similarity or equivalence or even equality, but precisely the stark and severely sharp relation of mathematical identity of its related terms.

Some further logical characters or properties of each of the above two relations are also here crucially important. The additive relation can be rigorously proven to be both associative and commutative and such that

$$a + 1 > a \qquad (8)$$

for every a. Hence, everywhere in arithmetic, if

$$c = a + b \qquad (9)$$

then

$$c = b + a, \qquad (10)$$

and if

$$c = (a + b) + d \qquad (11)$$

then

$$c = a + (b + d). \qquad (12)$$

Finally, it can be rigorously proven that the relation of mathematical identity is transitive, and such that if

$$a = b \qquad (13)$$

and

$$b = c \qquad (14)$$

then

$$a = c. \qquad (15)$$

In the metricized physics of length, for example, to choose the simplest case as paradigm, there exist in terms of operationally defined experimental fit both the juxtapositive relation between lengths of some given material, and the satisfactorily-approximate-coincidence-of-end-faces relation whereby, let us say,

$$C \, [=] \, A \, (+) \, B \qquad (16)$$

where capitalized C, A, and B indicate lengths of some physical material to which have been arbitrarily but systematically assigned appropriate numbers of given units of metrical scale, and where the identity sign is enclosed in brackets and the addition sign in parentheses to avoid in each case the logically and notationally inexcusable solecism of employing a single and undifferentiated symbol to represent two different relations at the same time. It is undeniable that the physical and juxtapositive relation between lengths of some arbitrary material *and* the mathematical and additive relation between certain appropriate numbers are not the same relation. It is also instantly clear that the mathematical relation of identity between a given pair of numbers and their unique sum is not the same as the physical relation of satisfactorily-approximate-coincidence-of-end-faces between lengths of some given material, for no two lengths of physical material can possibly be identical with a given third.

But it does turn out under certain clearly specifiable boundary conditions and to a certain recognizable and satisfactory degree that (1) the physical and juxtapositive relation between measured lengths is in a certain formal sense isomorph to the mathematical and additive relation between appropriate numbers insofar as both relations, although completely different in existential conditions, are in the same identical sense associative, commutative, and such that C is longer than the juxtapositive join of A and B exactly when

$$c > a + b, \tag{17}$$

and (2) the physical relation of satisfactorily-approximate-coincidence-of-end-faces of lengths of material is in a formal sense isomorph to the mathematical relation of identity between a given pair of numbers and their unique sum insofar as both relations, although completely different in existential conditions, are in the same identical sense transitive, and such that if A is just as long as B, and B is just as long as C, then A is just as long as C, in precisely the same way that if

$$a = b \tag{18}$$

and

$$b = c \tag{19}$$

then

$$a = c. \tag{20}$$

Two central conclusions emerge from this analysis. The first is this: The physicist has reasons of his own, which he sometimes revises in the face of recalcitrant fact, for believing that numbers a, b, c are not only unambiguously assignable to lengths A, B, C, but even so assignable that

$$A \;(+)\; B \;[=]\; C \tag{21}$$

exactly when

$$a + b = c. \tag{22}$$

The second conclusion is this: It is technically economical but semantically elliptical—and therefore seriously misleading to the linguistically naïve—to say aloud and in public that one adds measured lengths, or to write in strictly mathematical notation and symbolism without the protection against ambiguity that brackets and parentheses afford:

$$A + B = C. \tag{23}$$

The central and decisive conclusion for the physiognomist of physics now appears: More elaborate instances of successful interpretation in more complexly mathematicized theories of physical science are simply more elaborate isomorphisms established under certain discoverable boundary conditions between (1) certain ideal and prefabricated mathematical relations and (2) certain real and empirically uncovered physical relations. The aim of such a mathematicized physics is the exploitation of abstract mathematical patterns for the description and comprehension and control of physical measurements. The success of this scheme—and there is no automatic rule of thumb for achieving it—depends upon the correct interpretation of physical parameters and their proper identification with the appropriate mathematical entities. If these correlations are endorsed by nature, then observable relations among the physical objects are predictable by the algebraic properties of the corresponding mathematical entities. And it is precisely that fundamental kind of task—the reciprocal reduction of native and naïve cluster-concepts to further irreducible elements, the conscious confrontation for correspondences, and the correlation for structural identities—which faces every conscientious collaborator in the scientific enterprise of mankind who aspires to construct some sound schema for comprehension and control of repeatable patterns of interplay of empirical phenomena in any domain by effectively linking them with the relations and relata of some one or other mathematical system, already preconstructed, precomprehended, and precontrolled.

It is for these reasons that the only valuable—and as yet unwritten—history of physics is one that periodizes its subject, not according to an alien and irrelevant system of chronology for general history, but precisely according to the changing choices of a primary mathematical instrument for the ordering of phenomena. In the beginning of modern physics, that tool was naturally the elements of geometry. After sundry other phases, the physics of the nineteenth century worked its way through the theory of derivatives, the theory of integrals, the theory of differential equations, and the theory of integral equations. If we further choose relativity and quantum mechanics as specimens of later revolutions in physics, the same analysis holds true. Relativity chose as its primary mathematical tool the theory of differential invariants—and so, in effect, except for the wordbound—supplanted relativity with invariance. And quantum physics, as it grows, chooses now matrix algebra, now group representation theory, and even abstract algebra.

The history of physics is, thus, a progressive search for more suitable isomorphisms for the better comprehension and surer control of other and more complex physical relational situations. For his own professional reasons and prompted by his own artistic motivations and aesthetic ideals, the mathematician creates and preserves an expanding stock of classes of systems of abstract relations. Now and again, at moments of crisis, the physicist fumbles and falters until he finds in the mathematical warehouse a new system that fortunately fits, and then he exploits the coincident isomorphism, so long as it lasts. The prescription for such success is simple and straightforward: (1) inventory and then reduce the items in your scientific problem area to further irreducible elements of objects and relations; (2) for the moment become quite candidly a genius, seek single-mindedly to discover a correspondence with some currently available mathematical system of relations and relata, and then capitalize on that isomorphism, so long as it lasts; (3) if no mathematical system is now available for a start or for replacement after a challenging impasse, impound under a moratorium present physical research funds, divert such resources consciously to stimulate some newly subsidized mathematicians to don their thinking caps in earnest and increase their current stock in trade. It is axiomatic to the historian and philosopher of science that the quantity and the quality of scientific advances in any given area are each a function of the reserve supply of readily available or forthcoming isomorphism classes of mathematical systems of abstract relations.

I said at the start that it was the high purpose of these present pages in the newer perspective to attempt to exhibit in briefest compass for the benefit of intelligent and interested outlander layfolk the authentic face and genuine form of physical science. It is now time at the end to redeem that pledge in capsule form.

The physiognomy of physics is determined by one central process of inference and two coordinated logical procedures. The single central process of inference is reductionist methodology that pulses and oscillates healthily between predominantly regressive and predominantly progressive phases. The first coordinated operational procedure is a meticulously critical attention to the concepts and statements which together constitute its relevant, global antecedent sentence in the schema 2 paradigm. The second allied operational procedure is a conscious and deliberate awareness and use of the logical fertility latent in the mathematical apparatus embedded in the reductivist reasoning process.

There are, therefore, at least four logically relevant criteria for appraising the worth of various scientific theories. The first scrutinizes and measures the degree of clarity and precision with which the critically important total antecedent sentence is formulated and, in particular, how conspicuously the logical relationships of its ingredient elements to each other and to expressions phrased in observational terms have been rendered explicit. The second concerns the relative degree of explanatory or predictive power with respect to observable phenomena. The third centers on the criterion—notably somewhat vague and still problematical —of formal simplicity, and assays how much explanatory or predictive power is obtained per unit element of theory. The fourth and last estimates the extent to which the individual components of the total consequent sentence in the schema 2 diagram have been confirmed to date by experimental evidence, especially at logically strategic points.

Such, at any rate, as I now see it, is the physiognomy of physics. It is, I think, a spectacle of beauty to transport the soul of Plato and convert even a convinced Freudian psychologist to public respect and even private reverence for the human psyche.

JOSEPH T. CLARK, S.J.
The Canisius College of Buffalo

Science and Some Other Components of Intellectual Culture

> If it were as easy in other matters to verify reasonings by ex-
> periments, there would not be such differing opinions. But the
> trouble is that experiments in physics are difficult and cost a
> great deal; and in metaphysics they are impossible, unless
> God out of love for us perform a miracle in order to acquaint
> us with remote immaterial things.
> —Leibniz
> Preface to the *General Science* (1677)

To WEAVE IN WONDROUS WISE the warp and the woof of a complex
pictorial Bayeux tapestry from a multitude of single varicolored strands is
a consummate work of art that requires both a delicate aesthetic sense
and the exceedingly deft touch of a professionally practiced hand. It is a
challenging task of creative synthesis.

Patiently to unravel the interwoven threads of a segment of some such
complex pictorial tapestry in order to discover at close range the specific
function of each thread in the composition of the complete pattern is also
a consummate work of art that requires a keen sense of values in
perspective and the exceedingly gentle touch of a humanistically reverent
hand. It is a challenging task of diagnostic analysis.

And it is precisely that kind of diagnostic and analytical task which
these present pages undertake to perform. For it is our explicit purpose to
examine the given complex pictorial tapestry of our contemporary
intellectual culture—such as it is, woven long since under other skies and
in other times and by other hands than ours—and then to try to discern
therein the specific function of at least three predominant strands. The

first is the thread of science. The second is the thread of philosophy. And the third is the thread of religion, or more properly perhaps, the thread of its explicitly intellectual component, theology.

Such is our present purpose: to find out, if we can, just how our contemporary intellectual cultural complex was originally put together. And such is our present plan: to trace the intricate involutions and multiple criss-cross connections of its three main threads: science, philosophy, and theology. But our motivation is not antiseptically archeological and antiquarian. We do not merely want to discover, as an incidental point of dispassionate information about the long sepulchred past, how it was that our ancestors constructed the intellectual cultural complex that we confront at the first moments after our uterine existence. We want, in fact, also to find out, if we can—precisely because the design of the total human tapestry is still far from finished and may still be refashioned by fresher fingers—just how we may ourselves best proceed either to perpetuate its developing pattern, or perhaps for the future shift its focus, balance its elements, or reorient to our own preferences its present perspectives.

Precisely what, then, is it that science, as such, effectively contributes to the general texture of our contemporary intellectual culture? This is our first and fundamental question.

To construct a clear and completely satisfactory reply to this basic inquiry, one must previously establish the relevance of three important distinctions. One has to do with the procedural operations of science itself. The second is concerned with some important differences between science and technology. And the third is derived from a subtle point made in the contemporary theory of knowledge.

The first preliminary task, then, is to distinguish clearly and effectively between two discernibly different phases in the ongoing scientific enterprise itself. Let us agree to call the first stage *science-in-possession,* and the second stage, *science-in-pursuit.*

By the first stage, or science-in-possession, I intend to refer to those vast areas of accumulated scientific knowledge that have been so strategically, so frequently, so spectacularly, and so unexceptionally confirmed by repeated experiences of phenomenal behavior that we have come in time to regard such items of information as assured matters of fact and reliable points of departure for further research into the numerous problem fields that fringe such central nodes. I thus refer, to choose some simple and stock examples, to what are still called by semantical inertia the atomic theory of matter and the cell theory of the structure of organisms. But everyone knows, even though there is still so much more to be known about the presently known, that the discrete and reticulate structure of gross matter is a fact, as is likewise in its fundamental elements the cell structure of living tissues.

By the second stage, or science-in-pursuit, I intend to refer to those vast and inviting reaches of frontier research where ignorance still persists, problems remain, questions multiply, and rival theories strive and compete. But by theories in this present context I do not mean wild speculations, mystical insights, incommunicable intuitions, or the fables and fictions that narrators invent. I refer, rather, to scientific theories in a properly professional sense. Such a scientific theory is indeed as yet only a tentative and provisional explanation for a given set of reliably ascertained phenomena. But it is important for our diagnostic purposes to recognize that such a theory has already been qualified as scientific by meeting, first of all, the stern demands of a methodology designed to achieve internal logical consistency. Such a theory, moreover, is not only logically consistent and hence physically feasible and actually realizable in our world, it is also and in a more profound sense still scientifically respectable, insofar as it has been acknowledged by the associated craft of the physicists to meet satisfactorily the rigid requirements of a certain minimum scientific style. But it remains true, nevertheless, and it is important for our further purposes to press the point, that the theories characteristic of stage two, science-in-pursuit, have been to date insufficiently confirmed to warrant a confident transfer into the more settled realm of stage one, science-in-possession. Here I refer, for example, to the theory of antimatter in cosmic physics, or to the theory of an expanding universe in astronomy, or to the theory of continuous creation in astrophysics.

The second basic distinction, prerequisite to a clear and completely satisfactory reply to our first question about the function of physics in intellectual culture, is made mandatory by the obvious differences which exist, despite some close resemblances in procedural techniques, between science and technology. To highlight such differences, let us agree to call the discoveries and inventions and products of technology "thingama-jigs." And then we may without attendant ambiguity refer to everything else in our universe and our environment—including for ourselves, of course, each other—that is not a thingamajig, as a thing, a thing pure and simple, presented to us in naïve experience by what we have come benignly to call nature.

The third basic distinction, likewise indispensable for the construction of a suitable reply to our initial inquiry about the contribution of science to intellectual culture, concerns two different senses of the little but vital word, "true." For in a certain context one may say with respect to a given object *x* that it is true *to* a certain object *y*, as for example a portrait may be said to be true *to* a person insofar as its form and texture and tone and color correspond point for point and area for area with the original. In other contexts, and perhaps the only and significant ones for intellectual culture, it makes sense to say, not that some concept or idea or notion *x* is true *to* some thing or object or entity *y*, but only that *x* is true *of* some *y*.

This distinction is immeasurably important for our diagnostic purposes, for once we have devised a theory that *really* works and have contrived a conceptual scheme that *really* fits the contours of our experience tolerably well, we can quite easily and all too quickly fall into the simply simplicist error of supposing that we have, at long last, discovered the *really* right explanation of phenomena, the one and only unique and correct theory that is true *to*, and not only true *of*, the things in our world. But this emotive mistake would be fatally to forget the irreducible differences that there are between things that are and our thoughts about them. To think of phenomenally perceived objects, we must creatively and constructively conceptualize them in some organized way, just as to speak of objects we must endow them with arbitrary but systematically appropriate names. But since things in the raw state of naked existence do not have proper names, it is a vain and foolish pursuit to try to discover what such names *really* are and an inexcusable effrontery in sophisticatedly educated circles to suppose or to boast that we have finally found one or more of them. The point is, and it is well worth repeating, that what science knows and transparently reveals about the things to which it refers may indeed be reckoned as true *of* them without ever pretending to be true *to* them. Nor do I imply by this remark that there exists somewhere and somehow some such true-*to* knowledge of such things which happens, however, to be inaccessible to the peculiar and perverse methodological procedures of a purblind science. I rather mean that since no such true-*to* knowledge of such things is available anywhere or anyhow, it is self-delusion of the most insufferable sort to suppose that one possesses it, and it is a crime against humanity to burden science with the impossible responsibility to produce it in public.

Equipped now with the requisite major distinctions between (1) science-in-possession and science-in-pursuit, (2) thingamajigs and just plain, simple, straightforward, homespun things, and (3) alleged knowledge that is true *to* and familiar knowledge that is true *of*, let us repeat and then reply to our first and fundamental question. It is this: Precisely what, then, is it that science, as such, effectively contributes to the general texture of contemporary intellectual culture?

The answer that these present pages in the newer perspective are prepared to suggest presupposes in the first place that it is of paramount importance for the purposes of our diagnosis to realize in the deep of one's soul that science is a volunteer enterprise. Its sustaining motivations spring spontaneously from the perpetually ebullient depths of an incurable and insatiable curiosity. Every present advance opens new and inviting future vistas, and every answer is ancestor to a new and multiple progeny of inquiries. The methods of science thus require and will not ever passively forego the fullest franchise of freedom in research. The quester must without question or querulous qualification be allowed to follow the lead of his prepossessing question. The single and simple-minded goal of science is knowledge, pure and simple, despite the fact that such knowledge is itself the secret and the source of multiple other rewards and incidental by-products. The penalty, moreover, for neglecting or repudiating science is not some positive form of pain or punishment, but simply continued ignorance. But such ignorance is merely a state of mind, and not itself a disease, despite the fact that it is often the source of multiple further woes. For both such reasons it is an indisputable fact that science cannot ever be successfully commanded or compelled by any external force, although its professional personnel can be commandeered in a crisis or organized into group efforts to accelerate research as a team.

The forthcoming reply further presupposes that an adequate comprehension of the genius and spirit of science requires, in the second place, careful attention to the structure of its highly specialized and supremely functional language. In every range of the flexible vocabulary of physics one central component is always an ingeniously contrived conceptual scheme that fulfills two different but correlated functions: (1) At the strategic terminal points of originative problem and final test such a conceptual scheme makes contact at first hand with the raw data of phenomenal experience, whereas (2) in the interim the conceptual scheme transcends this level and moves with grace and ease at more rarified heights of abstraction. When, therefore, as often happens, such expertly devised and carefully correlated concepts successfully capture and thus allow predictable control over portions of experience, it is important to note that such a conceptual scheme is in no sense a merely photographic or ideographic reproduction of the original phenomena.

The answer that we await, however, also recognizes that such conceptual schemes are a common, run-of-the-mill ingredient in every scholarly discipline that purports to explain. What is, on the other hand, significantly distinctive about physical science is the careful fusion of such concepts with a highly sophisticated mathematicized syntax. It is, moreover, highly important to observe that the ratios and proportions of the two elements in this mixing recipe vary very widely from occasion to occasion. There are, for example, some significant sentences in physics, such as Boyle's Law, which are heavily weighted with empirical elements and less heavily loaded with mathematicized expressions. But there are many other sentences in physics, in contemporary nuclear research for example, where only the initiated can appreciate the fact that such formulas are still physical, so heavily mathematicized is the syntax and so thin and evanescent the residue from empirical contacts.

Here, then, in fully prepared context, is the reply to our first and fundamental question: It is the volunteer task of science in society more and more reliably to report in a suitable language invented for the purpose (by blending mathematical syntax with creatively constructed concepts) exactly how things observably are and interact in the universe which all men inhabit, or as they very likely may be in terms of some logically possible, scientifically respectable, but as yet insufficiently confirmed theory.

If such, then, be precisely the effective contribution of science, qua science, to the general texture of contemporary intellectual culture, it becomes for some analysts a perplexing puzzle and a vexing problem to find some further and comparably appropriate function for the enterprise of philosophy.

This resultant and problematic issue thus introduces us to our second but still basic question. It is this: Precisely what *else*, then, is it that philosophy, as such, effectively contributes to the overall pattern of contemporary intellectual culture?

In order to construct a clear and completely satisfactory reply to this second but equally fundamental question, it is first necessary to dispose of at least two pretended solutions to this problem that still survive in certain sequestered quarters and effectively obstruct modern insights. The first derives from Greek antiquity via the Latin middle ages and is based upon an intrasystematic distinction between a *general* and a *special* science. The second originates with nineteenth-century methodologists and rests upon some differences in nuance which analysis uncovers in certain classes of *how-questions* and certain classes of *why-questions*.

Proponents of the prior solution persuasively argue that it is logically and methodically an official responsibility of career philosophers first to conduct a broad and wide and general and panoramic survey of nature's terrain and in the course of that sweeping enterprise to raise and to answer some big and important general questions about our world. In this view, the corresponding professional task of the career scientist is then to pose a derivative set of specialized queries in quite minute detail, and thus in a kind of mop-up operation to work out the corresponding class of appropriately specialized answers. To make the same point by means of some egregiously inept metaphorical terms from optics, one may say that in this view, career philosophy employs a telescopic lens of extremely wide angle curvature, whereas science uses an electron microscope with highest resolving power but with a single eyepiece. For in this view of a general and a special science of nature the difference that makes a difference is precisely one of relative scope in the same identical visual field.

If I read the representative literature literately, it would on this view, for example, be construed as a native task of philosophy to explore the pandemic or universal phenomenon of change or alteration or mutation in general and, after due analysis, to explain, in Aristotle's terms for instance, that change in general is the actualization of the potential, precisely as potential. It would also on this view, if I see it in correct perspective, correspondingly be the cognate task of physics, for example, to explore in microscopic detail the structure of a specific type of change, such as that undergone by bodies in free fall to the surface of the earth, and after analysis to explain the observed rate of change, in Galileo's terms for instance, as proportional to the square of lapsed time intervals.

But it seems to me after some bovine rumination on the point that this intrasystematic distinction between a general and a special science of nature, no matter how valid and pertinent it may be in other areas, is here irrelevant, immaterial, obscure, and—what is far worse—*obscurantist*. I fail to see in any way how one can successfully maintain that some such statement as Galileo's renders specific some such statement as Aristotle's general observation. Galileo does not merely fill in the blank spaces in Aristotle's general statement with specific detail. Rather, it appears to me that Galileo makes an entirely different kind or type or genus or class of statement. Of course, Galileo's statement is not vapid nor vague nor vacuous and can therefore correctly be said to be specific.

But the pertinent point is that Galileo's suitably specific statement about the acceleration of free fall downward to earth is not a specification on the content of Aristotle's general statement about change. The difference is crucial, for Galileo provides us with a genuinely *functional formula*, whereas Aristotle delivers only *a general formulation for a general function*. And, ironically enough, it is the functional formula of Galileo that can best be designated as general, because it contains the variable g, the value of which must be further specified for each specific locality and specific altitude above sea level. Moreover, as we shall see later, the thrust of Aristotle's statement is significantly *other* than supposed in this first view.

For these and other similarly cogent reasons I find the *general* and *special* theory of science altogether unsatisfactory and completely unacceptable as a methodological device for distinguishing effectively between the respective cultural contributions of science and philosophy.

The second pretended solution to our present problem, as systematically developed by consciously careerist nineteenth-century methodologists from the initial insights of their innocently naïve seventeenth-century predecessors, is simple enough to state: Whereas science asks and is adequately equipped to answer satisfactorily all but only the how-questions about the perceptible phenomena of our world, it must be the case that philosophy poses and claims at least to be adequately prepared to solve satisfactorily all but only the why-questions about the same phenomena, if any some such significant questions there be. The same contrast may be phrased more dramatically, perhaps, by stating that in this view issues of teleology or final causality or purposes or ends are rigidly proscribed from the problem areas of science, but just as rigidly prescribed as the single professional prerogative of philosophers.

Two critical comments on this pretended second solution are perhaps appropriate at this point. The first comment claims that this second view of the matter grossly misunderstands and seriously misrepresents the authentic enterprise of science. The second claims that this alternate explanation also seriously misconstrues and misleadingly represents the genuine endeavor of philosophy.

It is thus, first of all, noteworthy that contemporary methodologists of science, as modern scientists themselves, have long since successfully outgrown, or at least sublimated, an adolescent Francis Baconian fear of the presence of purpose in research. The horrendous spectre of teleology no longer terrifies and haunts the scientific conscience, nor is "finality" any longer masked by blunt biologists with the transparently false face of "organic function." It is a fact, of course, that no person alive is willing to revive and reinstate the notorious excesses of that undisciplined spirit of teleological inquiry which the hardy pioneers of the scientific revolution rightly lambasted, lampooned, and eventually laughed out of court. But it is also a fact that contemporary researchers are no longer content to be deprived of all the possible why-questions in the full book of interesting inquiries simply because of an autocratic ukase by inherited group prejudices. If I read the mood of current and representative scientists correctly, it is the case at the present time that if and whenever a soberly disciplined why-question proves useful, as it often does in biological and psychological and sociological research, then investigators have the moral right to ask that type of question and the corresponding obligation to exploit such a methodology to the full. But if science may quite properly pose both types of question, then—as has been charged—this second pretended solution to our present problem misreads and misrepresents the authentic enterprise of science.

This second alleged solution, moreover, as is further charged, also misreads and misrepresents the genuine endeavor of philosophy. If so, the relevant reason is certainly not because philosophers fail to ask what they regard as significant why-questions. Philosophers do ask, and very frequently indeed. But, more importantly for our diagnostic purposes, it is equally an irrefutable fact of intellectual history that philosophers also and often ask relevant how-questions too. If so, then the dichotomy which serves as the logical basis for the second alleged solution dissolves and disappears. If both scientists and philosophers often enough ask each type of question, then no effective distinction between their respective contributions to intellectual culture can be contrived merely on the basis of alleged differences in nuance between certain classes of how-questions, reserved exclusively for the concerns of science, and certain classes of why-questions, reserved exclusively for the concerns of philosophy.

Despite this double failure of both the general versus special science theory, and its rival, the how- versus why-question theory, our original second inquiry—precisely what *else*, then, is it that philosophy, as such, effectively contributes to the overall pattern of contemporary intellectual culture?—remains important and in need of a suitable reply.

In order to establish a clear and completely satisfactory answer to this persistent question, it is first necessary to reread with an unbiased eye the actual record of the history of philosophy and to distinguish effectively, in somewhat the same way as was heretofore done between *science-in-*

possession and *science-in-pursuit*, between *philosophy-as-primitive* and *philosophy-as-sophisticated.*

This latter distinction is important for our diagnostic purposes on at least two counts. The first reason is this: It sometimes uncomfortably happens that a primitive philosopher is prepared to pose a really profound puzzle and to provide the formula for an equally profound solution to the same, each of which, both the question and the answer, survives intact and remains relevant even in the vastly changed perspectives of the historically later and more scientifically sophisticated philosopher. The second reason is this: No such comparable phenomenon occurs in the constantly changing and constantly contemporary intellectual contexts of an accumulatively progressive and historically advancing science. The moral of the story for us is that whereas the point, the thrust, the significance, the merit, the relevance, the value, and the validity of scientific questions and answers vary as a direct function of the historical context in which they are posed and supplied, and are hence inevitably dated—up to date at one time and then later hopelessly passé and out of date—authentic philosophic questions can with annoying frequency transcend their historical context and become in fact perennial, if not altogether perpetual.

It is therefore a fatal mistake in otherwise competent and conscientious analysis to rate by rote according to a ready rule of thumb the value of a primitive philosopher's insight into the structure of a puzzling problem as a direct function of the degree of his scientific sophistication. Let us illustrate the relevant lesson by two simple examples, each drawn from familiar materials. The first derives from the kitchen chemistry of boiling water and refrigerated ice cubes. The second relates to standard items in a problems-of-knowledge course conventionally prescribed in a core curriculum for first-year men or women in distinguished liberal arts colleges, such as my own.

It is, happily, historically accurate as well as dramatically effective to cast ancient Aristotle in the protagonist role of a primitive philosopher of low-grade scientific sophistication in the first illustrative sketch. There is copious evidence to show, for example, that Aristotle observed and was profoundly impressed by the spectacular and strikingly different sets of phenomenal properties, associated respectively with liquid water at room temperature, steam vapor above its boiling point, and solid ice below its freezing threshold. And there is equally copious evidence to show that Aristotle did not know the molecular constitution of water, the mechanical theory of heat, and the physics of the triple state of matter. Aristotle therefore thought that he had observed in the kitchen a remarkable and startling performance of nature in which, altogether paradoxically, one thing, essentially this, became another thing, essentially other, and thereupon promptly asked himself, as a volunteer vicar for the rest of humanity, this profoundly provocative question: How can things *be* as they observably are, namely, substantially intertransmutable? This question is provocative and profound because the awful penalty for failure to answer it satisfactorily is the acutely traumatizing and painfully psychotic state of perpetual puzzlement in the presence of a constantly changing universe that utterly confounds intelligence by generating, as fast as possible, unresolvable contradictions.

It is now known by courtesy of the well-established physics of science-in-possession that the locus of Aristotle's question was mistaken, that its incidence in that area of kitchen chemistry was enormously misplaced. But we also now uncomfortably know from highly sophisticated modern physics other loci in cyclotron-equipped laboratories where such substantial transformations of fundamental particles seem, at least, to us just as realistically factual as Aristotle's own kitchen instance seemed to him. If so, then the pertinent point for our present purposes of diagnostic analysis is that Aristotle's question survives intact and remains relevant to contemporary philosophical research, despite its drastic relocation to other and more sophisticated scientific contexts. For wherever and whenever one thing, no matter what, becomes another thing, no matter what, it is an inescapable burden of responsible intelligence to discover, if possible, how such things can possibly be as they paradoxically are, intertransmutable?

The second simple illustration centers on the apparent paradox that whereas the things which men presume that they know are singular and contingent, the knowledge which men think that they possess of them is universal and necessary. Is that not precisely the way that things are and behave, and is that not exactly how human knowledge is and appears? But the singular apparently, at least, confounds the universal, and the contingent appears, at least, incompatible with the necessary. Such is the framework of fact whence derives the notoriously persistent philosophic problem concerning the very possibility of such cognitive experience of such existent objects: How can our knowledge be as it actually is?

Here Plato conveniently fills the conventional role of primitive philosopher who first pinpointed this professionally problematic paradox in a contemporary context of low-grade scientific sophistication concerning the physics of light and heat and sound, as well as the physiology, psychology, and neurophysiology of the generally accepted psychosomatic apparatus of sense perceptions. The Platonic answer to this question is that such knowledge can *be* if and only if the singular and contingent things encountered in empirical experience are but illusory replicas of universal and necessary Ideas. Aristotle feels the pinch of Plato's problem, repudiates however Plato's solution to its puzzles, and supplants it with his own to the effect that such knowledge can *be* if and only if universal and necessary natures lie beneath and beyond the phenomenal surfaces of things, to be released and disclosed for the scrutiny of inquiring intelligence by a filtering process of native abstraction. Aquinas resumes in the Middle Ages the violently interrupted research on the same problem that bewitched the wits of his ancient Greek predecessors, repossesses Aristotle's answer from the slag pile of Arabic commentators, and retools it to read that such knowledge can *be* if and only if there is a *real* difference between the composite nature of the thing and its vibrant and actual existence.

Descartes precipitously discards general medieval perspectives but resolutely retains for the modern era the same ancient paradoxical problem of knowledge, but proceeds characteristically to streamline its contours in a slightly more sophisticated scientific context, and finally replies that such knowledge can *be* if and only if all the secondary qualities of familiar things are reinterpreted as merely subjective illusions of the reagent perceptual apparatus in men, while matter alone and the mathematically necessary laws of motion are uniquely the constituents of the world of observable events. Spinoza next undertakes to rework Descartes' radical reply by disemboweling all contingency from physical interaction, and asserting that such knowledge can *be* if and only if absolute necessity alone is real, and contingency a fiction of the mind in bondage to the imagination. Leibniz restores to its pristine glory the ancient and primitive form of the question, recognizes indeed the precise point that Spinoza makes at the price of espousing pantheism, but personally replies that such knowledge can *be* if and only if each of the multiple monads which crowd the Leibnizian universe itself reflects the entire pattern of an inescapable necessity.

Locke in turn transports the Cartesian version of the problem across the English channel, reports its central points to the British empiricist temper, and answers in effect that such knowledge can *be* if and only if its universal characteristics and pretensions to necessity are realistically reconstrued as only imaginative make-believe. Berkeley drives the logic of Locke's solution to the edge of desperation, and pronounces in summary that such knowledge can *be* if and only if the things to which it purports confidently to refer are not things at all, but only ideas. Hume bypasses Berkeley's defeatist solution, retools Locke's empiricist reply, and responds in the end that such knowledge can *be* if and only if its apparently universal and necessary character is diluted and then dissolved into the elements of a colossal illusion generated by the subconscious mechanisms of animal habit. Kant on the continent cannot either escape the nib of Hume's point that the singular and contingent in empirical encounter provide no philosophic purchase whatsoever for the universal and necessary in scientific knowledge, nor bring himself to disbelieve in the universal validity of the theorems of Euclidean geometry or in the necessity of Newton's universal law of gravitation. The Kantian solution therefore states that such knowledge can *be* if and only if the native engineering design of mind is such that it inevitably and unerringly but unconsciously projects such a priori perspectives into the aboriginally and initially amorphous no-man's-land-of-God-alone-knows-what-if-anything-lies-behind-and-beyond the automated structural panoramic surface of phenomenal experience!

This second illustration, a brief excursus into the long history of epistemological exploration, like the first, a quick glimpse into the kitchen chemistry of Aristotle, pays double dividends for our present project of diagnostic analysis. For each of the illustrations conspicuously reveals (1) precisely what kind of question it is that philosophy preferentially poses for itself, and (2) precisely what kind of language it is that philosophy preferentially employs for expressing its replies. The characteristic structure of the preferred philosophic question is clear: Given that certain things are in scientifically observable fact thus and so, how can they *be* as they (paradoxically) are? And equally clear is the preferred language of reply: The language of philosophy is not, like that of science, mathematical in syntax, but rather metaphorical. For Plato it is the metaphor of sight and visual image; for Aristotle and Aquinas, plastic art; for Descartes, the architectonics of engineering; for Spinoza, the paradigm of parallelism; for Leibniz, the transparent crystal; for Locke, impressions on wax; for Berkeley, the implications of self-sight; for Hume, animal behavior; and for Kant, plaster molds.

Without *some* scientific knowledge, no matter how primitive and low grade in sophistication, there can, of course, be *no* philosophy at all. This is the primordial dependence, for one who does not in *any* way know how things actually are in the world, experiences no sense of wonder or compulsion to inquire how things can possibly *be* as they paradoxically are. With some scientific knowledge, no matter how primitive and low grade in sophistication, there can nevertheless flourish some first-rate philosophy. The primordial dependence is not, therefore, of functional type. For it is possible to speculate quite appositely how things can possibly *be* as they paradoxically are, even when what one knows about their actual structure and condition is minimal and superficial. Functional dependence fails here precisely because the language of philosophy is metaphorical, not syntactically mathematical. Accordingly it does *not* follow that in a context of optimum and maximum contemporary scientific knowledge, as sophisticated as possible, philosophy is automatically and necessarily at the peak of its performance—but it could be, and ideally should be. It would seem that one who knows quite extensively and quite reliably how very, very many things in the world actually are and operate, is in the best possible position to wonder and to inquire just how such things can possibly *be* as they actually are and interact. And yet it would be folly to campaign for a moratorium on philosophy until science is finished, and for two sound reasons. First, science is *never* finished. Second, although philosophy requires some indispensable bare minimum of science in order to get started at all, and should ideally prosper *best* with the most science, it is surprising how little technical science is needed to stir the metaphysical impulse to full activity in intelligence.

Precisely because such is the type of question that philosophy feels forced to ask, and precisely because such is the language that philosophy prefers to employ in fashioning apt replies, philosophers are prone to appear to the general public, not like antiseptic scientists in the aloof role of volunteer teachers, but rather in the guise and full reformist panoply of compulsive preachers. For whereas the penalty for ignoring science is simply survival in a given state of relative ignorance—which can be bliss —the penalty for ignoring philosophy can only be construed *by* philosophers as the catastrophe of downright and damnable error. And whereas scientists, as such, can learn to ignore voluntary ignorance with icy composure, no philosopher can preserve peace of mind in the presence of even wilfully wanted and wantonly enjoyed error. And that is why scientists discreetly invite public attention, while philosophers feel professionally compelled to command and demand it.

Since the immediate foreground has now been conveniently cleared of distracting debris, and philosophy-as-primitive satisfactorily distinguished from philosophy-as-sophisticated, and the metaphorical language of philosophy suitably contrasted with the mathematical syntax of science, we are now in an optimum position to repeat our original second inquiry: Precisely what *else*, then, is it that philosophy, as such, effectively contributes to the general texture of contemporary intellectual culture? and to offer the following reply: It is the analytical task of the spontaneous but compulsive career philosopher in human society to explain to his equally perplexed public in a suitable metaphorical language invented for the purpose (by distilling and systematizing the analogical residues of the metaphorical concepts and syntax of ordinary language) just how things can consistently *be* as they are observably known to *be* by science-in-possession, or as they very likely may be in terms of some testable theory proposed by science-in-pursuit.

But the realm of contemporary intellectual culture presents for diagnostic analysis, despite Auguste Comte's superficial conceit that science alone would survive, not only the enterprise of science and the endeavor of philosophy, but also the puzzling phenomenon of theology. For if science contributes to intellectual culture reliable reports on how things observably *are* in the world of experience, and philosophy follows in the footsteps of emergent paradoxes to explain how things can consistently *be* as they observably are, it is at least a problem to specify precisely what *else* it is then, if anything, that theology bestows.

In order to construct a clear and completely satisfactory reply to this third, and final, question, it is necessary only to distinguish briefly between (1) theology as *positive*, and (2) theology as dogmatic, or perhaps better, as *speculative*.

Positive theology professionally concerns itself with the authenticity of whatever happen to be the alleged, at least, sources for a given religious revelation, and conducts its researches in two dimensions: one historical, and the other semantical. In the historical dimension, positive theologians are indistinguishable from scientific historians in general. In the semantical dimension, positive theologians are indistinguishable from linguistic scholars in general. For in each case the methodology of investigation, the rules of procedure, the tools of the trade, the standards of accuracy, the canons of competence, and the steps in an acceptable proof, are one and the same for all. If classical scholarship can successfully establish the text and interpret the sense of ancient documents that discuss wars, plagues, famines, and infidelities of one sort or another, there is no *systematic* reason why a positive theology of comparable technical competence cannot with comparable success establish the text and interpret the sense of ancient documents that discuss prophets and prophecies of one type or another. The task, therefore, of the positive theologian in the context of any given creed is straightforward: reliably to report from historically accredited sources exactly how some God says that things *are.*

But if the positive theologian is, thus, intellectual kin to the natural scientist in so far as each reports just how things observably *are,* or, as reported by contemporary observers, observerably were, one on the basis of observation, and the other on the grounds of accredited testimony, the dogmatic or speculative theologian is intellectual cousin to the career philosopher. For the puzzles and paradoxes that erupt from a knowledge of the way that things observably *are,* are child's play in contrast to the puzzles and paradoxes that emerge from the knowledge of the way in which some God says that things *are.* The task of the speculative theologian is, thus, equally straightforward: to explain to his equally perplexed coreligionists exactly how things can consistently *be* as some God is reliably reported to say that they actually *are.*

It turns out, happily, from this diagnostic analysis that none of our protagonists—the scientist, the philosopher, the theologian—*needs* the others in the precise performance of his professional task in the service of intellectual culture. It follows, also quite happily, that none of our protagonists can effectively interfere—despite some acrimonious pretensions to the contrary on some regrettable occasions in the quietly sepulchred past—or logically contradict the others.

But it may just be the case, and this circumstance I also happen to regard as a happy one, that a marvelously magnificent but simultaneously miserable mankind requires all three, if we are ever to achieve—as we have not yet done—a total knowledge of total reality, either personally encountered in individual experience, or rendered accessible to us through established channels of social communication.

Such, at any rate, at the moment, are one man's thoughts about science and some other components of contemporary intellectual culture.

Part II / COSMOS

THOMAS GOLD
Cornell University

Cosmic Processes and the Nature of Time

> It appears that the solution of the problem of time and space is reserved to philosophers who, like Leibnitz, are mathematicians, or to mathematicians who, like Einstein, are philosophers.
>
> —Hans Reichenbach
> "The Philosophical Significance of the Theory of Relativity" in *Albert Einstein, Philosopher-Scientist,* I

MUCH OF OUR UNDERSTANDING of the world is based on the particular sense organs we have. Our preoccupation with geometry, the geometrical configurations of all things around us, is no doubt due to the excellence of the eye for acquiring such information. The idea of expressing basic laws of physics in terms of forces no doubt arose because our muscles are equipped with sense organs that signal the force applied. These may all be perfectly sensible ways of analyzing the outside world; but they may be not as unique as we are tempted to think. There may be other ways—that we cannot now conceive—that are as good or even better for obtaining an understanding of the physical world around us.

This, I think, is the situation with time. We all have, as the most basic proof of our consciousness, the sensation of the passing of time. Just as we cannot conceive describing the outside world without reference to its geometrical properties, so we cannot describe it without reference to the passage of time.

Yet is that really the only way of describing the world? Is there really a uniform flow of time within which events occur?

We are familiar with describing an event in terms of the three coordinates of three-dimensional space—*where* it occurred—and one coordinate of time—*when* it occurred. An object may in this framework occupy any region of the space coordinates, or continue to remain in one place; but it cannot fail to slide along the time coordinate. Who is pushing it? Why can it not stand still? Why does it move in the one direction and not in the other along the time axis? These questions may be silly; there may be no answer to why-questions, if that is how the world is constructed. Explanations in physics can explain any particular thing only in terms of something more general. A particular occurrence can be explained in terms of laws of physics, the most general descriptions we have found. But how could we ever "explain" the broadest generalizations? Time flows—that is a law of physics; that is how the universe operates.

It is difficult, however, to leave the question there, to be satisfied with such a statement, if one knows certain things about the physical world. Perhaps the flowing of time is only a description of a subjective impression. Perhaps our minds create the illusion, and force us to describe the exterior world in these terms. Perhaps there is no feature of the exterior world that demands such a flow of time, but the need to describe it in terms that fit our consciousness, forces us towards it.

Let us try to understand the position of time in the framework of the laws of physics. It is used there as a coordinate, and any interval along the direction of this coordinate can be measured by an instrument called a clock. If we did not have clocks we could use certain types of physical processes that are known to run at a constant rate—the falling of sand through an orifice, the swing of a pendulum, a weight oscillating on a spring, etc. These processes are known to run at a standard rate in the sense that one can keep comparing them against each other and the results do not change. They give the impression, therefore, of an even flow of time underlying all processes we see. "Mathematical time," as Newton called it, is the ideal, and actual clocks differ in their indications from it through their individual imperfections. It is implied that there is only one "mathematical time," and therefore that "perfect clocks," whatever their principle of operation, will all go alike. What does that mean? What definition can we give of two clocks going alike? Obviously not that they tick at the same frequency, since I can arbitrarily adjust the rate of ticking of a pendulum or a weight-and-spring. But what is assumed to be constant is the *ratio* of the number of ticks made in any given interval. A given pendulum and a weight-and-spring may have any ratio of their frequencies but, it is assumed, if nothing changes in their construction they will always have that same ratio. It is just as with a measuring stick that is assumed to be of constant length, though not necessarily the same as another. But, if no changes take place in their construction, it is assumed that they both will measure in the same ratio, no matter whether the object being measured is in Sydney, New York, or on the moon.

It is, of course, an assumption that there is a "mathematical time" as Newton clearly realized, and that there is only one type. Milne realized this and challenged the assumption by looking into the consequences of having two different ones, depending on the physical principle employed. If gravitation is the force involved in making the oscillation then one type of time would be measured; if atomic forces were involved, then it would be the other. We shall not discuss this possibility further here.

The assumption of one "mathematical time" can be expressed as the assumption of the homogeneity of space-time. *Homogeneous* means *uniform* in position; any place is like any other. If the laws of physics make a weight-and-spring beat in a certain ratio with another periodic device at one location of space-time, they do so at another. The laws of physics operate in a homogeneous space-time. This could all be described on a space-time diagram in which we fix the units along the time coordinate by means of one clock, and along the space coordinates by means of measuring rods, and where we would then find another clock described in the diagram marking off even intervals along the time coordinate, wherever it was placed (so long as it is in uniform motion).

Does this tell us anything about the flow of time? We would really like to know why time progresses at all, and I have not discussed any more than that it progresses at the same rate at different places and different times. That has not got us any further yet. Any feature of the entire physical world can be described on space-time diagrams, as the world lines of all the particles of matter. Even if we could not make a diagram comprehensive enough to depict the entire universe, past, present and future, we can still contemplate having a sample of a representative locality. Suppose we had a very substantial piece of this diagram in front of us. Would we see in it any reason for the apparent "flow" of time?

The physical laws would all be represented in this comprehensive diagram as certain regularities in the pattern. The discovery of laws of nature is, after all, nothing other than the recognition of certain regularities in the great pattern of world lines. The fact that we think of ourselves as drifting along the direction of the time coordinate through this pattern was in no way essential to the discovery of these regularities —had we seen the entire pattern at once we could have spotted them at least as well.

But let us be quite clear about this. All of the physical world is contained in this great pattern. Yet in it, there is nothing that suggests any intrinsic division into past and future, and an edge representing the present, sliding relentlessly along. In fact, as one knows from the Special Relativity theory, there would not even be the possibility of such an edge representing the present, being defined in a consistent way so that it could be meaningful for observers no matter in what state of motion they were. This sliding edge has a meaning for each one of us, but it clearly is wrong to think of it as existing in an absolute way in our great pattern. In other words, the physical world as a whole is not divided into past, present and future. We make these concepts and then try to force them into our understanding of nature. Why?

All I can hope for is that at the end of this essay we will be a little closer to an understanding of the central problem: *Why it is that we live with this firm impression of the passage of time, and how the physical world around us has given us the possibility of forming such an impression.* In the process we will have to understand many more strange things about the nature of the physical world, but, what is more difficult, we will have to unlearn things that have become apparently self-evident. "It ain't what a man does not know that makes him a fool; it is what he does know that ain't so!" That is the famous saying of a comedian who would have made a good physicist.

The Sense of a Clock

Let us start with clocks. We have discussed them already, but really only one aspect of them—the ticking, the marking off of equal time intervals. But that is not all one requires of a clock. Just a pendulum swinging on a wall would not be satisfactory. It has to show the time; and that means not only that an indicating system has to count the ticks—that is trivial—but it has to know in what sense to count them. It has to know which is earlier and which is later. Now, of course, you and I know that without any trouble; why not the clock? It is easy to arrange for a clock to go round the right way. If it went round the wrong way we would just reverse some gears and put it right. There is no technical problem there —but there is one of understanding why all this is so easy.

The clock did not know in which sense it had to go, but *we* did. Our conscious awareness of the passage of time could always be used without fail to calibrate the sense of the indications of the clock. The sense any clock indicates for the progress of time is merely the sense some person knew was right. We still have not found the forward flow of time in the physical world, but only in ourselves.

The Time-Symmetry of Nature

But the story is much more mysterious still. Not only is it difficult to find a flow of time represented in simple processes, it seems to be impossible to find it in the very simplest. The basic laws of physics appear to be symmetrical with time; that is to say, they would represent the world just as well if time went the other way. Let us consider some examples of this. The laws of dynamics and gravitation, described first by Newton, make no distinction between the two senses of time. A process completely described by them can therefore occur just as well in reverse. The motion of the planets in the solar system is one such example—if we reversed all motions exactly, the system would still be just as good an example of Newton's laws, but its description would now be identical with that of the real one with the time reversed. The same thing is true in electro-magnetism. The motion, for example, of an electric charge in an electro-magnetic field and a description with the time reversed are both equally good examples of the laws of electro-magnetism. Also, there is no difference in the description of the emission process of light and a description of an absorption process with the time reversed. Quantum theory did not remove this strange symmetry either, nor did the theory of relativity. It seems that in each case the investigators responsible did not have any particular bias in favor of a time symmetrical theory, but it just turned out that way. Each new set of phenomena when it came to be understood and described in the most general terms, turned out to have no sense of time built in.

Just in recent times, this statement has to be qualified a little bit; because just now there is some discussion whether an elementary process in nuclear physics has been discovered which is not time symmetrical. It is not yet clear what this observation implies and perhaps we shall have to revise our discussion; but we must still regard it as very strange that all the major events in our surroundings are dictated by time symmetrical laws while we have so clearly an idea that time is unsymmetrical.

The Asymmetry of the Real World

Clearly, a lot of the actual things that happen are not time symmetrical. We only have to run a movie backwards to see that. Who could jump out of the water feet first and gracefully land on a high diving board upright? When has it ever happened that sand jumped up spontaneously off a heap and arranged itself neatly on a workman's shovel to be put carefully into a hole? Who has ever seen the fragments of a flower pot jump together on the floor and instantly weld themselves into a perfect piece in a person's hands? We do not have to look at a film for very long to see that it is reversed. Although to be sure, not all scenes would give it away. How is it now: which scenes would give it away, and which not?

Suppose you had a train running around a track. Would you know? You might say that it would be odd for the engine to be at the back, pushing, but not impossible. How about a car? You would say that no driver limited to the human range of skills could manage to drive the thing in reverse at sixty miles an hour and not smash up instantly; but could you prove that it is impossible to make a car that could go in reverse at this speed or find a driver who could master this skill? But then the scene in our movie might shift to a waterfall boiling and foaming at the bottom with the violence of the colliding water masses. Anyone would be sure there; the water is coming from the top and crashing down. No one could devise a way of making a boiling and bubbling mass of water and arrange to have emerge out of it a jet that gracefully coalesces and smoothly slides over the rock ledge a hundred feet above. That is just impossible.

Or there might be a scene of cream being poured into a cup of coffee and being stirred up. Again, no one would think it possible to have the coffee stirred in such an artfully contrived manner that all the cream droplets would coagulate together and form a single block.

Or suppose there is a scene of an airplane taking off. Could that be a landing in reverse? Could a plane fly backward? Of course not.

So the interesting fact emerges that there are some types of events that are strongly directional in time and there are those that are less so or not so at all. The closer we go to the simplest, most elementary processes, the most nondirectional, on the whole, things get. When we decomposed any kind of event into the elementary processes, then we lost the directionality that was clearly implied in the event as a whole. If we looked in detail at the molecules of water jostling each other in the waterfall's whirlpool, we would see many processes that could all go in reverse just as well. But if we look at larger and larger regions of this whirlpool it becomes less and less likely as a process in the opposite sense of time. If we looked at the flow of air over an airplane's structure on the microscopic scale we would not find any laws of physics infringed by the reverse flow. But again, if we look on the larger scale, the reverse flow would contain more and more events that we would say that are not in

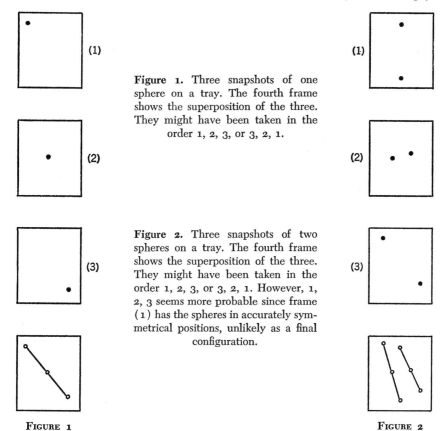

Figure 1. Three snapshots of one sphere on a tray. The fourth frame shows the superposition of the three. They might have been taken in the order 1, 2, 3, or 3, 2, 1.

Figure 2. Three snapshots of two spheres on a tray. The fourth frame shows the superposition of the three. They might have been taken in the order 1, 2, 3, or 3, 2, 1. However, 1, 2, 3 seems more probable since frame (1) has the spheres in accurately symmetrical positions, unlikely as a final configuration.

FIGURE 1   FIGURE 2

detail impossible, but are just extremely unlikely to go that way. Everything would look highly contrived and, while one would have to admit that the motion is a possible one with the detailed conditions of the position and movement of all the molecules involved, one would say that no one could have managed to contrive these initial conditions exactly such that the very unlikely results would follow.

Let us try to understand all this more clearly. Instead of classifying movies as those that do and those that don't have a sense of time, let us look at a simpler situation. Suppose we have a ball on a tray and we take some snapshots of it. We are told that the system was not interfered with during the entire period during which photographs were taken, but that it may have been interfered with before and after that period, and that it may, of course, have been left in a state of motion. If those snapshots are all shuffled, can you put them in the right order?

The answer is: You can put them in the right *sequence* if they represent sufficiently small time intervals. We can deduce the *sequence* but not the *sense in time*. 1, 2, 3, 4, 5 or 5, 4, 3, 2, 1; we cannot tell which. The laws of motion of the ball are time symmetrical and therefore either sense of its motion is acceptable. If the successive positions are just such that they would fit an undisturbed motion in either sense, then we will, no doubt, presume that this is the explanation and put the pictures in that sequence.

Or suppose that we have the same situation, but with two balls. Again we are told that during the period when the snapshots were taken there was no interference, but before and after there may have been. Again the snapshots can be ordered in a sequence—but now there may be a hint of the correct direction of time of that sequence. What if, for example, the two balls were lying in precise symmetrical places at one end of the sequence? Would we then not suppose that somebody started it out that way? Is it not too unlikely to find a neat arrangement at the end of the period?

With two balls, the probabilities are perhaps not too terribly small against the latter having arisen by chance, so we cannot be quite sure. But what if we had two thousand? Then surely any very systematic pattern would have to be at the beginning of the interval, for how could you think that it would have happened by chance at the end after a lot of random looking arrangements.

This is how we could tell the sense of the sequence if the arrangement in fact had been a favorable one for our purposes at the beginning. But if it was not, then we still could not tell. If the configuration at the beginning looks as random as that at the end, there is no possibility. The strange conclusion then emerges: with a few balls in the field we cannot be quite sure ever. With a lot we can be very sure if we happen to have a very particular situation set up at the beginning. If not, the *sequence* can be inferred but not the *sense*.

How does all this compare with the situation with the clock that we discussed before? There we decided that it was a person who knew the

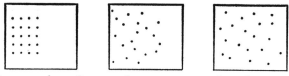

Figure 3. Three snapshots of many spheres on a tray. The order 1, 2, 3 now seems much more probable than any other, since the regular configuration on (1) would be unlikely to be the end product of the motion. (2) is likely to be intermediate, with the motion having not yet led to as random an appearance as (3).

sense, not the clock. Here we have it that we are prepared to infer that a person had set up the system at the beginning in some particular way and that the application of the laws of nature would then take it further away from this particular condition. Again, the intervention of a person is required for the sense of time to be inferred. Is that always the rule? Is there nothing other than people who know which way time runs?

What about the waterfall? Here we have a natural phenomenon which has a sense built in. Here also a lot of objects are involved—all the droplets into which the water can break up—and indeed if we look closely enough, all the molecules. That, as always, seems to help. But in this case it was not necessary for the initial condition to be one contrived in some particular way by a person. With snapshots taken in close succession, we could easily recognize the paths of many droplets and we would then arrange the sequence such that the water falls down on the whole and not up. The sense of flow of the water going upwards is not one that could be expected even though it is not quite impossible.

What is expected? It is always that an ordered or systematic system would give way to an unordered random one. All systems that show the sense of time have this in common. They are all systems of sufficient complexity so that order and disorder are meaningful. They all start out with a state of high order and go to one of more disorder. In the case of the waterfall, the water before and after falling may seem equally orderly, but it would not be if we looked in detail, for all that violent disorder at the bottom, when it gives way to a smooth stream again, will still have left its effect on the water. Instead of the big droplets rushing around in a disorderly fashion, it will eventually be the molecules of the water that will do so individually, since the water is now somewhat warmer. The increased disorder is still there, even if it is more difficult to see it.

Order and Disorder

What is order and disorder? Can we always define it properly? In some cases the definition seems obvious, as in the case of heating a perfectly regular crystal lattice of a solid material and causing it to melt into an irregular, nearly random, arrangement of its molecules. But I could invent other cases, for example with the spheres on my tray, where a precisely systematic pattern may go unnoticed. What if I set up the spheres to occupy the positions on a coordinate grid of precisely the prime numbers? It might not look very systematic if one did not look for this particular effect. If one did, it would suffice just as any other systematic pattern to tell the sense in time of the snapshots. But if one did not recognize the particular regularity, one just could not find the sense of the sequence of snapshots. If we do not have a good definition of order and disorder, then it only means that in all the doubtful cases we might not be able to recognize the sense of time in the system.

We now see clearly why we usually need a complex situation described on our snapshots. The more objects we can see on our snapshots, the easier it will be to recognize order and disorder.

To be able to find a sequence in our snapshots, we required not only the complexity but also that in fact in the beginning there must have been some recognizable order. This could have arisen either from a person having done it, having disposed the objects in some systematic pattern, or from nature having produced somehow an orderly situation in some natural way; either will do. If the system is then allowed to go on for long enough, it will eventually end up in a less orderly configuration and our snapshots will show the effect.

In practice, we often have systems with such vast numbers of particles that order and disorder are extremely meaningful concepts. It is for these circumstances that one has devised a measure of the disorder of a system and has given it the name of *entropy*. In thermodynamics one discusses the relation between this entropy specifying the degree of disorder of a system and its content of heat and of energy that could be made available in the system. Order and disorder, or entropy, assumes a new significance when it becomes possible to define in those terms the available energy of a system. Order and disorder and energy seem very different things, so how do these two come to be connected?

It is quite easy to understand the connection between energy and order-disorder by means of a simple example. Suppose we have a very well heat-insulated box and in it we have two large pieces of copper, one very hot and the other very cold. We know that if we left them in the box for a long time they would eventually assume the same temperature—the hot piece would have cooled itself and the cold piece would have got heated until there no longer was a temperature difference and nothing more would happen after that. The heat energy contained in the box as a whole would not have been changed by that. What is happening there is not very different from the discussion we had about the spheres on the tray. Here again, we have a highly ordered situation at the beginning, namely that nearly all the heat energy is concentrated in the one piece and very little in the other, and if we leave it to itself it will get itself into the more disordered condition in terms of the energy content of the individual molecules. Again, as before, it would not, in principle, be impossible for all the heat energy to concentrate itself back in the one block, but it is now a process which is so exceedingly unlikely that we need not discuss it. If we had only two molecules, then it would not be very unlikely. But since we have a very large number, all statistical probabilities are virtually certainties.

In this case a thermodynamicist would speak of the entropy of the system increasing as heat flows from the hot body to the cold body. He would then point out that, at the beginning, it would have been possible to extract energy from the system by placing a heat engine, say a steam engine, to be heated by the hot block so as to have its radiator (where it gets rid of heat) connected to the cold block. The shaft of this engine would then have made available energy that could have been used in any way one likes. If, on the other hand, one lets time elapse and hence entropy increase, then eventually when the two blocks have reached the same temperature, no engine could be made to work using this heat energy. The energy would still be there, of course, but it is now in such a state of disorder that we could no longer see a way of getting hold of it.

In the language of the thermodynamicist, entropy in any system appears always to increase. If entropy somewhere is seen to decrease—if for example someone is setting up the hot and the cold blocks by means of, say, a flame and a refrigerator—then one can inquire what the other effects of this equipment are; it will always be seen that, if one encompasses the system as a whole that contains the flame and the refrigerator and its fuel and so forth, that that system as a whole would have suffered an increase of entropy, even though some subsystem had suffered a decrease. It seems that things can only be ordered at the expense of making more disorder somewhere else.

Why did we get into all this for the discussion of time? We wanted to see what it was that characterized those systems in which the sense of time was evident. The hot and the cold blocks in our box are now a very good example, for there we do not need to know too accurately how to specify order and disorder. It is quite clear in which sense things will go. Is it true that all systems that contain a sense of time are of this kind? Is the arrow of time given only by the sense in which disorder increases?

A simple answer to this question is "yes." All the systems that we have discussed and all the others that we might equally have used as examples are of that kind. Even the clock might have been included if we had gone a little further with its discussion. The clock, in addition to ticking away intervals, has in fact a process going on which is not time symmetrical. I am referring to the fact that the mainspring will get unwound and the energy that was stored up there will reappear as heat throughout the mechanism. Energy has gone from an accessible form to one of so much disorder that it is inaccessible. Entropy has increased.

As we look around and find that every mechanism which shows time asymmetry is of this same basic kind, we must wonder whether this is also true of ourselves. Could it be that these same statistical tendencies which so heavily pervade all our surroundings and, no doubt, our own physical and chemical mechanism, are the ones that give us the time asymmetry of which we are so very conscious? I could certainly see no case for invoking anything different for biology when this biology is in fact placed in the real world that possesses all the asymmetry needed to explain the effect. It seems to me desirable not to make any special explanations for biology when there is no clear need for it. Let us understand as much as we can about biology in terms of the physical mechanisms.

What Makes Order?

We still have to search further, however, before we can understand all this. It is only in systems that have a certain state of order that the asymmetry in time shows up. If a person set it up we can readily understand why it should be ordered. But how is it in nature? If all systems get disordered, then how come that we still have any that are ordered? You might have thought that in the age of our solar system, 5×10^9 years, anything would have gone to the maximum disorder that it could reach. As we have said before, in the example with the heat insulated box, no effect of progressing time would then be in evidence. Why has all this not yet happened?

The situation here is essentially different just because we are not in a heat-insulated box. The radiation can, and does, escape from our locality. Where does it go? Into the depths of space. Just from our system? No; presumably from all other stars it is just the same. A great amount of radiation goes out and only very much less comes in. Our local system did not get to the maximum state of disorder because it could radiate away all the time. Had we had a heat-insulating box around the solar system, all would by now be at a uniform high temperature.

If we want to see the reason for the statistical tendencies on any one scale of things, it seems that we always must look to the next larger scale. Each system we look at is not in practice completely insulated from the rest of the world and it is the outside influences that determine the way things go. When we keep seeing fresh order generated, as for example when water keeps being delivered to the river above the waterfall to have its ordered energy dissipated into heat at the bottom, this is not infringing the general rule that entropy increases. What is happening is that we are not looking at an isolated system and that, for the apparent decrease of entropy, for every apparent ordering of things there is, on some larger scale, a greater increase of disorder. On our lives, the dominant influence is the sun shining radiation into the depths of space. We must think of ourselves and of all the activities around us in which order seems to be regenerated, all those things that are not just running down, all the clocks that are being wound up, all the waterfalls being replenished, as being connected with little heat engines that derive their input heat chiefly from the solar radiation and that are cooled by radiation into space. It is this heat flow from the sun out into space which, by being interrupted a little, can be made to generate order locally, but only at the expense of generating even more disorder on a larger scale. More heat energy is later widely distributed in the universe where before it was concentrated in the sun. This is the greatest disordering and running down process in our part of the world.

A heat engine is able to generate some order, but it needs a source of heat and a sink of heat into which it can reject heat at a lower temperature. For your motor car you have a radiator, and for any other heat engine there is some means of getting rid of heat. Without it, it would all merely heat up to a uniform high temperature and nothing more would happen. In the universe, the largest heat engines are driven by a source of heat, namely the stars, and a sink of heat, namely the cold space. Is it not strange that, after all this time, space is still cold? It seems to be able to accept heat being dumped into it indefinitely without getting hot. What is the explanation for that?

One answer might be that there is just so much space, that all the stars in the time in which they have been shining have not been able to fill it up with radiation. If we went on long enough, then eventually stars and space would all become equally hot and all heat engines would cease. No fresh order could be generated anywhere then, and no processes would then be seen in which there is a gross difference between the two senses of time. We do not have to trouble to explain how people's minds will then single out one sense of time because in that circumstance there would be no people. But so long as space is cold and the heat-flow from the hot stars continues, heat engines can work; all the statistical tendencies that we have discussed will continue to be in existence. These tendencies from which we judge the sense of time are thus clearly related

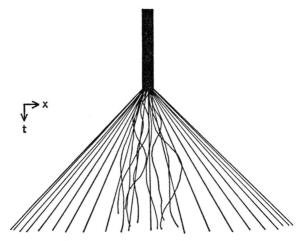

Figure 4. A space time diagram showing an explosion. This is a common feature in the all embracing pattern in the one sense of time, but rarely occurs in the other sense. Photon clouds often expand but rarely contract.

to the *overwhelming tendency in the real world* for radiation to expand outwards into space rather than for radiation to come inwards and focus on objects. It is this one overwhelming tendency in the real world that fixes the statistical behavior of systems on all other scales, for they all depend on heat engines that use space as the sink of heat. Clouds of photons, the units of radiation, have an overwhelming tendency to expand rather than contract. That seems the most basic statement to be made about the statistical tendencies in our universe. We have traced the effect to a property of the universe which it possesses at any rate at the present time. It is a separate but interesting problem why the universe has this property.

The Universe as a Heat Sink

You may have heard that one has discovered the universe to be expanding. What one has discovered is that, as one looks at very distant aggregates of stars, one observes their light to be a deeper red color than it would be from similar objects nearby. This effect is just of the kind that would be produced if the distant objects were rushing away from us at a high speed and their light was therefore subject to the Doppler effect which transposes it to a lower frequency.

If the universe is expanding in this way, then we could immediately understand why it does not get filled up with radiation. As fast as radiation is being poured into it, the spaces that contain it increase their volume. It is like pouring water into a barrel which fails to fill up, not because it has a leak but because it is increasing its size all the time.

We can look at the same thing in another way. If we pursued a particular direction of looking far enough into the distance, then, if the universe is big enough and is pervaded by stars everywhere, such a line of sight will eventually end on the surface of a star. But if in each direction of looking we saw the surface of some star, then all the sky around us should be as bright as the surfaces of stars, and everything in it would then be as hot as the stars. This is clearly not the case. Either lines of sight do not all end on the surfaces of stars but just go on forever into nothingness or—and that is the solution more commonly adopted—they end on surfaces of stars mostly only at a very great distance, and at that distance the stars are rushing away from us at a very high speed. As a result the light is so far transposed to low frequencies that it represents no visible light any more and that, in accord with the Doppler effect on light, the energy content of it has become very low. This is saying no more than that a very distant star which is rushing away from us cannot deliver much energy at us because it is spending almost all its energy to put light in transit on this ever-increasing path. The observed expansion of the universe thus gives an explanation for the dark sky, even if the

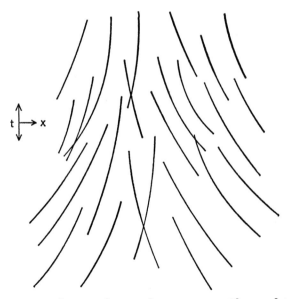

Figure 5. A space time diagram showing that symmetry with regard to sense along the time axis can be absent, yet the average properties need not be changing. (This is "homogenous" but not "isotropic.")

universe does not thin out, and if stars continue as far into the distance as you could ever see.

If we adopt the expanding universe explanation for the dark sky, then a little bit more of the story falls into place. The tendency for radiation to expand rather than contract is then clearly just related to the tendency for matter on a large scale to expand rather than contract. The reason for a dark sky was that the space between objects was for ever increasing and that is now precisely the reason why radiation is generally expanding. On a small scale we saw a statistical tendency dictated by the fact that radiation expands. On a large scale we see that this expanding radiation merely follows the expansion of the universe. *The radiation is the main link between the large and the small.*

Let us look again at a space-time diagram, but now one drawn for a very large scale. World lines of galaxies are now moving apart in the sense in which we normally regard time. Radiation in spaces in between is also moving apart. Now, if we have time-symmetrical laws of physics and we look at this diagram without our native prejudice as to sense of time, we should be able to interpret everything just as well in reverse. A contracting view of this universe would have to be just as acceptable so far as the laws of physics are concerned. If possible we would also like to explain that we would choose to regard this universe as an expanding one.

The Universe in Reverse

What happens if we try to describe the universe in the other sense of time? As you recall, the process of emission and reception of light can be regarded equally in either sense. All the places that in the one sense were the emitters will now become the receivers and *vice versa*. In this reversed picture most radiation would therefore come from such objects as the extensive dark clouds in galaxies, namely the objects which to the normal way of thinking absorb most of the starlight, and from these dark clouds the light would go usually a very long way. In the contracting universe it would then be severely shifted to the blue, and its intensity greatly increased. It would mostly converge onto the surfaces of hot stars and in the view we would then take, it would be the cause of their heat. In the star the heat would go into nuclear transformations that use up energy. All this is no more than merely describing all the radiation moving in reverse in a universe that is itself going in reverse. Now in this universe, the sky is not dark and radiation is generally contracting. All the statistical tendencies, if our previous arguments were correct, would now be in reverse. Disordered systems would tend to order themselves; radiation would tend to converge onto objects and heat them; heat in general would flow from cold bodies to hot bodies and entropy would in general decrease. This is the description of our universe in the opposite sense of time. It sounds very strange but it has no conflict with any laws of physics. If we think of the universe not in terms of an object progressing through time in a certain sense, but, as I have said before, of the existing totality of world lines, if we think of it as the great pattern on the wall of our space-time diagram, then either description is equally valid. Our strange description is not describing another universe, or how it might be but isn't, but it is describing the very same thing.

You might be puzzled by some features of this. For example, you might say that you know for sure that you are living in an expanding and not a contracting universe. Clearly, you say, when I turn the telescope to look at a distant galaxy it makes its mark on the spectroscopic plate on the red side and not the blue. There is an objective mark on the photographic plate in the place which means expansion and not contraction. There is no mark on the blue side of the spectroscope. Is this not an objective way of describing it? But this argument was not conducted sufficiently carefully. If we regard the universe as contracting then heat flows from cold bodies to hot bodies. All the statistical tendencies are reversed. A cold photographic plate is thus the last place on which to try and find the effects of radiation from a hot body. We need to go to hot places, not cold ones, in order to see the radiation arrive from the depths of space. The surfaces of stars or a flashlight held out of the window, these would be the places that would attract radiation from afar. This view is consistent since the emission and reception of light are indistinguishable processes.

Think of these processes as described on our great pattern on the wall; there is no question of describing things as likely or unlikely. That is the pattern which is there. You may describe it this way or that way in terms of a progressing time and you will then invent in each case the appropriate description of the statistical tendencies, and of the cause-effect relationships. But think of it as a given pattern in which you can recognize certain regularities, namely the laws of physics. The idea of a cause and effect relationship now becomes meaningless. You may see relationships within the pattern which are of the kind that in the conventional description one would be called the cause and the other the effect. In the description with the opposite sense of time you would just have to reverse these roles. But in the timeless description in our pattern

328   :   *Thomas Gold*

on the wall they are only related events but with nothing in the nature of a cause and effect relationship.

Time and Consciousness

Now having arrived this far in the argument, can we understand why in our consciousness we have singled out one peculiar way of describing the little piece of the pattern on the wall of which we have a knowledge? Why is it that instead of a static description of the pattern, or indeed one in the other sense of time, we pretend to know that we are sliding in one particular sense along the time coordinate?

We ourselves are, of course, little patches in this great diagram, finite, alas, in all four coordinates. What can it mean when we speak of having knowledge of the past? It means no doubt that there is some relationship between world lines interior to us and exterior world lines. Some code has been established, as in a computing machine, between events outside and configuration in our memory unit. Will this relationship be equally close with events displaced in either sense along the time coordinate? In each case we have facts at our command, namely the configuration of our memory, and we use them to infer something about the outside world. We say we are "remembering" or that we are "predicting," depending on whether this inference is concerned with the past or the future. It seems to me that our principal notion of the progress of time stems from the fact that these two operations seem so different to us. They are different mainly in the degree of certainty that can be acheived. The past we think we may know without any doubt, but the future is much less certain. Can we now understand where this difference comes from?

In terms of the great pattern on the wall, in which our brain box is represented as a little patch, we would now like to understand that the relationship between the interior of this patch and the outside is closer in the direction that we call the "past" than in the direction that we call the "future." Of course all this is placed into a diagram with an overwhelming asymmetry with regard to the two senses along the time coordinate. We are concerned with the world lines of a very large number of particles and for that reason, statistical probabilities become nearly certainties. The difference in the statistical tendencies of looking along the pattern in one sense or the other then appears a difference in principle and not merely a change of probabilities. Our brains can compute the past from their present configuration more accurately than they can compute the future, and because the difference in the quality of this computation is so great, we think of it as a difference in principle.

The great pattern has, after all, the quality of spreading out, of diffusing itself, of making things more random in the one sense of time, and therefore it is not surprising that the computation does not work so well in that sense.

If one had the great pattern plotted, all one could say from it is that the correspondence between inside and outside the brain box was much closer in the one sense of time than in the other. But as we have said, that diagram would then contain all the information there is. This must be the only reason for developing the notion of the passage of time.

Let us sum up these remarkable conclusions. The real world can be completely described by a pattern of lines in four dimensions where each particle of matter is represented by a line. Because of the large-scale architecture of the universe, that pattern is mostly unsymmetrical with respect to the two senses along one of the coordinates. This asymmetry shows up in any region containing a large number of lines, but as we look on a smaller and smaller scale the asymmetry disappears. We who are parts of this pattern have such a relationship with it that we create the fiction of a "time" which for ever progresses and which transports us along with it.

It may be very difficult for us to change our ways of thought. Even as I explain all this I am thinking that this essay is nearly finished, that I have already said most in the past and that I will only say a little bit more in the future. I do not really think of myself as a patch existing in this great static pattern and of these sentences representing some relationships between the interior of my brain, the air molecules in the room, and the interiors of your brains. I know that I am thinking of it instead as a process in time involving my own free will and decision and influencing the future but not the past. It is hard to do otherwise even though I know I have no justification for this point of view. When we come to discuss physics, however, it may complicate matters to discuss it with concepts that are subjective and have their origin in introspection only. The passage of time is a notion of that kind.

I cannot tell you whether it is important or not to try to understand these matters. Progress in science is often dependent on a new way of looking at things and on finding a less subjective way of describing the exterior world. I do not know whether this will be so here and I suppose most people would say that "only time can tell."

HENRY MARGENAU
Yale University

The Philosophical Legacy of Contemporary Quantum Theory

The agreement of these considerations with experience together with Planck's determination of the true molecular size from the law of radiation (for high temperatures) convinced the sceptics, who were quite numerous at that time (Ostwald, Mach) of the reality of atoms. The antipathy of these scholars towards atomic theory can indubitably be traced back to their positivistic philosophical attitude. This is an interesting example of the fact that even scholars of audacious spirit and fine instinct can be obstructed in the interpretation of facts by philosophical prejudices. The prejudice—which has by no means died out in the meantime—consists in the faith that facts by themselves can and should yield scientific knowledge without free conceptual construction. Such a misconception is possible only because one does not easily become aware of the free choice of such concepts, which, through verification and long usage, appear to be immediately connected with the empirical material.

> —Albert Einstein
> "Autobiographical Notes," in *Albert Einstein, Philosopher-Scientist,* I

WESTERN NATIONS tacitly embrace a doctrine which asserts the *philosophical neutrality of science.* This doctrine holds that scientific knowledge has nothing to do with philosophy, that it is compatible with almost any metaphysical interpretation, that it tolerates with equal liberality the theses of rationalism and empiricism, of idealism and realism, of positivism and existentialism, these being either matters of taste or based on trans-scientific evidence. When thus formulated the view is shocking;

many scientists will disavow it, but most of their acts and writings support it nonetheless.

It draws support from another Western fashion. Ever since the vogue of empirical positivism, orthodox science has been identified, at least in the popular mind, with the collecting of data, with an addiction to a kind of objectivity that shuns interpretation and relies on theory as little as possible, with an activity that culminates in accurate reports of observations and in the discovery of observational regularities called laws of nature. Science was largely meant to satisfy curiosity, not the deep desire for understanding. Hence, the frequent assertion that science merely "describes," while philosophy "explains."

It is hardly necessary to refute the characterization of science thus implied, for its fallacy is clear when it is fully stated. Nor, as I have said, do many scientists believe it. Their pragmatism, their lack of concern for philosophical interpretations of their own discoveries has a double reason: (1) the breathtaking rate at which their work succeeded has left them little time to worry about meanings and about ties with other branches of learning; (2) they did not like what philosophers made of their results.

The consequences of this attitude are also twofold: (1) Knowledge of what scientific discoveries *imply* has been ripening too slowly; there has appeared the so-called cultural lag, i.e., the gap between basic understanding and technological competence, creating as the public image of science the grotesque half-truth of a soulless monster which measures, analyzes, predicts but is forever unable to capture the spirit of things. (2) The second consequence is that the interpretations of science are often erroneous. The temporal lag behind science coupled with its inaccuracy has caused philosophy of science to lose status in our culture. This is probably the reason why today it is so frequently and so erroneously identified with history of science.

The present essay is meant to expose this situation and to attempt a small contribution to its cure by showing what specific modifications the quantum theory, in the form now most widely held, induces among the philosophic ideas that were compatible with the older branches of physics which are now called classical. Our scope will of course be limited to issues in the philosophy of *science*, which I regard as a disciplined study of the basic presuppositions of science together with the logical entailments of these presuppositions concerning other fields of human interest. Inasmuch as science is a dynamic, progressive, never-ending enterprise which harbors no stagnant certainties, philosophy of science likewise is a changing field of knowledge which, though it may ask questions of eternal relevance, does not pretend to give eternally valid answers. My best hope is therefore to be able to offer an exposition of certain novel features in the philosophy of science that are called for by the best scientific evidence *now* available.

This will be attempted in three sections. In the first a general, very neutral (in the sense of including the essential elements of many divergent representations) but structurally complete account of the epistemology of science is to be presented. The second section formulates the important concepts and axioms of current quantum theory and confronts them with their classical counterparts. In the last section philosophical consequences of this confrontation will be drawn with respect to the items surveyed in the first, and the important changes will be noted.

The sequence goes from the rigorous and specific developments in Sections 1 and 2 to the more popular and philosophically more general contents of Section 3. This comment should not, however, be taken as an admission that the article degenerates from science to "mere philosophy." If that happens it is not intentional. For it is my firm belief that science is more than observation, laws, formulas and rigorous theory, that its account is incomplete without a picture of its philosophical commitments, that it is filled with the spirit of adventure and engages man's heart as well as man's reason. Indeed, I hold that any part of science which is confined to formulas and factual prediction, refusing to reveal its significance in popular and philosophically meaningful terms, is either barren and therefore uninteresting, or still immature.

Epistemology of Science

Science may be called the principled endeavor to "understand," to make rational sense of a certain part of human experience. Hence it behooves us to analyze, first of all, the meaning of the word *experience*. The Latin verb *experiri* adverted to all possible phases of awareness, to perceptions, visions, hallucinations, feelings, thoughts, judgments, decisions, actions, and innumerable other unnamed conscious processes man can undergo. Mainly through the teachings of British empiricism (Locke, Hume, and their dissenting disciple, Kant), the range of denotation of the word contracted until it came to designate only the activities which are involved in or immediately consequent upon external perception. Some see in this transformation a perversion of the meaning of experience; be that as it may, the claim that this narrow sense of the word contains all that is vital to *knowledge,* a claim made by extreme empiricists, is certainly a perversion of philosophy. Hence, we return here to the original meaning of experience, allowing it to include what has been called the affective, the emotional, the conative and all the rest.

One might ask whether the use of so embracive a term will not result in wholly uninteresting and pointless statements. This is not the case, for the term retains exactly that discriminating power which is so important in philosophy: it allows the distinction between what is within experience and what is outside it, giving occasion, for example, to the meaningful inquiry concerning matters that transcend experience, making possible the time-honored distinction between epistemology (which remains within experience) and ontology (which may transcend it). We do not wish to ask such questions here but must record their validity, even while acknowledging the very extensive span of the term experience.

But now we trim it down; we select from the large domain a certain class of experiences called *cognitive.* Roughly, they are the ingredients which lead to knowledge or understanding as distinct from purely affective moods, appreciative or depreciative attitudes, decisions, and actions. These terms are admittedly vague, and there is nothing we can do about it. Experience does not come in neatly classified compartments; it is a multiform flow of conscious items with certain accentuations which we recognize and which we label "feelings," "thoughts," etc., much in the way we call a color blue. None of these elements of experience is strictly definable, each is a primitive in a logical system that contains them. Bearing this in mind we characterize *cognitive* experience by listing the words commonly employed to denote its fluid components, naming sometimes the psychological activity, sometimes its results in mind (since both are experiences, one active, the other contemplative) as follows: sensory awareness, perception, external data, observation, abstraction, judgment, analysis, thought, concept, reasoning, inference, conclusion, induction, assumption, prediction, verification, and many others, including above all that synthesizing bond, which makes for unity of experience, namely the memory of previous contents of awareness.

Traditionally, these elements of cognitive experience are often divided into two large groups: perceptions yielding external *data* on the one hand and reasoned judgments yielding *concepts* on the other. Memory, though not ordinarily included, must be considered to hover above the scheme, ready to be called upon when needed. Several motives have induced different philosophers to make the distinction between data and concepts; some intended to convey the origin of the experiences, assigning data to external objects and concepts to men's minds; others wanted to distinguish their reliability, data being incontrovertible while concepts are derivative and subject to error. The reverse position as to order of reliability was held by some rationalists. A third motive for wishing to distinguish between data and concepts is one which has seemed most significant to the present writer;[1] it lies in the clear introspective testimony of so-called data as to spontaneity and coerciveness, whereas concepts are distinctively of our own making. We have, we receive, we accept, we suffer the data which assail us through our senses; we abstract, select, contribute, engender the concepts with which we reason. There is a sense of fatefulness about the acceptance of what perception and observation deliver, a sense of responsibility about the results of reason. In the latter instance we feel ourselves involved like an architect in the structure of a building, in the former only as an agent who acknowledges the receipt of building materials.

The difference just sketched is incorporated into the method of science. Because the scientist has a right to disclaim responsibility with respect to data, he may treat them as independent of his own procedures, as "given"; to look upon them as something ultimate which he needs to accommodate in other phases of his experience. Figuratively speaking, datal or perceptory experience is a crude, suggestive forerunner of more elaborate and rational kinds of cognitive experience, much in the way in which the *protocol* of an ancient book, i.e., the leaf pasted inside the cover carrying the verbal plan of the book, forecast its contents. I have borrowed the word protocol from Carnap, whose early writings use it in a similar sense. This kind of experience which, roughly speaking, is not of our making, will here be called P-experience. The reader may think of P as standing for protocol, perceptory, or primary. In science, P-experience carries a measure of authenticity which concepts lack.

Whether sense data, observation based on and involving perception are alone in having this P-quality is a question we need not answer here. It is my belief that there are others which can also claim this property, cognitive experiences which are as coercive, spontaneous and reliable as perceptory data. Natural science, however, has not used them as such, and our analysis is here limited to the domain of natural science.

To signify the components of cognitive experience which stand at the other extreme of the range, far away from P, we shall use the letter C, which may be regarded as an abbreviation of *concept*. This word has unfortunately become the bearer of terrific burdens. In philosophy alone it seems to designate anything that can be thought, from the image of a particular object presented in sensation to the abstract universal, "being." Add to this the meanings of our military writers who are displaying increasing fondness of the word, and its suitability becomes highly questionable. For these reasons, and also because a reference is needed to the distinctive fact that concepts are of our making, I have employed the word *construct* previously,[1] and *C* may be taken to allude to it. The danger here, of course, is that the word might be mistaken to denote "mere, subjective, mental" constructs, following the usage of other writers. Such adjectives do describe the initial psychological situation in which constructs first arise, but they ignore the possibility of confirmation by comparison with *P*-experiences which lifts certain constructs out of this primitive subjectivism and converts them into *verifacts*, to use again an earlier terminology. F. S. C. Northrop[2] speaks of concepts by postulation and concepts by intuition; these are similar to the present writer's *C* and *P* experiences.[3]

The difference between *P* and *C* is not merely semantic or linguistic; in fact language frequently obscures the difference. To note this is especially important for a fuller understanding of the method of science, and a few examples will now be introduced to clarify this point.

A force may mean a *P*-experience, something immediately apprehended, such as a muscular sensation, a push or a pull. In the physicist's language force has a different connotation; it refers to something rather more abstract, existing apart from tactile and kinesthetic sensations yet related to them in a unique and measurable way. Newton's law speaks of it as mass times acceleration and implies an entity clearly different from sensed pushes and pulls. We are facing here the *C*-aspect of force, a new component of scientific experience for whose genesis *we* are responsible, for it is not given as a simple perceptory presentation. There is no reason to suppose, for example, that Leibniz's experience of the muscular sensation called force was different from that of Descartes, yet they differed in defining the construct force, Leibniz taking it to be mass times velocity squared, Descartes as mass times velocity, both disagreeing with Newton. Clearly, then, as a construct the idea of force is not immediately given.

One of the purposes served by the *C*-meaning of any term is to regularize it, to allow measurement, to quantify it in a more reproducible manner than direct sensation affords; another is to make the term more "objective." Indeed, ordinary language often speaks of *P* as the subjective, of C as the objective aspect of force. Precisely how the two are related, and what the word objective implies, will be considered later. Let us for the moment continue to look at the contrast between P and C in connection with a few other physical quantities, every one of which, as we shall see, presents this dual aspect without its being recognized in our language.

Temperature may mean hotness or coldness, something given in immediate sensation. It goes without saying that this sensation is not what is to be inserted in the equations of thermodynamics, nor what is registered by thermometers. To be sure, when reading a thermometer, visual sensations take the place of the sensed temperature. Yet the visual sensation of the scale mark which coincided with the top of the mercury column is not identical with the construct, temperature, either. C-temperature arises in a complex way out of a specific group of P-experiences plus certain inferences from them; P-temperature, on the other hand, is the direct sensation of hotness. The P-aspect of color is the seen hue in its sensory vividness, the C-component is the frequency of an electromagnetic wave. Consideration of these and other examples show that all words denoting measurable physical quantities, such as sound intensity, noise, pitch, energy, momentum, length, time, mass, etc. have this dual reference once to protocol experiences and once to scientific concepts.

How are the two aspects related? In the instances cited they are related by instrumental (or operational) definitions. The push I feel in my arm, the hotness I sense in my finger, the blue I see, are not sufficiently "objective," i.e., are too dependent on extraneous circumstances, on my own state of mind; in a word they are unmeasurable by themselves. If a science were to be based on them it would remain descriptive and unsatisfactory. Coerciveness and esthetic immediacy are on the side of these P-experiences, but systematic relations are not. Hence, we set up an instrumental arrangement, for example a spring with an attached scale called a dynamometer, and allow the agent against which the force in my arm reacts to pull out the end of the spring. The mark on the scale opposite the end of the spring is the value of the force thus "objectified" and measured. In a certain sense, difficult to justify logically, this procedure *defines* the force, and the definition is called an instrumental or an operational one. In the present terminology, it provides the passage from P to C.

The instrument performing this function for temperature is a thermometer, for color it is a spectroscope together with auxiliary apparatus, and so on. The use of instruments in the transition from P to C is a very general scientific procedure, employed in the psychological and social as well as the physical sciences.

The significance of instrumental definitions in science and elsewhere has been subjected to a great deal of discussion.[4] Detailed comments on this topic may be found in Reference 1, where it is shown that operational definitions are a special form of a wider class of epistemological relations called *rules of correspondence,* or, in Professor Northrop's terminology, *epistemic correlations.* They are not purely logical relations, and certainly not identities, although they have often been mistaken for these. They mediate between P- and C-experiences and are of great importance in modern philosophy of science. Though far from being implied or dictated by the constituents of the P- or the C-field, they are still not arbitrary. Scientific theory involves a matching of P-experiences against the C-field by suitable rules of correspondence, and this matching process is governed by principles which will be discussed in the sequel.

Instrumental definitions take us from a P-experience to certain simple concepts like force, temperature, and color. Science often requires further passages into the field of very abstract concepts, where meaning is related to P in remoter fashion. For instance, out of a number of quantities like the position and velocity of a body, all of which are operationally definable, science constructs the "state of motion" of the body and places it in a causal context with later states. Evidently, the rules of correspondence connecting a state with immediate sensation are here more elaborate than operational definitions, but they serve the same purpose of linking a C-experience with P. By compounding certain rules of correspondence with more abstract relations, passages from P to very remote parts of the C-field can be established.

In the far reaches of the C-field, away from the P-plane, transempirical principles play an important role. For one asks of a theory more than that it shall provide an epistemic link with protocol experiences; the history of science shows this to be an insufficient criterion for acceptability, often incapable of deciding between rival constructs which are equally successful in explaining known empirical data. The additional requirements to be imposed are spoken of somewhat vaguely as economy of thought, the use of Occam's razor, simplicity, elegance of conception, logical fertility, extensibility, and so forth. Attention must now be given to them because some of them, particularly the principle of causality, have changed their meanings and their roles in quantum mechanics. These guiding principles, which do not originate among the protocol observations but regulate our thinking about them, may well be called metaphysical if that word is taken in its old, time-honored sense. A survey of them, more complete than is necessary here, has been given elsewhere.[1,5] For present purposes I shall review those three principles which have undergone greatest changes in recent physics.

The first, loosely called the requirement of *logical fertility*, insists that the constructs used in science (and for that matter in all meaningful reasoning about the world) be suggestive of relations with other terms or constructs, entail a maximum of implicative or predictive information. The idea of a God who, having created the universe and set its laws, leaves it to its own devices, allowing it to run by itself without interference, is too aloof and singular to be of scientific interest; an entelechy that achieves purposes without observational entailment, or an unconscious "experience" which never exposes itself to test but hovers mysteriously behind man's drives—these are constructs which violate the principle in question. So a neutrino was invented only for the sake of explaining beta decay. The difference between a neutrino and an entelechy (of the kind here hypostatized) is that the former, upon further researches, did come out of hiding to lead to (1) important and fruitful connections with other constructs and (2) observable results, whereas the latter did not.

Classical physics had its own way of insuring the enforcement of the principle of logical fertility: It cast all constructs corresponding to existing entities (the physical systems of the following section) into the form of visual, mechanical artifacts. This method of achieving clarity, the famous *clarté géométrique Cartésienne,* is the simplest and most inviting one that guarantees a maximum of easily ascertained implications. For if the model that explains a certain set of observations is some sort of mechanism with moving parts of definite shapes and sizes, then the rules of correspondence which link the mechanism to P may be used by geometric intuition to relate the parts to P, and thereby engender a whole class of predictions capable in principle of being verified. In this way, which began with Aristotle, forces became interactions of rigid bodies through contact, space became a material medium (like a fluid), the ether an elastic solid, the atom a miniature solar system, chemical valence the stretching of arms, and—to follow this manner of explanation beyond science—God became an old man with a beard.

I should be going too far if I asserted that classical physics always adhered rigidly to the use of mechanical models. There were action-at-a-distance theories of forces; Newton's conception of light was non-mechanistic, and when Maxwell's equations of electromagnetism were formulated the sheer symmetry of their mathematical form almost suppressed the wish for visual models. But the basic tendency was always there, and it found expression in Maxwell's own philosophy in which an explanation, to be completely acceptable, had to be a machine in minature.

Sciences closely associated with physics partook of this fondness for visual clarity; others, notably psychology and the social sciences, manifested it in a lesser degree; but all of them without exception adhere to the principle that constructs of explanation must have suggestive implications beyond those that led to their original use.

Another principle of interest is that of *causality*, which requires that, within a closed system, i.e., a group of physical objects not dynamically influenced by others which are not included, a given situation predetermines all later situations. More particularly, if everything that can possibly be observed in connection with a given physical situation is known completely, that situation evolves in a precisely predictable way.

As an example, consider the translational motion of a particle. Its state of motion is completely described by means of its momentary position and its velocity, q and v. The principle of causality requires in this instance that $q(t)$ and $v(t)$ can be predicted if $q(0)$ and $v(0)$ are known. We shall not enter here into the fine distinction between prediction and predetermination: Causal predetermination shall here denote the state of affairs exemplified, where knowledge of certain variables obtained by observation, "implies" knowledge of the same variables at a later time. The implication is not some mysterious, dynamic enforcement, but rests simply in the laws of nature which are so formulated as to warrant predictability: In the present instance the law is Newton's law of motion, which allows calculation of q and v at t when q and v at $t = 0$ are given as initial conditions, to which the constants of integration are adjusted.

A similar state of affairs is seen to prevail in other branches of physics. In all classical field theories, field quantities like stresses and strains in an elastic medium, flow vectors in a fluid, electric and magnetic intensities in an electromagnetic field are the quantities fixed at $t = 0$ by observations. These are then inserted into differential equations which permit the calculation of the same quantities at any other time t. The observables are said to be propagated "causally," in the sense outlined, as time goes on. A breakdown of causality occurs when this mode of description fails, and this can happen for a variety of reasons. For instance, a given causal theory may lead to predictions which are at variance with the observations. Under such circumstances one does not ordinarily speak of a breakdown of causality, but tries other causal theories until success is at hand. Empirical failure of causality would have to be admitted when all causal theories encounter falsification by the facts. This contingency, however, can clearly never be certified in a convincing way, for one can never be sure that all possibilities have been examined. Empirical failure of the causal principle can therefore hardly be established. This is in line with the fact that *causality is a methodological, nonempirical regulative maxim which belongs to the metaphysical domain.*

A greater threat to it resides in those scientific developments which succeed in providing causal descriptions but pay for them by unreasonable and implausible complexities in the constructs they employ. The so-called ether theories of the last century were able to account for all aspects of light propagation at the expense of simplicity. Models like that of McCullagh, which introduced ether molecules with magnificently intricate internal structures, were not shown wrong vis-à-vis the facts but lacked plausibility and, to hark back once more to the requirement of fertility of constructs, suggested no observable consequences. On this occasion causality was saved by renouncing the use of simple visual models and accepting constructs devoid of some mechanical features; the theory of relativity with its formal reliance on the idea of invariance replaced the mechanical ether.

The philosophical doctrine of determinism is dominated by the thesis that all human experience is understandable in terms of the causal schema we have described. It is difficult to falsify because of the near impossibility of establishing a causal debacle. Nevertheless conditions may arise in which its maintenance proves highly inconvenient and methodologically unwise because of the easy success of some noncausal formalism, or at any rate of a *formalism which is noncausal in the classical sense.* This is indeed what has come to pass in the quantum theory.

In the foregoing discussion we have found it expedient to refer, somewhat vaguely, to another metaphysical principle which I shall call the requirement of *simplicity and elegance.* This has replaced to some extent the older criterion of mechanical intuitability or visual clarity of explanatory constructs. Great scientists have always been impressed by it, for they have sought simple laws, differential equations of low order, spherical shapes for fundamental entities, small and where possible integral numbers for basic constants, and so forth. True, they did not always get away with simple choices, and they replaced the naïve maxim of the simplicity of nature by the methodological injunction that simplicity must always be sought but perhaps ultimately distrusted. We should also note the logical ambiguity of terms like simplicity and mathematical elegance.

Yet, despite all these concessions, the scientific method is not correctly portrayed if such esthetic criteria are left out of sight. Books like Bunge's *The Myth of Simplicity* [6] do not deny their powerful and persuasive action among scientists but impugn their logical definition, proving not that there is something amiss with esthetic principles in science but rather the present incompetence of logic to encompass them. I shall not pause here to recite the use of them in classical physics, which is ample and is manifest in the history of theoretical physics; instead, I prefer to move on toward a brief study of the foundations of quantum mechanics, intending to return to this matter at the end of the next section in an attempt to show that modern theories place even greater emphasis on the metaphysical principle of simplicity and elegance than did classical physics. And it may also be said that they have made its meaning more precise.

Thus far my account has left out altogether the important matter of empirical verification. We need not dwell on it for it is never subject to dispute and has been fully treated elsewhere.[1] Suffice it to say that the principles named do not suffice to insure validity; they must be complemented by empirical procedures which confirm the constructs by reference to P. These procedures can be pictured as circuit-like passages from an observation in P, or a set of them, to the C-field by rules of correspondence, followed by a movement within C (calculation, logical inference), and finally a return to P, via rules of correspondence. This return is called prediction, and the verifying circuit is considered successful if the observations called for in the prediction are in agreement with it.

Foundations of Quantum Mechanics

Scientific quantities like position, momentum, energy, etc., which in accordance with Section 1 are related to observations in the P-field by rules of correspondence, are called *observables*. These observables are related to certain other constructs called *states;* the relation in question, however, is different in classical physics from its counterpart in quantum mechanics. States and observables are said to refer to objects in nature, which are called *physical systems* and are exemplified by rigid bodies, point masses, atoms, photons and the like. A *physical system* is regarded as the carrier of *observables* (observable properties) and these are somehow combined into, or represented by, *states*.

In classical physics the connection between the three concepts is simple and visually clear. A system is often a tangible object, more or less immediately given in sensation, or else a small imagined replica of one. There is a tendency to assign the pictorable qualities of large-scale objects to all physical systems even if they are not directly accessible to sense, and the resulting constructs are then called *models* or, more specifically, mechanical models. Some classical physicists saw the goal of science in the discovery of mechanical models for all observable phenomena.

This tendency is natural in the part of the world which is open to visual inspection. It creates minor difficulties even in classical physics when the system is only mediately apprehensible, as in the case of submolar structures or electromagnetic fields; but classical reasoning overcame them easily by inventing atoms patterned after planetary systems and a mechanical ether with molecules of great mechanical complexity.

The observables characterizing these systems were simple attributes, assigned to them in a possessive and inalienable sense: a moving object *has* position, velocity, mass, size, etc. at all times. The model for the system-observable relation is that of Aristotelian logic which recognizes substances (systems) and accidents (observables). The latter, being measurable, are represented by numbers, since numbers are the outcome of every measurement.

These numbers, however, change in time. To satisfy the requirement of simplicity, classical physics assumes that they change continuously—thus making a postulate which *P*-experience can in principle never confirm. An observable or, more exactly, the representative of an observable therefore becomes a continuous function of the time, $f(t)$, the values of which are made manifest in consecutive measurements.

The state of a system is the collection of all observables that can be assigned to it, a vaguely conceived set of innumerable continuous functions $f_i(t)$. The present state of a moving object is the present value of its position, its velocity, its energy, its orientation, the wavelengths and intensities of the light it reflects or emits, its temperature and so on indefinitely. Fortunately not all this information is relevant for a limited description of the system. If interest is confined to the motion of an object some of the attributes just mentioned are useless items, for it turns out that causal predictions regarding the motion can be based on a small set of observables: position and velocity alone, and all others may be disregarded. This restriction, which makes possible the statement of laws of nature in finite terms, leads to the definition of *causally significant states*, i.e., states which are collections of a small number of crucial observables, each of which is a function of the time.

In the terms of Section 1 an observable is a numerical (quantitative) construct which is directly related to the *P*-plane by a rule of correspondence. The *P*-experience to which it corresponds is called measurement. Analytically, the construct, observable, is a function of *t*. By definition, several observables are compounded to form a state, and that state is the objective characterization of another construct called the physical system. If the procedure involving these connections "succeeds," as explained at the end of Section 1, the construct, physical system, ceases to be hypothetical and becomes a part of reality, and the state is said to denote a real situation at the time *t*.

We note for future reference that the rule of correspondence which links a measurement to the value of an observable is one to one; that is to say, a single measurement determines in principle the value of an observable, and a finite set of measurements determines a state at *t*. This connection is somewhat encumbered by errors of measurement, and our version of it is oversimplified. But the philosophic context is correctly rendered because it is a tenet of classical physics that observational errors can be eliminated if sufficient care is taken; therefore they do not play a basic epistemological role. As we shall see, the isomorphism of the rules of correspondence, their one-one character, which is assumed in classical physics, is repudiated by the quantum theory, to which our discussion must now turn.

The factual discoveries, the new observational findings which made necessary a revision of the basic tenets just outlined are too numerous to be reviewed. Suffice it here to say that they (1) contradict the assumption of continuity in the temporal change of the observables, thus threatening to make the various $f_i(t)$ discontinuous functions with which mathematics found it difficult to deal; (2) violated the assumption of an isomorphism between an observation and the value of an observable, a difficulty closely related to 1; (3) indicated clearly that certain observables take on only specific discrete values when measurements are made, suggesting the occurrence of "quantization"; (4) created paradoxes in connection with the use of pictorial, imageful mechanical models.

The contradiction noted under 1 was evident from the fact that repeated observations on a given state of a physical system yielded irregular, discontinuous results; this likewise occasioned 2, which found its clearest expression in the uncertainty principle, e.g., in the well known proposition that an exact measurement of the position of an electron followed by a momentum measurement necessarily causes the latter to be indeterminate, to have a statistical dispersion which no observational skill can eliminate. Fact 3 was first recognized in spectroscopy, where the appearance of sharp spectral lines required the hypothesis of discrete energy levels, and 4 finds expression in the so-called dualism between the particle and the wave nature of electrons, photons, and all other systems of very small mass.

Quantum mechanics responds to these challenges by altering, indeed by extending, the connections between *P*-experiences, observables, states and systems. The role of observation and measurement as starting points of scientific reasoning cannot be changed because it belongs to the protocol domain of scientific experience over which philosophy has no control. But the linkage between observation and the *C*-field, i.e., between observation and observable, *can* be modified. There is, to be sure, an important restriction: observations, when made in the precise form of measurements, yield numerical values (or at any rate answers that can be converted into numbers); hence, whatever the new definition of an observable, it must have reference to *numbers*. Classical physics made the obvious choice and identified an observable directly with the numbers that appear in measurements, taking it to be the function which assumes these numbers as its values. The troubles we have reviewed counsel against this simple choice. There are, in fact, many mathematical constructs which entail numbers; among them are linear operators which generate numbers called eigenvalues. If, then, we associate linear operators with observables, we are sure of making contact with *P*-experience through numbers. Furthermore—and herein lies the amazing success of quantum mechanics—the eigenvalues turn out to be exactly the quantized results given in measurements when the operators are properly constructed.

This success, however, is not attained without sacrifice. The price one pays is the intuitive directness in the meaning of observables. They are no longer the measured numbers but assume a more abstract nature and withdraw, as it were, from immediate adjacency to the *P*-plane to a place further back in the *C*-field.

Correlated with this change in the definition of observables is a more profound one in the meaning of states. To understand it one is best guided by the mathematical consequences of what has just been said. If observables are operators which generate eigenvalues as their counterparts on P, then a meaning must be found for the eigenfunctions that appear in the process of constructing the eigenvalue equations. These functions are, in fact, the states. The artificiality of this identification disappears when its consequences are realized. For it is exactly the necessary step that brings the physicist to a position where he can utilize all the tools provided by a relatively recent but powerful and graceful mathematical discipline, the analysis of Hilbert space. He thus enjoys advantages quite similar to those which made the classical definition of states so attractive, the latter being so contrived as to enable him to use the older kind of functional analysis familiar from Newton's calculus.

Finally, we turn to the idea of a physical system, whose representative in classical physics was a mechanical model. Having already surrendered the intuitive immediacy of observables and states, quantum mechanics is no longer bound by the restraints of visual perception. It can and does use models of a more general and a more formal kind. Some would even claim that it uses no models at all. At any rate, most physicists no longer feel obliged to say whether the electron is a particle or a wave. Such statements seem to them as absurd as the assertion that the electron is red or blue.

The contents of the quantum theory will now be developed succinctly by way of a few basic propositions. Those chosen here serve as the foundation of a large part of the theory, but the list is not complete. Nor is it unique. There are other equivalent ways of choosing the axioms.

1. To every physical observable there corresponds an (Hermitean) operator. It is the business of physics to discover the appropriate operators for different observables, just as it was the problem of classical science to find the functions $f_i(t)$ that corresponded to them. In discovering the correct operators, classical physics has been an important guide.

2. Let 0 be some observable, e.g., position, momentum, energy, etc., and denote its operator by Ω. The eigenfunctions φ_i and eigenvalues ω_i of Ω are then given by the equation

$$\Omega \varphi_i = \omega_i \varphi_i, \tag{1}$$

which becomes definite and solvable when certain conditions are placed upon the φ_i. The present axiom declares—and every atomic observation confirms—that the only numerical values that emerge in a measurement of 0 are the eigenvalues ω_i. The ω_i sometimes form a continuous set, as all measured values do in classical physics; sometimes, as in the case of angular momentum, they form a simple discrete set of equally spaced numbers. Energy values, which are the eigenvalues of the Hamiltonian operator, are sometimes continuous, sometimes discrete, and often the same system has ranges in which they are discrete and other ranges in which they are continuous. Quantization is said to occur where the ω_i are discrete.

The mathematical form Ω is known for the most important physical observables, about ten in number. The success of the procedures implicit in this postulate, however, has led physicists to suppose that in general every possible observation, not merely those of fundamental interest in atomic physics, has associated with it an Ω and that, perhaps, every hermitean Ω corresponds to some physical measurement or observation. About the generality of this scheme, however, one can prove no more than about the thesis that in classical physics every observation corresponds to some continuous function of simple variables. The claim of universality of the eigenvalue postulate is just as legitimate as the corresponding claim of classical description, and no more legitimate, both being extrapolations of limited scientific successes.

At this stage, classical physics and quantum mechanics appear to be in conflict, the latter claiming validity in the atomic realm and the former in the molar world. In fact there is no conflict, for it can be demonstrated that the ω_i for large systems are indistinguishable from the continuous results of Newtonian dynamics. Quantum mechanics is, therefore, the more embracive discipline, of which classical physics forms a special limiting case.

3. The third axiom is best stated in two parts:

a) The state of a physical system is represented by a continuous function, φ, of certain variables, here called **r** collectively, which may be regarded as denoting points in configuration space. This sentence leaves the physical meaning of $\varphi(\mathbf{r})$ wholly undetermined; it sets up a construct in C without giving its rules of correspondence to P. The latter are provided in:

b) When $\varphi(\mathbf{r})$ is given, the probability of the outcome of every possible measurement upon the system is fixed. In particular, if 0 is measured many times (the state φ having been reprepared after every measurement) and the measured values are recorded, their arithmetic mean, $\overline{0}$, is given by

$$\overline{0} = \int \varphi^* \Omega \varphi \, d\mathbf{r} / \int \varphi^* \varphi \, d\mathbf{r} \tag{2}$$

where $d\mathbf{r}$ is the element of configuration space. From (2) follows an immediate but important consequence, which we do not prove here in detail: the probability $p(\omega_i)$ that in a given measurement of 0 the value ω_i will appear, is

$$p(\omega_i) = |\int \varphi^* \varphi_i \, d\mathbf{r}|^2, \tag{3}$$

φ_i being defined by (1). As a special case of (3), the probability $p(\mathbf{r})$ that the system will be found at $\mathbf{r}$ when a measurement of its position in configuration space is made turns out to be $p(\mathbf{r}) = |\varphi(\mathbf{r})|^2$.

This result provides a simple interpretation of the meaning of a state function in terms of probabilities of location.

So far we have written φ as a function of $\mathbf{r}$. Just as in classical dynamics, states can also change in time. Hence, we must anticipate that $\varphi = \varphi$ $(\mathbf{r}, t)$. In classical dynamics, force laws like Newton's $m\mathbf{r} = \mathbf{F}(\mathbf{r})$, control the change of states in time. The force law of quantum mechanics is given by axiom

4. States develop in accordance with Schrödinger's equation

$$\frac{\partial}{\partial t} \varphi(\mathbf{r}, t) = \frac{i}{\hbar} H\varphi(\mathbf{r}, t) \tag{4}$$

where H is the operator representing the energy of the system. (4), which is in general a partial differential equation with independent variables $\mathbf{r}$ and t, is used in the following way: When the function φ $(\mathbf{r}, t_0)$ is given, it is made to serve as initial condition for the solution of (4), which yields φ $(\mathbf{r}, t)$ at any t.

That function then exhibits a remarkable feature deserving of special mention. Suppose the system to which φ refers is a molar one of large dimensions, for which the probability distribution $|\varphi(\mathbf{r}, t)|^2$ has a negligible spread. That is to say, the spread will still be appreciable on an atomic scale of magnitudes but unimportant in ordinary observations. We would then expect $\overline{0}$, given by 2, to be not merely the mean but the actual value of an observation made at t, since the statistical spread is small. Now it may indeed be shown that the ratio $\int *(\mathbf{r},t)\Omega\varphi(\mathbf{r},t) \, d\mathbf{r}/\int *\varphi d\mathbf{r}$ reduces to the classical function $0(t)$, computed in accordance with classical laws of motion. Again, classical dynamics emerges as a limiting case of quantum mechanics.

In recent years an extensive literature dealing with the theory of measurement in quantum mechanics has sprung up.[7] Its purpose is to give an account of the way in which measured values emerge through the interaction of a system in a specified quantum state with a measuring apparatus.

The logic of many attempts in this area is not very clear, nor is it always obvious what purpose they are to achieve. Let us note first of all, therefore, that if the postulates enumerated in the foregoing context are accepted, a detailed dynamic theory of measurement is quite unnecessary. For if that theory contradicted postulate 3, which is a well-confirmed cornerstone of elementary quantum mechanics, it would have to be judged in error, or else it would bespeak an inconsistency in the set of axioms. This has not occurred. If, on the other hand, the theory is in accord with the postulate it merely shows consistency and rubberstamps the axioms. This last event, while logically somewhat redundant, is nevertheless a useful exercise because it might yield physical insights which the bare logical structure obscures.

In every attempt of showing how postulate 3 conforms with the detailed analysis of the measurement process two essential points should be observed. First, the definition of measurement should be taken sufficiently wide to include all acts which the physicist normally associates with that word. Second, a minimum of further axioms, and preferably none at all, should be invoked.

It has become customary, in developing theories of measurement, to invoke an additional axiom, called the projection postulate; it supposes that every measurement suddenly converts a quantum state which is a superposition (not a mixture) of eigenstates of the measured observable into a single eigenstate, namely the one corresponding to the measured value. In the terminology of Hilbert space, every measurement "projects" an arbitrary state vector onto the ray characteristic of the measured eigenvalue. The lack of critical appraisal with which this semiclassical conjecture has been allowed to creep into the philosophy of quantum mechanics is amazing.

Beginning with von Neumann, who used the postulate as a tool, most mathematicians and physicists base their philosophical discussion upon a premise such as this. "As is well known, a quantum mechanical state can undergo two kinds of change: one sudden and acausal, the other continuous and controlled by Schrödinger's equation." The first of these is supposed to occur during measurement, it reflects the projection postulate. Often this postulate is regarded as a crucial tenet of the so-called Copenhagen interpretation of quantum mechanics. This, in my opinion, is not correct, but it is difficult to disprove because of the amorphous character of the beliefs which make up that philosophy.

I have discussed the projection postulate in a number of papers,[8] examining it in a more technical way than is called for here. The main results reached are these. The logical structure of the quantum theory is complete without it. There are many perfectly acceptable physical measurements which obviously violate it, and to reject these would seriously impair the verificational phase of quantum mechanics. The literal use of the postulate invalidates actual physical theory.[9] Finally, there is a serious mathematical difficulty associated with the projection postulate, since it does not allow the construction of joined probabilities for the measurement of non-commuting observables in a meaningful way.

Matters related to the projection postulate and other problems which are still under dispute were treated by Feyerabend[10] in the 1962 volume of this series. A few comments, made partly to confer further emphasis upon the points he made, partly to correct what seems like a misunderstanding, may be appropriate in the present context. Feyerabend's conclusion that a uniform interpretation worthy of a single name, like the Copenhagen view, does not exist needs special stress. His doubts about complementarity, which he shows to be conceptually unnecessary, should be taken seriously; my own view is even stronger, for I regard complementarity in the sense in which philosophers and theologians have used the concept, as absurd.

I do not understand, however, what is meant when Feyerabend denies continuity between elementary quantum mechanics and classical mechanics. Certainly, no discontinuity has ever been discovered, and the fact that every wavepacket, when sufficiently compact, behaves as if it were a particle controlled by Newton's laws provides as smooth a passage from one field to the other as can be desired. It is true, the wave packet describes a time-varying probability; but a confined probability of encountering an object which moves through space along a trajectory is indistinguishable from a moving object.

One point, however, should again be emphasized: the quantum theory is the more general one, and it reduces to classical mechanics as a special case. There is no distinction in principle. Hence, it is misleading to speak, as did Feyerabend and Bohr, of a classical domain of experience as distinct from a microdomain; of classical measuring apparatus in opposition to microsystems. In a theory of measurement every apparatus can and must be treated as a quantum mechanical system if the theory is to make sense. The trivial fact that most measuring apparatus are large in size so that man can handle them, and the consequent truism that observables of large systems have closely spaced eigenvalues (which follows from quantum mechanics) are not sufficient to justify the distinction.

For these reasons I could not subscribe to the statement on page 253 of the last named reference: "The methods of quantization which have lead to such tremendous successes in the quantum theory of particles and fields will continue to succeed only as long as there exist classical theories which after proper reformulation can be subject to quantization." Current tendencies seem to suggest that we depart even farther from classical description, that we take the radical features of quantum mechanics even more seriously, and certainly as primary relative to the time honored, visually direct conceptions of classical science. We may use the latter as inductive guides, but never as anterior logical premises.[11]

Philosophical Consequences

The philosophical consequences of the quantum theory are contained in the foregoing section. To expose them to view I shall project them against the methodological background sketched in the first section, "Epistemology of Science." They affect, as we shall see, the metaphysical postulates which regulate the C-field. Although they leave their essence unchanged, the details of these regulative principles suffer alterations, mainly in four respects.

1. *There occurs a wider utilization of nonmechanical, nonvisual models.* The systems concerned here are atomic and subatomic entities which in classical theory were regarded as particles or assemblages of particles performing motions of the ordinary kind. To be specific, they were thought to follow continuous paths, such that to every instant t there was conjoined, as we have seen, a position q together with other observables. As a result of this functional association a particle could not be in two places at once. An entity satisfying this kind of description can, of course, be certified to be indeed a particle, a small region full of stuff, impenetrable, and coherent.

To be sure, classical physics employed other visual forms like waves, stress lines and vortices, and these did not need to satisfy the requirements just mentioned. But being addicted to visual clarity, prequantum explanation always maintained a clean distinction between all of these. Thus an electron had to be conceived as either a particle or a wave, and the renowned dualism, together with certain forms of complementarity, entered the philosophical scene.

In quantum physics it was realized that systems which, by their very size and nature are forever beyond visual perception, may also be beyond visual conception. Hence the use of mechanical models was abandoned; systems like the electron and other subatomic particles including light were defined in certain formal ways, were represented in a manner which, though more abstract, is nonetheless equally clear and definite. Instead of saying that an electron has the ability to pursue an orbit in a given field, one assigns to it a Hamiltonian operator; a spin operator of specific mathematical form takes the place of the imageful rotation of a little charged sphere about an axis. The particle character which will not allow it to be in two places at once is loosened to permit (unobservable) conditions in which it can interfere with itself, go through two holes without relinquishing its total mass or its total charge. While these statements tax our imagination—as all nonvisual propositions do—they are nevertheless logically consistent and follow from the Hamiltonian formalism that serves as the fundamental description of the electron.

We note in passing that this freer representation restores the symmetry of space and time which particles in classical physics do not respect. If an electron were truly a particle it could not be in two places at the same time but could be at two times in the same place. An electron, in its newer understanding, allows both statements in positive form.[12]

When viewed from this vantage point the dualism vanishes, for it becomes clear that the electron in its nonvisual conception need not be a particle nor a wave nor a vortex nor any other visual form. Though still far from such nonphysical constructs as "mind," which everybody nowadays conceives as nonmechanical and nonmaterial, electrons and photons have taken on some aspects of these abstracta in refusing to be pictured in customary terms. Rather than talk unphilosophically about a dualism we should, I think, recognize the regression from picturesqueness in the description of physical being that has occurred, and yet realize that this description remains unique and determinate, but that certain accustomed ways of representing physical systems have been found inadequate.

Bohr's complementarity principle, which in its correct version expresses this important insight, is often banalized and made to say that there *is* a dualism, that we *can* picture the electron as a particle or as a wave but forfeit thereby all success in an attempt to predict its behavior; on the other hand, if we want to predict we must renounce the picture. As a matter of reasonable fact the first alternative, which bolsters classical custom but proves unsuccessful, is strictly no scientific possibility at all, even though it may at times provide a heuristic device or a mental crutch.

To maintain objectivity it must be said before concluding that the interpretation of quantum mechanics here given does injustice to a small number of notable dissenters. Men like Bohm and De Broglie, under advocacy of what the first calls a causal (meaning, however, mechanistic) version of quantum mechanics, are pleading for a reduction of its nonvisual features to a mechanistic substratum of hidden variables, classical in kind. That this can be done is beyond doubt. Only its plausibility is questioned by most physicists. Hidden-variable theories, which at present have no P-plane consequences other than those of the normal quantum theory, are reminiscent of the ether theories of old with their repulsive encumbrances in the form of excessively complex molecules. They are not being rejected as wrong in any empirical sense; their fate is worse: they lack, so far, logical fertility. All this will change when and if they make a single significant correct prediction of which the normal theory is not capable.[13]

Other physicists, most notably Landé, proceed consistently by assuming electrons (etc.) to be particles so constituted that certain classical observations cannot be made upon them. The major features of quantum mechanics then emerge from the halo of uncertainty that surrounds their nature; in Landé's case from the assumption that only transition probabilities can be observed and are meaningful. The resulting scheme is then in harmony with the ordinary quantum theory and makes no pretense at having greater competence.

2. *New, stochastic rules of correspondence are employed.* In classical physics a single observation determines the value of an observable, and therefore a finite and usually a small set of observations determines a state. In quantum mechanics a state is a statistical aggregate, tantamount to a probability distribution and it cannot be fixed by a finite set of observations. The simple linkage between the construct "state of a physical system" and observed events in nature has been modified in an important way. If φ is given, what happens in a single event cannot be predicted; many different events may take place, and only their relative frequency is specified. Hence, φ is not related to P by single connections; each rule of correspondence breaks up, as it were, into a multitude of linkages with a large number of possible events, the probability of each being determined.

In a way, this change leads back to the old philosophical notion of possibility or latency in contrast to actuality. A state is a latent set of possibilities which are actualized in real observations or events. But the older concepts are now refined: latency (or potency) or possibility has become quantified by an assignment of probabilities to the possible outcomes. Also, as we have seen, the possibilities are often mathematically restricted by the phenomenon of quantization.

There is another trend in modern philosophy that has been reversed. The contrast between C and P, which found its historical expression in the perennial conflict between rationalism and empiricism, was thought by positivistic philosophers to have been resolved. For it was supposed that the C-field was nothing more than a compact description, a coherent representation of P-experience, that one was equivalent to the other, that reference to both was an idle appeal to an isomorphism between two realms, one of which sufficed to carry the weight of reality. It now appears that this isomorphism is untenable, that the full P-plane contains more in the way of actual, existential material than C implies. Here arises, then, a new situation which postpositivistic philosophy must meet.

3. *There is a change in the causal postulate.* Correlated with the change in the connection between the state construct and events or observations on P is a reformulation of the causal principle. According to it, a state is methodologically entrained by former states, and the entrainment is made possible by a law of nature. Now if we insist on the older definition of states even with respect to subatomic systems, it turns out that there is no law known to science by which such states are propagated in time. Hence, those who feel that an electron, for example, is still a particle and as such must be described by the good old Newtonian concept of state (position and velocity) are forced to admit that causality has failed.

The overwhelming success of quantum mechanics, however, suggests that the idea of state be redefined in order to *save* causality. The state concept is to be associated with the function φ, which we have already termed a state function, for it satisfies a causal differential equation, namely Schrödinger's, as postulated in axiom 4. The new kind of causality which is then introduced does not allow the prediction, or entail the predetermination, of P-events on the basis of other P-events; what it couples in deterministic fashion is probability distributions of whole aggregates of events. The name for the new relation is *stochastic* or *statistical causality,* the claim of its universality is embodied in *statistical determinism.* Strictly speaking, an infinite number of observations at $t = 0$ enables the prediction of all the probabilities, i.e., the relative frequencies, of all possible happenings (observations) at *t*. The rigidity of causal determinacy is weakened, just as the rigid rules of correspondence of classical physics have spread out into stochastic linkages.

This puts the question of freedom in a novel light. Suffice it here to say, under the strain of brevity, that classical physics, if allowed to govern all experience, leaves no room for true metaphysical freedom. Nor does quantum mechanics establish it. Freedom, in its proper understanding, involves objective chance *and* subjective human choice. Classical physics denied the former and said nothing about the latter; indeed what it might have said about it would have been irrelevant because of that denial. Quantum mechanics affirms objective chance and thereby makes room for freedom, but it, too, is silent about choice. Chance alone is never freedom, it is lack of determination and absence of motivation. One might say, therefore, that quantum mechanics solves the first problem of freedom, but leaves the second unattended.[14]

4. *Recent physics places increasing reliance on simplicity and elegance.* These two words, simplicity and elegance, designate a regulative maxim which, as indicated in Section 2, has always been operative in the selection of scientific constructs and theories. Whereas in the past their meaning was indefinite, involving sometimes the occurrence of few or no arbitrary constants in the laws of nature, sometimes the use of analytic functions, it has now crystallized into the concept of *invariance* with respect to specifiable operations or transformations. Physics has always restricted its consideration to laws which were invariant with respect to time translation, i.e., the translation $t' = t + \tau$ where τ is constant. Likewise, it sought in accordance with the philosophical principle of "uniformity of nature" only laws invariant with respect to space translation, satisfying $\mathbf{r}' = \mathbf{r} + \rho$, where ρ is a constant vector. In mechanics, reversibility was supposed to hold; this means that the laws remain unchanged under the substitution $t' = -t$. Until the advent of relativity and quantum mechanics, it rarely went beyond these simple requirements.

Now a new set of interesting transformations have entered the discourse of physics, ushered in by the Lorentz transformations of special relativity. Simplicity has taken on the form of invariance, and many excursions are taken in its name. An appealing equation, usually some sort of wave equation, has an a priori air of credibility, of likely application to some physical phenomenon, if it is invariant with respect to some or all of these transformations, and investigations of the properties of these equations before they are known to have empirical reference are conducted with gusto. The strange thing is that the effort is productive of verifiable results!

Such is the philosophical legacy of the quantum theory. Pondering the points we made, the philosopher asks, and has a right to ask, whether they are final. Or are they merely traits of an evanescent theory, one among many, that are bound to change as time goes on? Are they indeed aberrations that will fade away when classical reason is restored? No one can answer these questions, least of all the philosopher.

If the history of science teaches anything at all it is that there are no eternal verities which man can grasp and hold forever. Science is a flux of understanding, deepening and yielding ever greater satisfaction, it appears, but the river of discoveries is never dammed and made into a stagnant pool. Whether the points here noted are among those which future progress will substantially alter, or whether they will retain their essential validity and undergo only minor changes, can only be conjectured. But the issues run deep; they touch the most basic strata of scientific reasoning, and they can hardly be swept away by a casual discovery or two, no matter how challenging.

In any case, to record these matters is all the philosopher of science can do. Like the scientist, he is surrounded by a flow of attitudes and facts; there is no source of knowledge for him outside of logic and science. He must swim with the flow and try, if possible, to be abreast of it. He may be able to judge for some distance ahead where he is moving, but his final destination is also unknown.

NOTES

This essay was written with the aid of AFOSR Grant 249–64.

1. H. Margenau, "Methodology of Modern Physics," *Philosophy of Science*, 2 (1935), 48, 164; *The Nature of Physical Reality* (New York: McGraw-Hill, 1950).
2. F. S. C. Northrop, *The Meeting of East and West* (New York: Macmillan, 1946); *The Logic of the Sciences and the Humanities* (New York: Macmillan, 1947).
3. F. S. C. Northrop, *The Nature of Concepts: Their Interrelation and Role in Social Structure* (Stillwater: Oklahoma A. and M. College, 1951).
4. See, for instance, "The Present State of Operationalism," *Scientific Monthly*, 79 (October 1954).
5. H. Margenau, *Open Vistas* (New Haven: Yale U. Press, 1961).
6. M. Bunge, *The Myth of Simplicity* (Englewood Cliffs, N.J.: Prentice-Hall, 1963).

7. A sizable bibliography is attached to an article by the author in *Annals of Physics*, 23 (1963), 469, where a detailed theory is formulated.

8. (a) H. Margenau and R. Hill, *Progress of Theoretical Physics*, 26 (1961), 722. (b) Ibid., Ref. 6. (c) H. Margenau, *Philosophy of Science*, 30 (1963), 1; and *Philosophy of Science*, 30 (1963), 138.

9. See, for instance, p. 481 of Ref. 6, last paragraph.

10. P. Feyerabend, "Problems of Microphysics," *Frontiers of Science and Philosophy*, ed. R. Colodny (Pittsburgh: U. of Pittsburgh Press).

11. In Note 197, Feyerabend offers a rebuttal of my argument against the view that measurements invariably produce eigenstates. He describes a measurement, rather more complicated than most, of the spin of a photon and produces a clear diagram, to which the following remark refers.

    The inference that if no photon is found in beam II it must be in beam I—provided one has previously made sure that a photon passed through the analyzer *P*—is indeed correct. If this arrangement were used to measure the spin of a photon, it would clearly produce an eigenstate of the photon's spin.

    The argument, however, is irrelevant. To invalidate the general theory of measurement I proposed, which counts as physical measurements not only those procedures that fall short of, but also those which satisfy, the projection postulate, it is clearly useless to show that some measurements do conform to the postulate: It is necessary to explain why those which fail to conform are not measurements.

    Let me add, however, that the arrangement described by Feyerabend is somewhat unusual. It belongs in the category of *compound* measurements (position conjoined with spin); see H. Margenau, *Annals of Physics*, 23 (1963), 496. Noting the emission of a Compton electron in *F* (of the diagram), and subsequently the incidence or lack of incidence of a photon in II, should properly be regarded as a single compound measurement, and the probability for the emergence of a pair of observed values is not in general controlled by the projection postulate, as was shown in the last named reference.

12. This point is mine, fully treated in *The Nature of Physical Reality*, p. 160, Ref. 1.

13. For a more thorough discussion of hidden-variable theories, see the author's "Advantages and Disadvantages of Various Interpretations of the Quantum Theory," *Physics Today*, 7 (1954), 6.

14. See H. Margenau, *Open Vistas*.

Index of Names

Index of Topics